THE WORLD MUSIC CD LISTENER'S GUIDE

by Howard J. Blumenthal

GW00570871

Billboard Books
An imprint of Watson-Guptill Publications/New York

To people around the world who contribute to the Internet by building their own Web pages, communicate via newsgroups, and send helpful information to new, unseen friends via e-mail.

Senior Editor: Bob Nirkind
Managing Editor (Logical Extension, Ltd.):
Sharon Blumenthal
Design: Howard J. Blumenthal
Jacket Design: Barbour Design

First published in 1998 by Billboard Books, an imprint of Watson-Guptill Publications, a division of BPI Communications, Inc., 1515 Broadway, New York, NY 10036

Library of Congress Cataloging-in-Publication Data

Blumenthal, Howard J.
        The world music CD listener's guide / by Howard J. Blumenthal.
            p.   cm.— (The best on CD)
            ISBN 0-8230-7663-6
            1. World music—Discography. 2. Compact discs—Reviews.
I. Title. II. Series.
ML156.4.W63B58   1997
780.26'6—dc21

                                97-40492
                                CIP
                                    MN
Manufactured in the United States of America
First printing, 1998

1 2 3 4 5 6 7 8 9 / 06 05 04 03 02 01 00 99 98

This book was written to help you navigate through the world music section at a record store. It highlights the work of more than 100 artists whose CDs you are likely to find at any well-stocked store in the United States. I've personally listened to every CD, then written about 100 words to tell you why the CD is special, unique, and worth owning. There are no ratings: if a CD is included in the book, then it is a recommended purchase. Every CD in this book is currently available in the U.S. (with few exceptions, as noted). Within a review, you might also see a reference to another CD by the same artist. These are recommended as well; often, these CDs are not reviewed separately because of limited space in the book. Every CD review is "linked" to another review, my suggestion for a follow-up purchase. Often, the "link" CD is by an artist from the same country, or by one who shares a style or sensibility.

I selected the artists based on hundreds of conversations with journalists who specialize in world music, producers, record company executives, managers and buyers at record stores specializing in world music, and through e-mail and newsgroup conversations with people passionate about the music. Some artists were eliminated because their CDs were not easily available in the U.S.

For better or for worse, the focus here reflects what's sold in U.S. record stores, which means lots of Latin, reggae, Brazilian, African, Caribbean, Indian, Celtic and British, some Native American, Hawaiian, Scandinavian, and Eastern European music, but not enough from Eastern Asia, central Europe, Russia, the Arab countries, and the Pacific. I've compensated for some of this with a special section at the back of the book. This book is not intended to represent every country in the world (many do not support a thriving record industry), nor is it an ethnomusicological survey. It's a book about the many world music CDs that are in wide distribution—and I hope, a tool to help you build a collection of your own.

Most record stores stock only the most popular world music titles. For a wider selection, either visit the store's front desk for a special order, or visit a record store on the Web. Three mail order sources are especially useful: Stern's Music, which specializes in African music (598 Broadway, NY, NY 10012-3205; 212-925-1648), World Music Distribution (800-900-4527; info@worldmusic.com), and Multicultural Media (800-550-9675).

Howard J. Blumenthal
December 1997

Acknowledgments

A great many people shared their enthusiasm, opinions, and information with me. And many more supplied CDs so that I could listen to the music before writing about it. In particular, my thanks to Kevin Mallon at Claris and to the publicity department at Adobe, and to Terry Halper and Ted Swanson, who guided me through the wonders of databases. Here's an incomplete list of the many music industry professionals who helped to make this project possible. First, a select group who patiently answered a great many questions and gave generously of their time:

Jose Florez – Sonido
Kostas Theodoribasis – GVRT
j.poet
Drew Miller – Omnium
Chris Nickson
Ned Sublette – Qbadisc
Juan Gomez – Harmonia Mundi USA

Isabel Soffer – World Music Institute
Jacquie Juceam
Carl Youngblood
Ian Anderson – Folk Roots
Andrew Seidenfeld – No Problem
 Productions
(plus many newsgroup netizens)

And, my thanks to these music industry professionals:

A. J. Correale – SONY Music; Alison Tarnovsky – Caroline; Ann Pryor– Virgin; Anna Olivera – WEA Latina; Anne Ruth – Triloka; Annie Johnston– Arhoolie; Archie Meguro – SONY Japan; Ben Churchill – Dancing Cat; Bob Haddad – Music of the World; Brenda Dunlap – Smithsonian Folkways; Carla Sacks; Charles Barnett – Penthouse; Chris Mills – Multicultural Media; Cindy Byram – Shanachie; Dan Marx – Denon; Dave Wechsler –Qbadisc; David C. Broyles – Triloka; Debbie Mercado – RMM; Dennis Britton – Smithsonian Collection; Diane Fortier – Island; Dr. Terry Miller; Forrest Faubion – Allegro; George Naufel – MESA/Blue Moon; Glenn Dicker– Rounder; Glenn Kenny; Harriet Wasser; Howard Gabriel – SONY Tristar; Isabel Gomez – Polygram Latino; Jack O'Neil – Blue Jackel; Jacob Edgar – Tinder; James Goring – VP; Janeann Ardolino – Windham Hill; Jennifer Jaime – Concord; Jenny Adlington – World Circuit; Jesse Reuben Wilson – ARC; Jim Eigo – Dreyfus; Joe Boyd; Joel Cortright – World Music Distribution; John Reilly – Shore Fire; John Vlautin – Island; Jorge Luis Borrego – EMI Latin; JR Rich – Blue Note; Judith Joiner – Green Linnet; Karen Digesu – Ellipsis Arts; Karuna Davy – AMMP; Kate McLaughlin – IMN; Ken Braun – Stern's Music; Kim Ewing; Linda McKay Feldman – Dorian; Marc Zola – SUKAY; Marilyn Egol – BMG; Mark Schwartz – Luaka Bop; Martin Cohen; Marty Kirkman – starscape; Mary J. Khan – AMMP; Meg MacDonald – Vanguard; Meg Way – Shanachie; Megan Zinn – Red House; Mengual Heinstein – KAREN Publishing; Michael Galbe – WEA Latina; Michael Steinberg – Annie O'Hayon PR; Mike Gott– BGO Records; Nick Clift – Caroline; Nicola Sigrist – Putumayo; Nili Belkind; Paul Hartman – Dirty Linen; Peter Clancy – Nonesuch; Peter Elliot – Nimbus; Philip Yampolsky; Ralph Samuelson – Asian Cultural Council; Richard Klecka – Music of the World; Rob Thatcher – Sphere Marketing; Sandy Miranda; Sarah Weinstein – Island; Shahrokh Yadegari – Kereshmeh; Sharon Sherman – Earthbeat!; Sonya Kolowrat – Rykodisc; Sophia Alayou – Sony Discos; Sue Schrader – Narada ; Teri Williams – Celestial Harmonies; Tom Bee – SOAR; Tom Diamant – Arhoolie; Tom Horan – Kells; Viola Galloway – F.T.C.; Wesley Parks – Herschel Freeman; Yvonne Gomez – Rhino.

A real **Nigerian** prince born in 1946 (real name: Sunday Adeniyi). Adé's parents were active in church music, but reluctant to see their son become a musician. By 17, he had joined a traveling entertainment troupe and a high-life band. Adé then became interested in juju—working class music based on Yoruba tribal drumming. As the high-life dance craze faded, juju gained popularity and in 1966, Adé formed the Green Spots. The group's "Challenge Cup" celebrated a local soccer team and became the best-selling juju hit ever. In 1974, Adé started his own record label and a new band, the African Beats. He was voted King of Juju Music. Hoping to make Adé an interna-

tional superstar and looking to replace Bob Marley, Island Records signed him in 1982. Juju, however, lacked reggae's widespread appeal and English-language lyrics, so Adé was dropped after three albums. Still, Adé remains a popular feature in world music festivals.

JuJu Music   Mango 9712

After 40 top sellers in Nigeria, this was Adé's international coming-out. One of many outstanding features here is Adé's guitar, backed by two more lead guitars, a steel guitar (sounding vaguely Hawaiian), a rhythm guitar, and a bass. In juju music, instruments call and respond. The bubbling sound of three talking drums interact with Adé's sweet singing voice and a chorus. Talking drums play lead over bongos, congas, other drums, and siren-like echo effects from other percussion instruments. Sometimes this sounds like a Yoruba tribal gathering, but with slick commercial patches. Endlessly inventive. From 1982.

LINK➤ *I.K. Dairo — Definitive Dairo*   *Xenophile (Green Linnet) 4045*
Representative 1971 sampling of the work of a juju giant. Dairo is one of Nigeria's long-term finest musicians.

Synchro System   Mango 539-737

Adé's band, the African Beats, is largely un-changed for this 1983 album, but the sound has evolved with more emphasis on musical conversation between percussion and vocal group. On many songs the talking drums lead, and guitars fill in background. Best is the machine-like title cut; it starts with an extended talking drum solo and continues the factory beat with rhythm guitar, whooshes, guitar riffs, and Adé's high voice.

Whooshing sounds that sweep from one speaker to the other add a modern edge. Varied textures come from a wide range of instrument sounds. The pounding "E Saiye Re" will shake your room—great dance music!

LINK➤ *Prince Nico Mbarga — Aki Special*   *Rounder 11545*
Another fine Nigerian band, playing infectious dance music that will have you tapping your feet. The title track and the group's biggest hit, "Sweet Mother," were popular in the late '70s, released in the U.S. in 1987, and still feel fresh.

Aura   Mango 9824

"Ase" begins like a giant rattlesnake, a room-filling rumble, followed by ringing guitars, chanting from the male vocal section, the big drums, and, without
warning, the immediately recognizable Stevie Wonder on a harmonica solo.
The beat is relentless, and this train just keeps on moving. Again, the emphasis is on guitars—7 in an 11-piece band. The percussion pattern on "Gboromiro"
is dark and complex, periodically highlighted by the African Beats' signature
high guitar riff, answered by male chorus. Sumptuous group singing on "Ogunja."
Superior album for its varied textures, complexity, and overall sound quality.
Impressive growth; this was released in 1984.

LINK➤ *Various Artists — Africa: Never Stand Still*   *Ellipsis Arts 3300*
*Terrific introduction to African pop music. Includes influential performers whose
work should be better known: Orchestra Marrabenta Star de Mozambique,
Pierre Akendengue, etc. Released in 1996.*

Live Live Juju   Rykodisc 10047

A live recording, made during a 1987 tour date in Seattle. Just two micro-
phones recorded 20 musicians onstage, and this digital recording places each
musician with vivid accuracy on the stereo soundstage. The opening number,
"Drums/Gbe Mi Ro," is mostly percussion, as are the two closing tracks ("Drumming Interlude" is fantastically fast!), and the recording technique brings out
the depth, power, and nuance in the drum sounds. "Africa and America" is a
group vocal anthem accented by guitar riffs and kept moving by maracas,
conga drums, and powerful rhythm guitar breaks, plus a fabulous extended
lead guitar solo. The crowd's enthusiasm is infectious.

LINK➤ *Ebenezer Obey — Get Your Jujus Out*   *Rykodisc 20111*
*Adé's principal competitor for Nigeria's juju crown. This 1987 live album ex-
plains why. Juju is the perfect oxymoron: a relaxed beat that's perfect for fast
dancing, melodies that don't seem memorable until the song is over. And on
this record, outstanding percussion.*

E Dide/Get Up   Mesa 92644

Adé continues to evolve. This 1995 album, also recorded in the Seattle area,
stars Adé's deep and powerful drum machine. Overall sound is crystal-clear;
the male backup vocalists sound like individuals, not a faceless chorus. Keyboards, often buried beneath Adé's carnival of sounds, come alive. English
lyrics clarify the proceedings: in "Oshodi Oke," a man tries to convince a woman
to have sex with him (remember: this is dance music, where similar themes
are common worldwide). "Orisun Iye (Creator)" is a song of harvest thanksgiv-
ing. "Ope Ope (The Palm Tree Is Not Dead)" is a Yoruba folk song about the
cycle of life.

LINK➤ *Fatala — Gongoma Times*   *RealWorld (Caroline) 2331*
*From Guinea in West Africa, a look back at African dance music from the
1950s. Traditional instruments, lots of drums, and a swinging attitude. Very
good recording quality.*

One of **Greece**'s most popular singers, Alexiou and her family came from Thebes in Asia Minor (now Turkey). She was born in the early 1950s. Alexiou became well known after singing on Kaldaras's 1972 *Mikra Asia* (Asia Minor) album; it told of 1922's exile of one million Greeks from western Turkey and the massacre of a half-million more. Alexiou recorded her first album in 1975; it was a collection of folk songs that included "Dimitroula," one of the decade's best-selling singles. Through two decades, Alexiou has performed many types of music, from popular "laika" songs to "rebetika" (Greek blues), with stops along the way for serious art songs ("endechna") and the songs of Jacques Brel (sung in French and in German). She's an extremely popular concert artist in Greece, and in the large Greek communities throughout Europe and North America. In recent years, Alexiou has moved from dance music to quieter work and has gained renown as a songwriter.

I Balantes Tis Haroula (Ballads of Haroula) Minos-EMI 80023

"Haroula," a diminutive of "Haris," means "little grace." These heartfelt ballads by Alexiou offer a fine introduction to a voice journalists and fans have called "byzantine"—deep, smoky, and intelligent. This collection covers the 1970s and 1980s. "All the Sundays in the World" and "Everything Reminds Me of You" are two of many love songs; they are accompanied by acoustic guitar and the distinctive Greek bouzouki. In "The Ballad of Iphigenia," Alexiou envokes mythological characters to explain her life and her relationship with her mother. "Sundays in Katarini" recalls life in a small rural town. A delightful album, released in 1993.

LINK➤ *Giannis Parios — Island Songs*   *Minos-EMI 430*
From the early 1980s, another side of popular Greek music. Parios (who took his stage name from the island where he was raised) sings popular songs by Konitiopoulous, a folk singer whose work captured the soul of a sailor's life.

Gyrizontas Ton Kosmo (Around the World) Mercury 532-480

This fan's dream of an album includes a 36-page hardcover book, lovingly designed, and filled with color photos and remembrances (1992-96). "Cigarette Case" was a hit for Sophia Vempo during World War II; a man gives a woman a cigarette case, which she sees as a symbol of future unhappiness. "Tango to Evora" is a lovely blues. In "My Jealousy," one of Alexiou's big hits, a woman's lover is pushed out the door before her husband returns. Alexiou also sings "Looking into Her Eyes," a hit for the Greek rock group, OPA. Her cover of the techno song is calmed down considerably to suit her singing style. A nostalgic visit to an Athens neighborhood, "Aristotle Street," gets the audience singing along. Highly recommended.

LINK➤ *Nikos Ksidhakis & Eleftheria Arvanitaki — Konda sti Dhoxa Stigma*
Lyra (Import)
1987 album arranged by Ksidhakis featuring top Greek female vocalist Arvanitaki. She's accompanied by Ross Daly, an Irish musician who has studied and developed an expertise in older Greek and Turkish music. Original, but reminiscent of gypsy music.

Hossein Alizadeh

Born in Tehran, **Iran**, in 1951, Alizadeh is both a leading contemporary composer and a virtuoso on two string instruments: tar and setår. In the 1970s, he studied with Persian masters of traditional and classical music, and subsequently joined the National Orchestra. This led to a job as the conductor and soloist of the Iranian National Orchestra of Radio and Television, and the start of a solo career. Deeply committed to the advancement of Persian classical music, he established the Ãref Ensemble and works closely with the Shayda Ensemble. Alizadeh has composed various works for small and large ensembles, and for orchestra (some combine European and Iranian traditions, while others are more distinctly Iranian). He has toured the world. He teaches Persian classical music at the California Institute of the Arts, and heads Tehran's Conservatory of Music. (For more on Persian music, visit www.kereshmeh.com.)

Torkaman   Kereshmeh 102

The Persian setår is a four-stringed, long-necked lute with a sound somewhere between an acoustic guitar and a sitar. This is an album of setår improvisations that reflects a deep understanding of traditional Persian music and demonstrates extraordinary dexterity and musicality. The musical form, known as Råst (or Råstpanjgah), is based on modes and is enormously complicated. To Western ears, the formal structures by which "Darãmad-e Råst" establishes a sonic space (or maqãm) and the way in which "Zang-e Shotor" emphasizes rhythm, are not likely to make sense without musical education. Still, the varied rhythms of the guitarlike setår and Alizadeh's virtuosity allow this music to be enjoyed without formal training.

LINK➤ *Mohammed Reza Shajarian, Mohammed Reza Lofti —*
The Abu-Ata Concert   *Kereshmeh 107*

The connection between Persia's poetry and classical music is elegantly expressed in this 1981 landmark concert. Both musicians are masters. Shajarian's commanding voice and Lofti's virtuosity on tår make this CD essential.

Raz-o-Niaz   Kereshmeh 104

This wonderful pair of ensemble works was recorded in 1986. Alizadeh composed the music, performs on setår and tår (a lute), and serves as music director. The first work, "Råstpanjgah," begins with the entire ensemble performing "Chãhãrmezråb," an upbeat string piece (for Westerners: chamber music plus Pat Metheny). The mood is established by "Darãmad," played by setår, kamãncheh (a bowed lute common in Persian classical music), and a resonant male voice. "Song of Heavens" is punctuated by bursts of resplendent dance; the piece continues through three more sections. The second long piece is called "Shoushtari." Also try *Neyvana* (Kereshmeh 103). The album contains one concert for ney and string orchestra and another for Iranian instruments.

LINK➤ *Parviz Meshkatian — Dawn*   *Kereshmeh 108*

The radiant 24-minute "Segåh" is joyfully performed by Meshkatian on santur (a three-octave dulcimer). The 30-minute "Homâyoun" is more somber and introspective. Both are accompanied by tombak (drum). Highly recommended.

Altan is a lake in **Ireland** and also the name of a musical group formed in the 1970s by fiddler Gaoth Dobhair. The name was then adopted by two elementary school teachers, the husband-and-wife team of Frankie Kennedy, who plays flute, and Mairéad Ní Mhaonaigh, who sings and fiddles. In 1983, the duo released an album of Ulster dances with Ní Mhaonaigh's brother Gearóid on guitar, Ciarán Curran on citern, and Eithen Ní Bhraonáin on keyboards (she would later abbreviate her name to Enya and become a major new age star). Frankie, Mairéad, and Ciarán became one of Dublin's most popular traditional Irish acts. In time, the musicians left their day jobs to form a permanent, full-time group. With some personnel changes, the group has prospered, creating consistently excellent albums and wonderful live performances. Kennedy died after a two-year fight against cancer in 1994, inspiring the band with his dedication.

Altan   Green Linnet 1078

This is a 1987 album by Frankie Kennedy and Mairéad Ní Mhaonaigh with the same title as the band they would soon form. Several songs showcase Mhaonaigh's lovely voice; the striking "Ceol A'Phíobaire" ("The Music of the Piper") is an outstanding melody based on the sound of pipes. Flautist Kennedy's virtuosity shines on several reels. This is gentle, simple music from whose roots Altan will grow. But the overall sound is less elaborate than Altan's later music—a fiddle and a voice with subtle accompaniment provided by guitarist Paul Kelly.

LINK➤ *Frankie Kennedy and Mairéad Ní Mhaonaigh — Ceol Aduaidh*
**   Green Linnet 3090**
Delightful early work from the early 1980s: traditional duets performed as simply as they were in the duo's live performances throughout Ireland. The recording is lovely and intimate. Start here and listen to Altan develop over time.

Horse with a Heart   Green Linnet 1095

From the start, this has a fuller sound: a fiddle, a flute, and a rhythm guitar playing three original reels. Altan is a full-scale ensemble, no longer a duo with some backup, as fiddler Mhaonaigh and flautist Kennedy now share space with fiddler Paul O'Shaughnessy, Mark Kelly on guitar, and Ciaran Curran (who played on the first duet album) on bouzouki. Mhaonaigh sings three songs, each with simple accompaniment; here, her voice is darker, more sophisticated, mature. Spirited reels, very tightly played, are the heart of this CD; you can almost see the fiddlers smiling as they play. A 1989 release.

LINK➤ *Natalie MacMaster — No Boundaries*   **Rounder 7023**
Cape Breton Island (between Nova Scotia and Newfoundland) has a delightful fiddling tradition. MacMaster chooses her songs with great care and plays beautifully. From 1996.

Harvest Storm

Green Linnet 1117

Altan becomes a world-class band. The lineup now includes Ciaran Tourish on fiddle, whistle, and backing vocals. As before, Mhaonaigh sings several songs, and the band plays reels, jigs, and other traditional music. What made this 1992 work the breakthrough album? More imaginative arrangements, mainly. "Dónal Agus Mórag," one of Altan's best songs, begins with Donal Lunny's rhythmic bass line, then some distant voices, then Mhaonaigh, then the chorus. Far more complex than previous Altan work, this traditional wedding song typifies the album's surprise and delight. Instruments like the (Australian) didgeridoo and the bass bodhrán add texture.

LINK➤ *Talitha Mackenzie — Spiorad* *Shanachie 78003*
Innovative combination of traditional Gaelic songs linked with folk music from Serbia, Bulgaria, and Breton. Forward-thinking arrangements combine some jazz and new age.

Island Angel

Green Linnet 1137

An exciting, confident set of reels—one of Altan's best—starts this CD, "Tommy Peoples/The Windmill/Fintan McManus's," with the same band members (adding Dáithí Sproule on guitar) supported by Donal Lunny on bodran and Dermot Byrne on accordian. It's followed by "Brid Óg Ní Mhállle," a broken-hearted love song nicely arranged with visitors Lunny on keyboards and Neil Martin on cello. Produced in 1993 by Brian Masterson (and Altan), who had engineered *Harvest Storm* under P.J. Curtis, this is a terrific traditional CD with solid arrangements, but it doesn't hit the heights of Curtis's work with Altan.

LINK➤ *Altan — The First Ten Years 1986/1995* *Green Linnet 1153*
Good sampler of Altan's work with the best cuts from Altan, The Red Crow, Horse with a Heart, Harvest Storm, *and* Island Angel. *1990's* The Red Crow *(Green Linnet 1109) is the transition between straight traditional work and* Harvest Storm*'s more evolved approach.*

Blackwater

Virgin 2796

Fiddler Ciaran Tourish and accordion player Dermot Byrne provide the foundation for this 1996 release—Altan's first studio album without Frankie Kennedy. They can be heard in fine form on a pair of jigs: "Johnny Boyle's/King of the Pipes." Ciaran Curran's bouzouki and Mark Kelly's guitar open "Dance of the Honeybees," and they're soon joined by Tourish's melodeon and his fiddle. These are compelling affirmations of Irish tradition, perfectly performed and recorded. In addition to fiddling, Mairéad Ní Mhaonaigh casts her magnificent spell on "Tá Mé 'Mo Shuí (I Am Awake)," a song about a lovesick sleepness night, and skips happily with a children's song, "'Stór, A Stór, A Ghrá."

LINK➤ *Dervish — Playing with Fire* *Kells 9501*
The next generation of Celtic band plays and records with ultimate clarity, peak musicianship, and a rocking good sense of melody. This superb album was released in 1996.

Arrow's mega-hit recording of "Hot Hot Hot" has become one of the decade's most-played songs (if you missed it during hundreds of sporting events, you've doubtless heard the song on Toyota commercials). Arrow (Alphonsus Cassell) comes from the small island of **Montserrat** in the Lesser Antilles. He worked his way to the top of calypso but strived for a sound with greater international appeal. Many of his early songs are message-oriented, as is common in calypso. By combining various Caribbean styles, he re-emerged as a soca star and in 1983, recorded "Hot Hot Hot" to great success throughout the Caribbean, and later, throughout the world. Most of Arrow's high-energy music is intended for dancing. Apart from the albums released by Mango, most of his work has been released on his own Arrow record label. His career parallels the maturation of Caribbean music from older calypso through cadence, integration with Latin music, zouk, dance hall, and so on.

Knock Dem Dead   Mango 539-809

Great as this album is, the best ones are the releases on Arrow's own label (hard to find). Even so, *Knock Dem Dead*, released in 1988, contains some of the best dance music on record. At the time, Arrow was exploring the combination of soca with other hot dance formats, with consistently ecstatic results. "Rhumba Again" has those soaring horns and a hybrid rhumba-soca rhythm (credit the trumpet solo to Mac Gollehon). "More Arrow" is a great song for a conga line—a call-and-response with African touches. "Groove Master" gets three treatments: a straight mix, a dance mix, and an acid soca house dub.

LINK➤ *Various Artists — Best of Straker's: Ah Feel to Party*
                                                                 Rounder 5066/7
Granville Straker operated one of NYC's first gypsy cab services, and because the rental property had some extra space, he opened a record store. Five years later, he started producing calpyso greats like Mighty Sparrow, Chalkdust, Calypso Rose, and in time, added soca. This 2-CD set covers 25 years.

Soca Dance Party   Mango 539-878

Arrow's calypso roots provide a foundation for "Limbo Calypso," but the song doesn't fit the stereotype. It's set up as a battle between limbo's athleticism and soca's horns and gutsy rhythms. Released in 1990, this ultimate party music shows Arrow once again concentrating on good times. (Arrow is a very articulate social commentator, but not on his Mango releases.) This album is solely about horns and sirens, blazing beat, and fierce percussion as exemplified on "Fire." Arrow's style builds in cascading layers, starting hot and becoming (his words) a "furnace." He uses repeats often, always to fantastic effect ("bring water/to out the fire"). Remarkably tight arrangements cause listeners to sing and dance along. (You can't help yourself!)

LINK➤ *Black Stalin — Roots Rock Soca*   *Rounder 5038*
This essential 1991 collection includes many of the best songs by one of Trinidad's legends. Over a soca rhythm (heavy on horns and percussion), he sings out for "Caribbean Unity," and defends 1979's new soca as the latest evolution of "Black Man Music" and social reform.

Aster Aweke

Born around 1960 in the old capital city of Gondar, **Ethiopia**, Aweke's musical career was not the first choice of her well-connected family. Still, by the mid-1970s, she was very much a part of Ethiopia's music scene, first as a female vocalist working for several local bands, then as a solo singer who could belt out songs (she was influenced by Aretha Franklin and other R&B singers from the U.S.). Aweke recorded some hit singles in Ethiopia, and worked with the popular Roha Band, but by 1979, oppressive politics made the situation for a free-thinking female in Ethiopia less than ideal. She eventually moved to Washington, D.C. Aweke became well-known in that city's fast-growing Ethiopian community, frequently performing in clubs and restaurants. A Columbia recording contract came a decade later, and her career has become increasingly international, with concerts in Europe.

Aster   Columbia 46848

Multiple influences are at work in this album's arrangements: American soul music, Arab pop, traditional North African harp, and danceable Afropop. Add Aweke's varied vocal style, whose range includes Motown, 1980s pop, and quivering Arab nasal intonations, and the result is simultaneously accessible and exotic. Although the songs are varied, they do follow a kind of formula. "Selale (Name of a City)," for example, begins with big Memphis-style horns, but then moves into an Arab rhythm, with Arab lead vocals, and Arab chorus; the horns return for the bridge and elsewhere, often with a standard rock rhythm section of bass, guitar, and drums.

LINK➤ *Aretha Franklin — Amazing Grace*   ***Rhino 906***
This 2-CD collection of gospel songs provides the best opportunity to hear Franklin without too much production—the better to make your own decision about the similarity between the voices of Aweke and Franklin. (Even if you don't make the comparison, this is a fine purchase.)

Kabu   Columbia 47846

This 1991 album gets off to a pulsating, Western-style start with "Yedi Gosh (My Guy)," but both horn and percussion arrangements are more ambitious and varied than before, with less reliance on formulaic arrangements. There's also more space for lively instrumental breaks; even more confident than before, Aweke's having some fun with her hybrid Eastern-Western singing style. The title cut, which translates as "Sacred Rock," is a slow spiritual adoration with soft marimba accompaniment; it's her best work. "Eyoha," a spring celebration normally sung by young girls who trade flowers for bread, is one of several updates on traditional Ethiopian songs.

LINK➤ *Mahmoud Ahmed — Soul of Addis*   *Earthworks (Stern's) 35*
Ethiopian dance music from the previous generation. Thick rhythms, room-shaking percussion, and an enormously powerful voice. Rykodisc no longer carries 1986's Ere Mela Mela *in the U.S., but an imported version of the Hannibal disc might be found.*

Martin Cradick, a classically trained guitar player and passionate traveler, met
Graham Wiggins, who taught himself to
play didgeridoo (an Aboriginal instrument
made from a hollow tree) at Oxford University in 1988. They recorded a cassette,
aptly entitled *Didgeridoo and Guitar*, and
used the profits to fund an album called
Baka. (The inspiration was a TV documentary Cradick had seen on the U.K.'s
Channel 4; he became fascinated by the
lives and music of the Baka tribe of pygmy

people living in **Cameroon**.) Cradick and Wiggins subsequently added drummer Ian Campbell, French fiddler Paddy LeMercier, and Sagar N'Gom from
Senegal and recorded another album called *Outback*. In 1992, Cradick took
his wife, guitar, mandolin, and some supplies to the rainforest to make an
album of field recordings and an album of collaborations with the Baka people.
Two years later, he returned to Cameroon with LeMercier and N'Gom.

Heart of the Forest: Music of the Baka People of
Southeast Cameroon   Hannibal (Rykodisc) 1378

The companion to *Spirit of the Forest*, with similar cover art, contains unadorned Baka music recorded by Cradick in 1992. Starts slowly as the day
begins with just insects, then voices, then the morning river bath. Songs played
on "water drums"—women striking the surface of the river, making it sound
like a syncopated drum quartet—are amazing. The delightful "Nursery Rhyme"
is sung by young children led by an older man. After several songs on natural
string instruments, a party ends the day, when only insects can be heard.

LINK➤ *Louis Sarno — Bayaka: The Extraordinary Music of the*
Babenzélé Pygmies   *Ellipsis Arts 3490*
Cradick is not the only one fascinated with music from people who live in
African forests. Living in New Jersey, he heard them on the radio and moved
to live with the Babenzélé Pygmies in Central Africa. A very elaborate book
and CD project.

Spirit of the Forest   Hannibal (Rykodisc) 1377

This 1993 CD is unique among field recordings; Martin Cradick and Paddy
LeMercier play adaptations and cover versions of Baka music along with members of the tribe. The sound combines Baka voices, natural noises from the
forest, traditional instruments, and Western instruments like the guitar, mandolin, and violin. The result is easy to enjoy: simple acoustic music in a natural
setting. Songs are more obviously rhythmic than melodic, but a second listen
reveals handsome melodies in every song. Recorded in the rainforest in southeast Cameroon, additional instruments were added in a U.K. studio.

LINK➤ *Outback — Dance the Devil Away*   *Hannibal (Rykodisc) 1369*
In 1990, calling themselves Outback, Cradick and Wiggins recorded an gui-
tar/didgeridoo album: Baka (1357). For 1991's Dance the Devil Away (1369),
Outback added N'Grom, Ian Campbell and LeMercier. 1994's Out of the Woods
(1384) was made by Dr. Didg: Wiggins, Campbell, and Mark Revell (guitar).

Ray Barretto

Barretto was born and raised in NYC, started playing conga during military service in Germany, and became a part of the city's jazz scene in the 1950s. For most of his career, Barretto has managed one career in **Latin** music and another in jazz. He hit the big time as a percussionist with Tito Puente's band in the 1950s, but also played with jazz stars like Gene Ammons, Red Garland, and Lou Donaldson. He left Puente to make his own music in the early 1960s and recorded hit singles for Tico and respected jazz albums for Riverside. During the 1970s, he was the music director of the hugely popular Fania All-Stars. In the 1980s, he reinvented Latin jazz. All of this, plus appearances at big events, like the anti-apartheid Sun City concert, and TV work as a music director, plus a flow of new recordings, keep him busy, even as he nears age 70.

Barretto
Fania 486

Ray Barretto recorded a great many albums for Fania, Tico, and other Latino labels in the late 1960s and 1970s. This Fania album from 1975 is one of the best (if you can't find it, *Indestructable* [Fania 456] is a good substitute). In this energetic, hugely inventive take on NYC Latin music, three sounds predominate: the three trumpets on the frontline (sometimes, one is a fluegelhorn); percussion instruments like congas, bongos, and timbales; and two singers: Tito Gomez and Ruben Blades (who also composed two songs). Airtight arrangements sizzle; Barretto's amazing instincts bring in a flute or piano at precisely the right (often unexpected) moment. Endless surprises. Totally danceable.

LINK➤ *Fania All Stars — Live at Yankee Stadium, Vol. 1*   *Fania 476*
In 1975, salsa was the hottest music in NYC, and the Fania All-Stars were the hottest group in salsa. Santos Colon's "Soy Guajiro" is a highlight. Celia Cruz tears it up with "Diosa del Ritmo," and the crowd goes wild (what a voice!). Hector Lavoe sings "Mi Gente." 1977's Rhythm Machine (Columbia 57666) looks more toward fusion, but it's good, too.

Taboo
Concord Picante 4601

Times have changed. Barretto's New World Spirit is a jazz combo that uses some Latin rhythm. Bassist Jairo Moreno teaches music at Yale. Drummer Satoshi Takeshi grew up in Japan, fascinated by Afro-Cuban and South American rhythms; he lived in Colombia for six years. Pianist Hector Martignon is Colombian. Trumpeter Ray Vega came up through NYC's Latin music scene, like Barretto himself. Saxman Adam Kolker is a newcomer with no Latin training. "Bomba-Riquen," with its Cuban bomba beat, is Barretto's roots song. The more typical "Brother Tom," written by Stanley Turrentine, is straight jazz with subtle Latin influences. For a late-model Barretto salsa recording, try *Irresistible* (Fania 658), from 1989.

LINK➤ *Celia, Ray & Adalberto — Tremendo Trio*   *Fania 623*
For years, as the musical director for the Fania All-Stars, Barretto worked with salsa singer Celia Cruz. Here's a good opportunity to hear them together at their peak in the 1970s with Barretto's own orchestra. Adalberto Santiago is one of Puerto Rico's great singers.

Alan Reid, who plays keyboards, guitars, and sings for this **Scottish** band, was around at its beginning in 1969. The long story began in a Glasgow pub while Reid was a university student, and progress was intermittent until the early 1980s and some critical attention. Personnel changes through the 1980s and 1990s further complicate the band's history. Among its many members: Ged Foley, who played with the House Band and Patrick Street; Pat Kilbride, now a solo artist in NYC; Jamie McMenemy, who performed for a time with Kornog (a Celtic band in Brittany); and others who have left music to work in the theater, teach, write novels, raise a family, and so forth. Through three decades, endless concerts, and well over a dozen albums (and appearances on radio's *A Prairie Home Companion*), the Battlefield Band's mix of traditional and new music is one of Scotland's most reliable exports.

Home Is Where the Van Is   Temple 2006

So many fine bands reinterpret traditional Celtic music, it's sometimes difficult to identify the standouts. That this one is a clear winner is immediately evident in the fine quartet playing on "Major Malley's March & Reel," which opens the set, and Ged Foley's strong, clear vocals on "Bonny Barbry-O." Whether it's Foley's skillful manipulation of the Northumbrian pipes on "The Keelman Ower Land," Brian McNeill's hurdy-gurdy, or Duncan MacGillivray's bagpipes behind "The Boar and the Fox," there's real magic here. On any other album, the foursome's collaboration on "The Lads o' the Fair" would be truly remarkable. Here, it's just one more song. Beautifully recorded in 1988.

LINK➤ *Boys of the Lough — Sweet Rural Shade*   *Shanachie 79068*
Although Donal Lunny's fiddle is a joy, the 25-year history of this traditional group offers that and more (including Christy O'Leary's expressive vocals). Here's one of their finer efforts. 1987's Farewell and Remember Me *(Shanachie 79067) is another.*

Across the Borders   Temple 2065

Recorded live at the 1996 Edinburgh International Festival (one of the planet's best—mayhem and fine music), this CD captures the energy of a great live band. Reels, jigs, and airs are magnetic (and NEVER dull). Folk story songs "Tramps & Hawkers" and "The Arran Convict" are crowd-pleasers. Great big Scottish bagpipes get their workout on "Donnie MacGregor." The emotional favorite is an air, "Miss Kate Rusby." Special guests include Californian Eric Rigler, whose Irish ("Uillean") bagpipes are standout, Alison Kinnaird on the lovely small Scottish harp, and the Radio Sweethearts, who do a just-for-fun recap of the Flying Burrito Brothers' "Six Days on the Road" with "bluegrass bagpipes." Wonderful show!

LINK➤ *Maddy Prior and the Carnival Band — Hang Up Sorrow & Care*
Park 31

Yes, they're English, not Scottish!—but few from this part of the world project such a joy-filled attitude toward their traditional music-making. Tons of spirit! And former Steeleye Span lead vocalist Prior sounds powerfully happy.

Keola Beamer

The **Hawaiian** tradition dates it's a style of bines the music can and Spanish brought guitars to much older choral  slack key guitar back a century; playing that compled by Mexicowboys (who the islands) and and rhythmic sounds. Beamer traces his family to 15th century Hawaiian royalty. His great-grandmother was an accomplished composer and a respected dancer. His mother is an educator and composer. Beamer was born in 1951, learned to play at an early age, and in 1972 recorded an LP called *Hawaiian Slack Key Guitar in the Real Old Style*; he also wrote a book about slack key guitar (like the LP, it's no longer available). These projects raised public interest in the musical style and paved the way for one of the most popular Hawaiian albums, 1978's *Honolulu City Lights* (Paradise 808), recorded with his brother Kapono. Beamer currently teaches, makes records for Dancing Cat, and performs on a regular basis.

Wooden Boat   Dancing Cat (Windham Hill) 38024
On this popular 1994 album, Beamer performs 14 acoustic numbers, some with bass, drums, and other percussion. "Hula Lady" suggests a warm breeze and the allure of a Hawaiian dancer. The Hawaiian flute (sounding wooden and similar to Native American flute) opens "Dancers in the Land of Po," a moody duet about twilight dancers; Beamer plays guitar and flute."Po Mahina (Night Moon)" retains influences of the vaqueros (early Spanish cowboys); it's a duet with producer (and Windham Hill mogul) George Winston. The album's folky title song celebrates the Hawai'i Loa, a 57-foot canoe launched in 1993 to rekindle an old tradition. Very commercial.

LINK➤ *Various Artists — Hawaiian Slack Key Masters:*
Instrumental Collection   *Dancing Cat (Windham Hill) 38032*
Introduction to the Dancing Cat series of contemporary slack key recordings. Includes Ray Kane, Leonard Kwan, Cyril Pahinui, etc.

Moe'uhane Kikia: Tales from the Dream Guitar
                                      Dancing Cat (Windham Hill) 38006
From 1995, a superb demonstration of slack key guitar recorded with extraordinary attention to sonic detail. "E Ku'u Morning Dew" follows a slow pace with a dappling of slightly faster high tones to evoke droplets, and careful control of harmonics for the pastel images. It is a masterwork. A standard among slack key players for a century, "Lei 'Awapuhi" is also played with pristine virtuosity (and a warm heart). The innocent love song "He Panuhele No 'Oe" is often heard at a wedding, or a lu'ua celebrating a baby's birth. Listen for slight tempo variations suggesting the natural process of breathing in and out. *Mauna Kea* (Dancing Cat 38011), from 1997, is equally fine.

LINK➤ *Roy Kane — Panahele*   *Dancing Cat 38001*
Gentle, elegant approach to slack key by one of the older masters. Kane paints beautiful pictures with his music.

Jay Begaye is a **Navajo** from Steamboat Canyon, Arizona. He has lived on the Similkameen Band reservation since 1988, a part of the Okanagan Interior Salish. He is a man of considerable talent, not only a singer, but also a sculptor, painter, and rodeo contestant. Begaye learned to sing by listening to other Pow Wow singers. After attending his first Pow Wow in Salt Lake City, Utah, Begaye began to compose. The American Indian Pow Wows support a great many large singing groups; Begaye joined the White Eagle Singers, and eventually became the group's lead singer. He later founded his own Pow Wow singing group, the Cathedral Lakes Singers. Begaye strongly believes that the power of American Indian music transcends its culture, and that songs are of great importance in keeping humanity and families together.

Honoring Our Ways   SOAR 170

The album features modern chants and prayers from the Dineh Nation, released by a label specializing in modern digital recordings of Native American music. The crystal-clear 1995 recording brings out the best in Begaye's vital approach to song (mostly low tenor with occasional falsetto for emphasis). A single drum typically provides structure for Begaye's calls and yearning songs. His "Lord's Prayer," written by a relative, Arlie Naskahai, urges delivery from all evil forever. "Rodeo Prayer Honor Song" is a multitracked a capella vocal, one whose internal rhythm is so powerful that drums are insinuated, but never heard. Four songs simulate choruses through multitracking; the other six feature Begaye with the Cathedral Lakes Singers.

LINK➤ *Rio Grande Singers — Turquoise Dancer*   SOAR 168
Very spirited Pow Wow songs from New Mexico. Fantastic voices, excellent recording quality. One of the best of this kind.

Cathedral Lakes Singers: Pow-Wow Wow Songs, Volume One   SOAR 116

One of two albums recorded by the Cathedral Lakes Singers with Jay Begaye as lead singer. (The other is *American Pow-Wow* [SOAR 142].) This live album was recorded at 1990's Tuba City Thunderbird Pow-Wow. Ecstatic male and female chanting voices intertwine with vocal calls and a single intense drum on "Grand Entry Song." The lighter, less intense "Grass Dance Song" is very different in feeling. "Retiring the Colors" has an end-of-day sense of joyful exhaustion. The songs are generally sung in Navajo, and typically require a few auditions before differences between them stand out. Begaye's wife, Lauren, is a member (and their baby daughter, Tiinisha, is sometimes heard, too).

LINK➤ *Various Artists — Songs of the Spirit*
Worldly (Triloka) 697-124-137
Contemporary Native American music borders on pop, fusion, and new age. Collection includes Little Wolf, R. Carlos Nakai, Primeaux & Mike, and Rita Coolidge.

Maria Bethânia is the sister of top **Brazilian** singer-songwriter Caetano Veloso. Born in 1946 in the interior region of Bahia, Brazil's northeastern state, she'd planned to become an actress. In 1963, Bethânia and her brother moved to the nearby state capital city of Salvador, where she impressed audiences singing in a musical (written by her brother). Bethânia has been a professional singer ever since. While in Salvador, she and her brother became friendly with Gilberto Gil and Gal Costa, and the four led a significant cultural movement called Tropicálismo that changed Brazilian music and art. It was so radical that Veloso and Gil were exiled, but Bethânia and Costa kept the movement alive in Brazil. Bethânia is a dramatic singer whose versatility is matched by her desire to experiment with a wide variety of songs and genres, and a willingness to introduce works by up-and-coming songwriters.

Simply the Best of Maria Bethânia (Simplesmente)
Verve 836-335

Several Bethânia collections are available, and at least one more is in the works, but this is the best current choice; there are more songs (21) and a longer running time (61 minutes) than the others. Most of this work is lighter, more pop-oriented, less serious. Only a few of these songs appear on the other recommended discs; most are hits from the 1970s. Some are quite lovely: "Cheiro de Amor (Odor of Love)," "O Lado Quente do Set (The Warm Side of Being)," and "Negue (Say No)." Buy the others first, but this disc belongs in every Brazil collection.

LINK➤ *Elis Regina — Fascinaçao (Fascination)*   *Verve 836-844*
A singer with phenomenal range and a spectacular interpreter, Regina was one of Brazil's top performers in the 1960s and 1970s. The 20 tracks on this best-of include excellent songs from Baden Powell, de Moraes, Jobim, Bosco, and other superior songwriters. Essential.

As Cancões Que Você Fez Pra Mim   Philips 518-214

This 1993 album was recorded twice. One version was recorded with Portuguese lyrics (as above). The other, called *Las Canciones Que Hiciste Para Mi* (Philips 518-787), is in Spanish. Both are majestic. Each is a collection of 11 songs written by Roberto and Erasmo Carlos and sung with a small combo backed by an enormous string section (magnificently arranged by Graham Preskett). Bethânia's powerful, dramatic interpretations are affecting on both the Portuguese and Spanish versions, but her passion breathes life into the Portuguese versions of "Fera Ferida," "Palavras," and "Eu Preciso de Você." Analog recording, but sounds better than most digital discs.

LINK➤ *Clara Nunes — The Best of Clara Nunes*   *World Pacific 96866*
For fifteen years, Nunes was one of Brazil's top interpreters. The blending of her voice with samba rhythms results in a more traditional sound than Bethânia's best work, but the influences are clear.

Memory of Skin (Memória da Pele) — Verve 838-928

The title of this 1989 album refers to the haunting memory of a lover's skin. Here, and throughout the album, Bethânia's voice is darker, more worldwise, glorious with meaning. Veloso contributes the best song, "Reconvexo," a portrait of the culture and energy of Bahia, his "Black Rome." The song's percussion and hand claps are so engaging that it's tough to sit while listening—and Bethânia's so welcoming that it's nearly impossible not to sing along. The tranquil songs, with their wistful fluegelhorn solos, are the most sensual: "Morena (Dark Skinned Girl)" and Buarque's "A Mais Bonita (The Prettiest)." Very highly recommended.

LINK▶ Various Artists — Brazil Classics 2: O Samba — Luaka Bop 26019
Samba continues to play an important role in Brazilian popular music. Interesting to contrast Bethânia's more sophisticated MPB with samba. Important singers here include Clara Nunes, Beth Carvalho, and the romantic voice of Agepê. And singer-songwriter Martinho da Vila.

Álibi — Verve 836-011

The best-selling Brazilian popular music album of all time, recorded in 1978 (Brazilian popular music is called MPB). Although she sings in Portuguese, Bethânia is a magnificent singer with extraordinary taste in songwriters: Caetano Veloso, Chico Buarque, and Djavan, who wrote the title track. Her interpretations transcend language (but a Portuguese-English dictionary is also a good idea). Veloso's "Diamante Verdadeiro" poetically describes the "brilliant truth" in a lover's voice. Buarque's "O Meu Amor" is a duet in which two women sing about their lovers; the harmonies are especially attractive. Arrangements are subtle, breezy, and ideal for Bethânia's rich, deep voice.

LINK▶ Gal Costa — Mina d'Agua do meu Canto — RCA 26323
MPB vocalist interprets Veloso and Buarque songs. (Interesting that the songwriters were considered dangerous in the late 1960s, but the women who interpreted their songs were allowed to stay.)

Âmbar — Metro Blue 54174

A sophisticated work finds Bethânia continuing to blaze her own direction. Much of the creative soul here comes from Jaime Além, whose impeccable taste informs many of the arrangements. His acoustic guitar provides an elegant background for Bethânia's flawless alto voice on "Chão de Estralas" and "Âmbar." She sings two Carlinhos Brown songs: "Lua Vermelha (Scarlet Moon)" and "Allez y," the latter with a charming arrangement by Luis Brasil. Chico Buarque duets on the lilting "Quando En Penso na Bahia (When I Think of Bahia)." Zap Mama leader Marie Doulne arranged "Iluminada," an up-tempo novelty performed mostly a capella with vocal percussion (and some violin from Além).

LINK▶ Various Artists — Brasil: A Century of Song — Blue Jackel 5000
4-CD set is useful as a general introduction to Brazil's traditional music, not as strong on MPB. CD1 begins with Carmen Miranda and explores early pop, folk, and traditional music. CD2 is carnaval music. CD3 covers bossa nova, CD4 does MPB without Veloso, Bethânia, Costa, or Gilberto Gil.

The **Jamaican** group Black Uhuru was formed in the mid-1970s by Derrick "Duckie" Simpson, and after the first of many personnel changes, hit its stride in the early 1980s with Michael Rose as lead singer. Rose, a charismatic stage presence, brought in producer Prince Jammy and raised hopes for a new album. Its failure brought more personnel changes. Simpson and Rose found a new female voice in Puma Jones, an American from South Carolina. The new trio approached Sly and Robbie to play rhythm and to produce. This time, everything worked. Hit singles led to an Island Records contract. The group broke through in England and then reached out to U.S. audiences by opening for the Police. Change came again in the mid-1980s. Rose was replaced by Junior Reid, and Jones died of cancer. Eventually, Don Carlos and Garth Dennis rejoined—both were founders of the original band. "Uhuru" is the Swahili word for "freedom."

Liberation: The Island Anthology
Mango 518-282

Black Uhuru's six Island/Mango albums were crucial to reggae's development through the 1980s and into the 1990s. Sly & Robbie produced most of this music with surprising percussion, overgrown bass, and deft studio effects. (A perfect example is "Youth" from 1983's *The Dub Factor* [Mango 539-756].) From their best album, 1981's *Red* (539-625), "Youth of Eglington" encouraged armed resistance by calling out to the West Indian neighborhood in Toronto—and to all African diaspora communities—as Michael Rose rhymed the names of weapons. From 1982's *Chill Out* (539-752), "Wicked Act" is an angry comment on poverty punctuated by gut-punch percussion. An important 2-CD compilation.

LINK▶ *Sly & Robbie — A Dub Experience*   *Island 539-787*
Mostly, this is a closer look at Sly & Robbie's fascinating rhythms without the added layers of vocals, melodies, and such. This CD is part of Mango's Reggae Greats *series; it's a best-of issued in 1984.*

Michael Rose — Dance Wicked   Heartbeat 214
Like his 1995 solo album, *Michael Rose* (Heartbeat 144), this 1997 release was a tremendous dance-hall success. The Black Uhuru style is evident, but Rose is far more focused. Mafia and Fluxy have produced a recording dense with effects and big rhythm, but they've kept the mix clear and sharp.The railroad rhythm on "Happiness" shakes the room with bass, but with the tiny nuances of a ringing bell. Rose's songwriting has improved with time; his melodic sense is well developed. "Dreadlocks" not only maintains its own hook, but looks back to "Happiness" for quotations. Maxi Priest joins in for "Lion in the Jungle," adding some lower-toned street smarts to Rose's sweet high tenor.

LINK▶ *Maxi Priest — The Best of Me*   *Charisma 86259*
Shows his range from lover's rock in the late 1980s with "Some Guys Have All the Luck" and "Wild World," and his transition to dance hall. Released in 1991, so many 1990s hits (like "That Girl" with Shaggy) are to be found on later albums.

Born in **Panama** in 1948, Blades grew up loving American rock, but a 1963 military conflict with the U.S. changed his focus to Latin music. Blades sang with Latin bands while studying law at the University of Panama. When military action closed his school, Blades visited NYC, played some dates and recorded, then returned to Panama in 1974 to complete his degree. After working as a lawyer for the Bank of Panama and rehabilitating convicts, Blades left for NYC, where he worked in the mailroom at Fania, a Latin label. He next worked for Ray Baretto, then joined Willie Colon, and later became a member of the Fania All-Stars. Blades won *Latin NY* magazine's Composer of the Year award in 1976. More recent collaborators include Lou Reed, Elvis Costello, and Sting. Acting credits include *The Two Jakes* and *The Milagro Beanfield War* . Always politically active, Blades ran a close second in Panama's 1994 Presidential election. And in 1997, he debuted on Broadway in Paul Simon's *The Capeman.*

The Best   Sony Latin 80718

From 1977 until 1986, Blades recorded ten albums for Fania, some with Willie Colon. Globo, a large Brazilian entertainment company, compiled his Fania hits on this CD, released in 1992 by Sony Latin. "Pedro Navaja," the desperate story of a Barrio gangster shot dead by a prostitute, is one of three songs from 1978's *Siembra* (Fania 537), the best-selling salsa album of all time. Among work from 1979's *Bohemio y Poeta* (541) are "Paula C." and "Sin tu Cariño," two sad love stories. Other songs come from *Canciones del Solar de los Aburridos* (591) and *Double Filo* (645). Essential, though the individual albums are also excellent.

LINK➤ *Willie Colon — Grandes Exitos*   *Sonido 2001*
Blades came to stardom by working closely with the brilliant Latin arranger and musician Willie Colon. This greatest hits album (which lacks anything vaguely resembling liner notes) includes good work together, and recordings made by Colon without Blades.

Buscando America   Elektra 60352

In "Buscando America (Searching for America)," the country is mute. It has been gagged and can't answer. In "Decisiones," Blades describes a high school girl who might be pregnant, a man about to hit another in the head with a baseball bat, and a driver too drunk to comprehend what he hit and why it screamed—all to the recurring theme of "Ave Maria." "Desapariciones (Disappearances)" wonders about everyday people who vanish. "El Padre Antonio y El Monaguillo Andres (Father Antonio and the altar boy, Andrés)" honors a good man and a promising boy. Both are shot dead while delivering Communion. The killer was never identified. Remarkable storytelling. From 1984.

LINK➤ *Bruce Springsteen — Nebraska*   *Columbia 38358*
1982 all-acoustic album by one of the U.S.'s finest musical commentators. Songs include "Mansion on the Hill" and "My Father's House."

Agua de Luna
Elektra 60721
These story songs are less literal, more poetic. Blades's songs were inspired by the works of Colombian author Gabriel Garcia Márquez (notable for *Love in the Time of Cholera*, etc.). Blades tells the abstract, mythical stories, but gives his Seis del Solar band more space to perform. "Ojos de Perro Azul (Eyes of a Blue Dog)" is performed as a medium-tempo dance, but the lyrics speak of a dog "dementedly searching for reality, hoping to suddenly see the truth." The title song, which translates as "Moon Water," and "Claro Oscuro (Twilight)" offer mystical connections between life, death, tranquility, and dreams. From 1987.

LINK➤ *Joe Cuba — El Pirata del Caribe (The Caribbean Pirate)*
Alegre (Tico) 1434
NYC salsa and boogaloo star Joe Cuba provided the young Blades with end-less encouragement, and his influences obviously ran deep. Listen to "Mulata y Bella," "Y Joe Cuba Ya Llego," and "Que Mucha Gente Maseta."

Ruben Blades y Son del Solar...Live!
Elektra 60868
A wonderful live concert. Recorded in 1989 at NYC's Lone Star Roadhouse, Blades is relaxed and at his very best. There's less hardcore intensity, as well as more opportunities for the new band to excel and an adoring audience. The band, formed about year earlier, is an 11-piece ensemble called Son de Solar. The music is hot, but it's also sophisticated and smart, an evolved version of salsa and Latin jazz. Most songs are expanded versions of work found on *Encenas* (Elektra 60432), *Agua de Luna* (60721) and *Buscando America* (60352). The live versions of "Decisiones" and "Muévete" are great party songs.

LINK➤ *Los Fabulosos Cadillacs — Vascos Vacíos* *Sony Discos 81220*
Like Blades, Los Fabulosos Cadillacs have introduced rock audiences to Latin music. (Their live performances are legendary.) This 1994 album recaps most of their first decade. They come from Argentina, but influences are quite broad.

La Rosa de Los Vientos
Sony Tropical 81992
An album that deserves considerably more attention than it has received, this is a lovely return to Panamanian roots, and an extremely appealing introduction to the traditional music of Central America. The work is done by young Panamanian musicians on acoustic instruments native to the culture. On both the title song and "Alma de tu Flor," the mood is light and relaxed, the melodies easy, and the vocals warm and inviting. "Todo Mi Amor" is a ballad with spare accompaniment. Many of these songs recall salsa's early days. The Afro-Caribbean drum patterns, the horn arrangements, and Blades's singing style recalls the early days of salsa. Don't miss this!

LINK➤ *Totó La Momposina Y Sus Tambores —*
La Candela Viva *RealWorld (Caroline) 2337*
Self-assured female vocalist Totó La Momposino sings traditional music with a spirited, small chorus above thundering drums. With a voice like Celia Cruz, she has remained close to her family in Colombia. In other words: she's not famous, but she's a world-class singer.

Born in the **Ivory Coast** in 1953, Seydou Kone was raised by his grandmother, who taught him the Koran and native Dioula morality. Kone picked up languages easily, English in school, French from the Bible. He listened to U.S. rock and soul, and soon performed under the stage name Alpha Blondy (a nickname from his grandmother—Alpha means "first," and "Blondy" is a pun for "bandit"). In the early 1970s, he attended NYC's Columbia University, supported himself as a messenger, and hung out in Harlem's clubs. He met a producer and recorded, but the producer disappeared with the tapes, sending Blondy into a two-year depression. The turnaround came with videos seen throughout French Africa: he dressed as a Rasta, wore a hardhat emblazoned with a Star of David, and carried both a Bible and a Koran. His 1985 African tour played to huge audiences (250,000-plus), including heads of state; European tours followed. Blondy currently lives in Paris.

The Best of Alpha Blondy   Shanachie 43075
The ultimate Alpha Blondy collection, this best-of CD includes the cream of Blondy's four Shanachie CDs. The first cut, "Cocody Rock," is one of five recorded at Tuff Gong studios in 1987 with the Wailers on backup (the trip to Jamaica and the session were a dream come true for the African Blondy). It's a rouser, a true reggae classic. "Jerusalem," recorded with chimes and small chorus, begins with a Jewish blessing, then breaks into a reggae beat. The unifying Blondy sings in many languages: French, Dioula, English, and Arabic. Five cuts with his own Solar System Band are more elaborate productions.

LINK➤ *Mandators — Power of the People: Nigerian Reggae*
Heartbeat (Rounder) 156
Although South Africa's Lucky Dube is the other familiar name associated with African reggae, The Mandators have more recently been the top performers. Their greatest hits.

Apartheid Is Nazism
Shanachie 43042
Blondy at his political best. The title cut implores America to "break the neck of this apartheid." Songs are sung in English, French, and (mostly) Dioula; every tune is strong, but translated lyrics would have helped to sort out Blondy's pungent meaning. Arrangements are often thrilling; Blondy's Solar System Band includes two lead guitars, two rhythm guitars, two drummers, a very

clever percussionist (named "Lick"), three horns, four backing vocalists, and a keyboard player. With a less skillful mixer, this could be a muddy mess, but recorder/mixer Hervé Lecoz deserves special mention for extremely clean, slick production.

LINK➤ *Peter Tosh — No Nuclear War*   *EMI America 46700*
Former Wailer Peter Tosh in one of his angriest efforts. He takes on apartheid, nuclear war, and numerous other topical subjects. His final album (a short time after it was recorded, Tosh was assassinated).

The Bothy Band's members initially came together for a series of **Irish** radio broadcasts. Largely the creation of bouzouki player Dónal Lunny, the Bothy Band gave its first concert at Dublin's Trinity College in February 1975. The lineup changed a bit, and although a permanent unit, Lunny and fellow members also played with other bands (Lunny was often seen with Christy Moore, for instance). The Bothy Band attacked Irish music with the intensity of a rock band; live performances, according to all accounts, were riveting. Financial and management problems further clouded the future; here was one of Ireland's supergroups, more user-friendly and exciting than the Chieftains, but in August 1979, at the Ballisdodare Festival in Country Sligo, Ireland, the Bothy Band gave its last performance. Members moved on to other projects; Lunny, for one, joined Planxty and recorded with former Silly Wizard musician Andy M. Stewart.

1975—The First Album   Green Linnet 3011

Of all the Bothy Band albums, this is the one that set the standard. Recorded in 1975, it's filled with traditional Irish songs played on Uillean pipes, whistles, bouzouki, bodhrán, and fiddle—all traditional instruments. Still, this is a step toward a contemporary blend of rock rhythms (however subtle here) and an updating of Irish music. This is the only Bothy Band album with energetic fiddler Tommy Peoples, but Paddy Keenan's work on the pipes and whistles and Donal Lunny's bouzouki are also exceptional. For those beginning to explore contemporary Irish music, this is an excellent place to start.

LINK➤ *Tommy Peoples — The Iron Man*   *Shanachie 1995*
Peoples remains one of the finest Irish fiddlers, and now, there's a widely available album that states his case. Also on hand: Dáithí Sproule, who has played guitar for Altan (Sproule's own solo effort, Heart Made of Glass *[Green Linnet 1123], is also worth owning).*

The Best of the Bothy Band
Green Linnet 3001

An honest best-of covering all four albums: *1975- The First Album, Old Hag You Have Killed Me, After Hours,* and *Out of the Wind Into the Sun* (each is available on CD and worth owning). Standout cuts include a reel and song, "Pretty Peg/Craig's Pipes," and another song, "Do You Love an Apple?," both featuring the remarkable female vocalist Tríonna Ní Dhoumhnaill; "The Blackbird," which begins as a dramatic air, then breaks into a set dance, and concludes as a reel; and "The Death of Queen Jane," a sad vocal with a melancholy pipe solo from Paddy Keenan. "Fionnghuala" is Scots-Gaelic mouth music—a tight, fast, a capella surprise, perfectly executed.

LINK➤ *Planxty — The Planxty Collection*   *Shanachie 79012*
Recaps their three Shanachie releases and reintroduces the friendly discussion about whether Planxty or the Bothy Band was the more important in the 1970s folk revival.

In 1990, former Boukman Eksperyans members Eddy François (lead vocalist), Vladimy "Jimmy" Jean Felix (guitarist), and Evens Seney (one of several percussionists) formed a new group. A leading band in **Haiti**'s current roots movement, Boukan Ginen's orientation is strongly affected by voodoo passion. The word "boukan" refers to the fire or fire pit central to voodoo ceremonies; the word "ginen" comes from the name of a drumstick also used in these ceremonies. The connotations linked to African religious practices result in spiritual power and cultural identity. Boukan Ginen is a ten-piece band heavy on guitars and percussion. The band's work is angry and controversial; this resulted in an exile from Haiti after President Aristede's overthrow in the early 1990s (the musicians found shelter in NYC). By the mid-1990s, the situation in Haiti had settled down, and Boukan Ginen became well known.

Jou a Rive   Xenophile (Green Linnet) 4024

The group's basic formula features the clear, soulful voice of Eddy François atop a rhythm constructed by a hard-packed bass and percussion line. The music is accented by electric guitar riffs and a combination of alto and tenor sax and trumpet. A small street chorus joins in as well. "Sa Rèd" is an announcement that everyone has endured enough misery. "Lib (Free)" and "Jou a Rive (The Day Will Come)" are majestic, optimistic anthems to the bright promise of a nation's future; uplifting arrangements and François's vocals attract attention to these important songs. "Nati Kongo," which comes close to a reggae beat, praises Kongo ancestors and heroes like Bob Marley and Steven Biko. Recorded in the early 1990s, but not widely released until 1995.

LINK➤ *Various Artists — Caribbean Revels:*
Haitian Rara and Dominican Gaga   *Smithsonian Folkways 40402*
Field recordings from the streets provide an academically interesting look at some roots of current popular music. Made in the mid-1970s. Search the used bins for 1989's Konbit: Burning Rhythms of Haiti (A&M 5281), compiled by film director and Haitian art collector Jonathan Demme, for great work from Tabou Combo and others.

Rèv an Nou   Xenophile (Green Linnet) 4027

The musicians in Boukan Ginen begin their concerts with horns, drums, and guitars playing at full blast; "Salouwe (Greeting)" opens this album in the same way. The next track is the upbeat, chanting celebration "Afrika"; it's followed by "Zanfan Nago (The Children of Nago)," a thoughtful call for the reunification of the black nation. "Move Fanmi (Wrong Family)" and "Nèg Yo Danjere (Those Men Are Dangerous)" are challenge songs—variations  of traditional Haitian songs that point a finger at wretched leaders without the danger of actually naming names. Encouragement to speak out for the next generation is heard on "Timoun Yo (The Children)." The lyrics shout: "They are without strength, without support....We need people to defend their rights."

LINK➤ *Fela Kuti — Black Man's Cry*   *Shanachie 44013*
Recordings from 1975-78 by one of Africa's most outspoken talents. Strong lyrics, good solid jazz.

Boukman Eksperyans

Boukman was the slave who led the **Haitian** revolution against France in 1804, a struggle that helped create the New World's first black republic. A Vodou priest, Boukman taught his followers to fight oppression and to take pride in their heritage. The importance of these messages are the heart of Boukman Eksperyans, a radical dance band influenced by rara festival music and ceremonial drumming (their style is called Voudo Adjae). In 1989, 1990, and 1991, the group became famous through a series of songs criticizing Haitian leadership. The 1991 military coup ousted Aristede and placed the army in power; vicious actions against the band included the teargassing of a high school dance, threats with guns to discourage concert performances of political songs, and ultimately, a band member's death (due to an embargo and a need for medicine). In 1994 while touring, the band was left without a home country; Jamaica then became home.

Vodou Adjee   Mango 539-899

Boukman Eksperyans's career took off with the thrilling "Ké-m Pa Sote," a carnival song with a mighty edge, a street anthem with large-scale singalong choruses, street-smart drumming, police whistles, laughter, and the anger of a hurricane. (The English title is "My Heart Doesn't Leap [I'm Not Afraid]".) Hard rocking guitars and aggressive singing recall music from Zimbabwe on "Mizere' Re' (Misery Follows You)," summed up by: "the time has arrived to make a revolution." The vocalists' passion on "Nou Pap Sa Bliye (We Won't Forget This)," and pride in "Se Kreyeo'l Nou Ye (We're Creole)" once again explains why oppressive politicians are terrified of music's power. From 1990.

LINK➤ *Rara Machine — Break the Chain*   *Shanachie 64038*
New Haitian music from 1991 with greater emphasis on Latin drums and horns, and on traditional Haitian instruments. Without the political acidity; the "chain" in the title song refers to Haitian sugar cane farming—encouraging city dwellers to return to the rural life.

Freedom (Let's Take It!)/Libète (Pran Pou'l!) Mango 539-946

Haiti's political situation worsened in the first half of the 1990s, and the effect on the band was direct and forceful. "Jou Male (Day of the Shock)," the 1993 Carnival song's lyrics strafed the military—"A mafia is sucking our blood with no mercy" and "Spoiled food dressed in red" (uniforms were red)—and the song was banned. On "Libète," sweet voices of freedom from backup vocalists answer the yearning lead of "Lôlô" (Theodore Beaubrun, Jr.). Throughout this 1994 album, the four Beaubrun silblings show themselves to be potent singers and instrumentalists. Lead guitar from "Ti Bazol" (Mackel Jean-Baptiste) and complex percussion cast an intoxicating spell.

LINK➤ *Kassav' — Double Best Of*   *E.M.A.P. 472076*
The enormously popular zouk band from the French Antilles. Unfortunately, their best records are only available as imports. (This one was found in the World Music Distribution catalog—www.worldmusic.com.) A 2-CD collection of hits.

A controversial reggae dance hall deejay, Buju Banton has been one of **Jamaica**'s most popular 1990s stars. The youngest of 15 children, he was born in 1973 to a poor family in a ghetto near Kingston. His given name was Mark Myrie. Buju is a nickname assigned to overweight children. (It means "breadfruit"; young Mark apparently fit the description.) It's not clear whether the Banton name came from a local term used to describe a storyteller or from Jamaican performer Burro Banton (perhaps both). Late in his teens, Buju Banton was recording hit records that were harshly criticized—"Boom Boom Bye Bye" pressed for the murder of homosexuals. His songs about sex often involved violence and abuse. As he became a Rastafarian and a recording artist for a major label (Mercury), things changed. He founded Project Willy to encourage condom use, and now teaches religion. He also sings against violence.

Mister Mention   Penthouse 1997

Banton in the days before his realization of social conscience: the early 1990s. "Batty Rider" was a Number 1 hit in England and Jamaica, and throughout the dance-hall world. The song is about short shorts, and the way they ride up.... "Dickie" has girls tearing down a boy's back fence to get at his body part. In those days, taking a body at gunpoint seemed like a reasonable strategy to make sex happen, as described in the song "Have to Get You Tonight." None of these songs, however, was as controversial as "Love Me Browning," in which Banton expressed a preference for lighter-skinned women. He recanted this position in a later hit, also included here, called "Love Black Woman."

LINK➤ *Shabba Ranks — Cran Dun*   *VP 1450*
2-CD greatest hits by reggae rapper. Aggressive sexual energy from the late 1980s and early 1990s.

'Til Shiloh   Loose Cannon (Island) 524-119

Buju Banton's music combines three basic elements: a rap-like rhythmic style of speaking that sometimes resembles melodic singing, a sturdy rhythm track, and some samples. His voice is best in its lowest register. Fortunately, a lyric sheet is provided to make sense of his sometimes rapid-fire delivery. "'Til I'm Laid to Rest" is one of this 1995 album's best cuts. It's an intricate rhythm look toward roots in Africa with a catchy hook. "Murderer" pursues a different theme: "Murder! Your insides must be hollow. How does it feel to take the life of another?" Banton's duet with singer Garnett Silk on "Complaint" and the desperate optimism of "Untold Stories" are also highlights.

LINK➤ *Beenie Man — Maestro*   *VP 1486*
From a top deejay, skillful integration of speaking, percussion, horns, and keyboards. Slick integration of jazz and reggae, too. Charismatic stage presence. Clever, even at fast speeds.

Earl Bullhead born in 1948. He's a **Lakota Sioux**, a kin to the Nakota (in Canada) and Dakota (in the northern U.S.). Specifically, Bullhead is a Standing Rock Lakota, living with his people on a reservation in North Dakota. He started singing Lakota songs as a child, and he's been singing ever since. Bullhead stays close to home, performing in the Plains with a Pow Wow group that has become locally renowned. As with many Native American artists, one of Bullhead's motivations is education: he spends a great deal of time teaching young people about Lakota ways, Lakota language, and Lakota music. Some of his songs go back a long way; others he has written. Not all of Bullhead's songs are traditional. Many were written using traditional language and traditional instruments, but are lyrically modern. (Incidentally, the term "Sioux" is no great honor—it's derived from a derogatory word in French.)

Walking the Red Road   SOAR 141

Lakota songs old and new. This album, released in 1993, contains "Hesapa Oloowan Wan (Black Hills Song)," which begins with a soft drum, then a chant-like vocal that's a particular combination of falsetto and groan. The song is about taking personal responsibility for the Black Hills given by the Great Spirit (referred to here and in many of Bullhead's songs as "Grandfather"). "Sinakaki He Wakye (Family Camp Circle)" is a newer Bullhead composition that uses older images of teepees to rekindle an old, comfortable feeling. The lyrics: "All of the families are in their rightful spots....Come down friend, we do all these things for you and ask nothing in return."

LINK➤ *Vince Two Eagles — In America*   *SOAR 173*

Contemporary Lakota country-folk singer. Performed in English (with guitar, bass, and drum accompaniment), but the underlying messages are connected with Bullhead's work.

Sacred Directions   SOAR 185

One of the better introductions to Native American music, this clear and strong 1996 recording is lovingly annotated with a written statement of purpose, song histories, lyrics, and English translations. Bullhead's adopted father taught him "Wacekiya Olowan Wan (A Prayer Song)" to share the related values of humility and community prayer. From "Wakan Tanka Tokaheya (Large and Holy)," he learned the purpose of prayer and felt less alone during a difficult time (recovering from addiction). Many of the songs are about learning and personal growth through spirituality. Bullhead sings out with a reedy baritone, generally accompanied by a single drum.

LINK➤ *Black Lodge Singers — Pow Wow Highway Songs*   *SOAR 125*

From the Blackfoot tribe in Montana, one of the most popular family groups on the Pow Wow circuit. Lead singer is Kenny Scabby Robe. The album features pronounced drumming and singing that is a bit distant.

Winston Rodney took the name Burning Spear to celebrate Kenya's champion of independence, Jomo Kenyatta, a legacy that he has taken very seriously. Rodney grew up in St. Ann's, **Jamaica**, and started recording in 1969 at Studio One with producer Clement "Sir Coxsone" Dodd, but his rockers-like sound was neither understood nor accepted. He retreated and tried again in 1975, this time with producer Jack Ruby, and established himself as an important reggae talent with a series of successful albums. In 1980, Burning Spear appeared in the reggae film Rockers, showing off his remarkable voice in an a capella performance of "Jah No Dread." After more than 25 years in the music business, and dozens of albums, his concerts tend toward the mystical and ecstatic. Few performers are more sincere, or more powerful, advocates of Marcus Garvey, Rastafarian beliefs, the power of Africa, and the message of world unity.

Chat Down Babylon: Island Anthology Island Jamaica 524-190

Sadly, the majority of Burning Spear's albums are no longer available on CD. Happily, his best work is collected on this 2-CD set from Island Jamaica. The first CD covers the productive 1975-78 period when Burning Spear recorded "Marcus Garvey," "Slavery Days," "Man in the Hills," "Throw Down Your Arms," "Dry & Heavy," and other hits tied to social consciousness. While significant, they lack the variety of tempo and arrangement that brighten the second CD, which contains mostly 1990s music. "Mek We Dweet," "Jah Kingdom," and the Grateful Dead song "Estimated Prophet" are among many highlights.

LINK▶ *Mutabaruka — The Ultimate Collection*   Shanachie 45026

Outspoken, literate, brilliant dub poet tells stories essential to every reggae library. Included: "Great Kings of Africa," "The People's Court," "Witeman Country," "Drug Kulcha," and other works accompanied by reggae's best musicians. Acid humor. Solid commentary.

Resistance   Heartbeat (Rounder) 33

On this 1986 Grammy nominee, the featured horn section provides rhythmic accents and serves as a chorus, often answering Burning Spear's easy-flowing vocals. The hypnotic "Mek We Yadd" is constantly refreshed by the horns. "Holy Foundation" starts with a strong beat and chimes, and Lenford Richards's lead guitar is captivating, but a tenor sax answered by several guitars and horns adds the essential spice. "Love to You" is mostly a horn piece with sparse, underplayed lyrics from Spear. Two revolving motifs, a pretty blues guitar riff and horns quoting "Grazin' in the Grass," combine for one of his best recordings.

LINK▶ *Third World — Reggae Ambassadors:*
20th Anniversary Collection   Mercury 518-294

Through the 1970s, 1980s, and into the 1990s, Third World has expanded reggae's involvement in the world of pop music. A 2-CD set of their hits, plus some concert work.

Cafe Tacuba took shape in 1989, when a group of design students in Mexico City discussed ways in which the world might be changed, and eventually drifted into a realization. **Mexican** rock bands, by and large, did not do much with Mexican roots music. Moved to action, they formed Cafe Tacuba (the band was named for a local hangout). Anonimo (whose stage name translates into "anonymous") sings lead and plays guitar; he has changed his name several times during the band's short history (another name he used was Cosme). Joselo Rangel plays electric and acoustic guitar, and his brother Quique Rangel plays bass. Emmanuel Del Real completes the band on keyboards, programming, and guitar. Everyone sings backup vocals. Stylistically, they're not an easy band to pin down: GenX meets old Mexico, metal meets folk, and sometimes pop, free jazz, mambo, and hip-hop, as well.

Re WEA Latina 96784

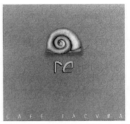

Their second album: an international multi-platinum success in 1994. The music is difficult to classify. Sung in Spanish, "El Aparato" begins with a typically Mexican acoustic guitar and vocal. More contemporary percussion undercuts the traditional. The song next switches to a slow tempo, then to a thundering fast tempo that is harder, more contemporary. "La Ingrata" is almost bubble-gum rock. "El Ciclón" is techno, harsh, street. "El Borrego" is more relentless and extreme. Jarring jump on "Esa Noche" to old-fashioned Mexican village harmonies is disconcerting. Maybe "24 Horas" is neo-punk. Rock music that began in a nearby non-U.S. culture. Is it "world music?" Or rock with Spanish lyrics?

LINK▶ Fito Paez — Circo Beat WEA Latina 98242
Paez is a leading rock star in Argentina and throughout the Latin world (also an actor and director). This 1994 album views life as a crazed circus; songs are about his life. It was co-produced by Roxy Music's Phil Manzanera. Solid commercial rock. Paez's best to date.

Avalancha de Exitos WEA Latina 16718

The over-the-top title refers to an avalanche of hit songs by other Latin artists. This 1996 album is filled with cover versions, often performed with a peculiar urban mix of reverence and attitude. Juan Luis Guerra's "Ojalá que Llueva Café (I Hope It Rains Coffee)" gets a full-scale Mexican traditionalist treatment. The album opens with "Chilanga Banda (Mexico City Crew)," a rap about a poor, drunk, bored teenager. "Metamorfosis" grows into something akin to either the Beatles' "I Am the Walrus" or something by Queen. Leo Dan's "Cómo Te Extraño Mi Amor" is also twisted into ska. It's more interesting if the original songs are familiar, but still potent if they aren't.

LINK▶ Juan Luis Guerra — Ojalá que Llueva Café Karen 29418
Top-selling album with a poetic title track (actually several songs are as lovely). The album includes some Dominican dance music by one of the country's biggest stars. Very appealing, even if the words are unfamiliar.

Singer Karen Matheson met Donald Shaw, who plays accordion and keyboards, at school in Oban, **Scotland**. Matheson had learned many traditional songs from her grandmother, a renowned singer in the Outer Hebrides. Matheson and Shaw played together in the mid-1980s; in time, Manus Lunny (bouzouki), John Siach (bass), and Charlie McKerron (fiddle) joined the band. Over the years, the personnel has changed, but Matheson, Shaw, and Lunny have remained the group's central force. A TV soundtrack for a documentary about Gaelic Scots led to a Scottish platinum disc, and their work on the film *Rob Roy* in 1995 encouraged more interest, particularly in the U.S. As a result of aggressive touring and consistently fine recordings (and numerous awards), Capercaillie has built a following among Celtic audiences in South America, the Middle East, Africa, and among many listeners who do not typically purchase Celtic music.

Sidewaulk

Green Linnet 1094

Dónal Lunny produced this 1989 release. It was the group's fourth album—the one that captured their energetic stage presence and caught the critics' attention. "Alasdair Mhic Cholla Ghasda (Alasdair, Son of Gallant Coll)" is sung to the unique rhythm of a cloth being beaten on a table (done to shrink a tweed fresh from the loom). It's a traditional song, performed by lead vocalist Karen Matheson and a male chorus. Amidst several medleys of tightly played reels, jigs, and other instrumental pieces, there's the beautiful anthem to an emigrant's old homeland, "Oh Mo Dhùthaich (Oh, My Country)." Matheson's inspiring voice sparkles on "Iain Ghlinn' Cuaich (John of Glen Cuaich)."

LINK▶ *Dick Gaughan — Coppers & Brass*   *Green Linnet 3064*
1977 album of Irish and Scottish dances (jigs, hornpipes, reels), all performed on by one man with his guitar (with some piano fill). An extremely talented musician.

To the Moon

Green Linnet 3117

Matheson's near-whisper over a mystical instrumental bed is sometimes interrupted by the resonant, otherworldly impact of the bodhrán on the traditional "A Nighean Donn." The song then breaks into a peppy near-pop arrangement of "A Ghealaich"—these two parts constitute the title song. Manus Lunny's "Claire in Heaven" is a contemporary folk-rock song with some fiddle and bouzouki instrumental breaks. Several songs begin with new age synthesized ether that breaks when Matheson starts to sing; then, the rhythm comes in while a dreamy background continues; this is the format of "Ailein Duinn," for example. Made in 1995, the album is a sophisticated, contemporary take on traditional music.

LINK▶ *Runrig — Mara*   *Avalanche 35*
Seek out this important Scottish band for their emphasis on culture, and their knack for portraying the land and its wonder in music. Sound combines Gaelic traditional with English rock. The name of the album means "sea," a concept supported throughout the album.

Folksinger Carthy was born in 1941 in Hatfield, **England**. His mother had been a folk dancer and singer in the 1920s and 1930s, and he often heard folksongs as a child. Carthy started his career as an actor, but at 19, switched to skiffle (a rough blend of blues, folk, jazz, and pop). By the early 1960s, he'd made the transition to folk music and eventually became a resident musician at London's best folk club, the Troubador. Many popular folk singers from the U.S. saw him there; Paul Simon adapted Carthy's "Scarborough Fair" for a Simon & Garfunkel album. Carthy toured and recorded, often with David Swarbrick on violin. In 1969, Carthy joined Steeleye Span for several years, playing electric guitar, then sang more traditional British music as one of the Watersons (with his wife, Norma Waterson). In the 1980s, he played with Brass Monkey and on a great many special projects.

The Collection
Green Linnet 1136

A 1993 compilation from five albums recorded in the 1970s and 1980s, of which only *Sweet Wivelsfield* (Rounder 3020) is generally available in the U.S. "Palaces of Gold" is a wry, cutting protest song about conditions of poor schoolchildren. Carthy excels with songs like "Bill Norrie," a labyrinth about a twisted relationship. He's also a master with old English ballads and gives a minstrel-like performance on the dark song "Lord Randal." Trickery plays a part in "Willie's Lady," a song about a surprising birth. Fair to say that much of this is musical literature, sometimes more compelling in lyric than in melody.

LINK➤ *Ewan MacColl — Black and White: The Definitive Collection*
Green Linnet 3058
Recordings made from 1972 to 1986 by one of Britain's greatest folksingers. MacColl shares Carthy's interest in old songs, but his political and social commentary connects just as often to Pete Seeger. (MacColl was married to Seeger's half-sister, Peggy, who often plays guitar and sings duets.)

Skin & Bone
Green Linnet 3075

A 1992 album with frequent partner Dave Swarbrick, who shares Carthy's passion for collecting old English songs and fragments thereof, and whose musical style is entirely compatible. Typical is "The Sheep Stealer," which they expanded from a kernel of a song supplied by Mrs. Woodberry in Somerset. Percy Grainger, who gathered songs and made field recordings, was a source for "The Mown Hay" and "I Courted a Damsel." Unafraid to tackle rough and taboo subjects, "Lucy Wan" deals with incest, and "Clyde's Water" with extreme parental control. Songs are always sweetly sung, and the pair are very much in command of the acoustic guitar and fiddle. Their 1990 duets on their *Life and Limb* album (Green Linnet 3052) are equally good.

LINK➤ *Fairport Convention — Liege & Lief*
A&M 4257
Swarbrick was not only Fairport's violinist, but also a key creative force in the band. He joined for this album, and went on to lead the band. Much of this early 1970s work is unavailable (best: Angel Delight, Babbacombe Lee, Rosie), but Full House *(Hannibal 4417) is in print.*

Chandra has approached the music industry on her own terms. Born to **Indian** parents and raised in England, she started working professionally at age 13 with regular appearances on a children's TV series. At 16, she was the lead singer for Monsoon, a band whose first single, "Ever So Lonely," was in the Top Ten (the band played dance music with Western and Indian instruments). At 17, in response to record company demands for a more commercial product, Chandra started her own label, along with ex-Monsoon producer and writer (and later, her husband) Peter Coe, recording highly original music. By the mid-1980s, at age 20, Chandra stopped working for four years, took time to learn more about her Indian heritage, and became fascinated with Islamic chants. More than most musicians, Chandra has not only absorbed these diverse sounds, but also successfully woven them into her music.

Out On My Own RealWorld (Caroline) 1783

Although Chandra would subsequently become well-known for chants, drones, and sound sculpting, this CD, her first solo work, is very satisfying Indian pop music. The songs are catchy, the instrumentation is unconventional (tabla, keyboards, sitars), and Chandra is already experimenting with vocalizations in place of lyrics. Recorded in 1983, this CD is more than a transition from the Monsoon pop/rock band to a solo career. As with many of her earlier albums, some songs are straight pop tunes that you'd hear on the radio, and others are more traditional Indian instrumentals, typically with some chanting or vocal percussion.

LINK▶ *Najma – Qareeb* Shanachie 64009
Another well-known world music singer who grew up in London's Indian community, and grew from Indian pop music to a broader agenda. This 1987 album blends the short lyric poem form known as ghazal with Western instruments. Very accessible. Beautiful voice.

Quiet RealWorld (Caroline) 1782

A radical departure for 1984, Chandra's second album has no lyrics, no pop melodies, no commercial potential. It's a lovely, complex, layered work that celebrates the human voice as musical instrument. Chandra updates many vocal styles, such as "spoken bols"—a rhythmic singing of a note's name as it is sung: "Sa," "Re," "Ga"... (these sounds are similar to the Western "Do," "Re," "Mi"...). Each track is called "Quiet," followed by a number. On "Quiet 3," Chandra overdubbed her voice 384 times to create a single chord. "Quiet 2" has a bluesy vocal; "Quiet 6" is inspired by reggae dub breath beats.

LINK▶ *Yungchen Lhamo – Tibet, Tibet* *RealWorld (Caroline) 2363*
From a vastly different culture, her remarkable voice sings out with spiritual devotion. At her best without accompaniment, Lhamo is sometimes presented with the Gyoto Monks, and with a mild acoustic instrumental background.

The Struggle
RealWorld (Caroline) 1781

Chandra's third solo album is an eclectic mix. It's fascinating to hear ideas later popularized by rap—pronounced drum tracks, repeated sample-like vocals—imposed on Indian and street rhythms. Most songs are commercial Indian pop whose lyrics try to reconcile tradition with the modern world. "Om Shanti Om" is a sacred Indian chant, but sometimes a blues guitar plays along. The title cut is like her later work: multiple percussion instruments, gongs, and cymbals in giant sheets of sound, and vocals that soar, repeat as percussion beds, and carry a lovely Indian chant-like melody, constantly pushing the limits of 1985's eight-track recording technology.

LINK➤ *Various Artists — Her Song: Exotic Voices of Women From Around the World*   *Shanachie 64077*
With Pura Fé (Native American), Kirsten Bråten Berg (Norway). Part of a mid-1990s marketing trend. Try also: Women of the World International *(Putamayo 119) with Amoya (Mozambique), Sophia Arvanitit (Greece), Anima (Tunisia).*

Weaving My Ancestor's Voices
RealWorld (Caroline) 2322

The title of this 1992 album refers to deep connections among musical traditions. "Dhyana and Donalgue" is an a capella rendition of a thousand-year old Irish ballad with some Muslim influences. "Nana" is a Spanish lullaby played over a drone (it recalls the Beatles' "Tomorrow Never Knows"). A ghat is a song in which an classical Indian vocalist demonstrates skill by singing variations. English folk song lyrics and ghat structure on "The Enchantment" make sense of the concept for Western ears. "Speaking in Tongues" uses rapid-fire percussive vocals; this was once a drumming teacher's tool; now it's a full-fledged Indian art form. *The Zen Kiss* (Caroline 2342) follows the vocal strand farther.

LINK➤ *Anonymous Four — An English Ladymass*
                    Harmonia Mundi France 90780
NYC quartet recreates 13th and 14th century chant and polyphonic song. Not only is this music beautiful, it's soulful. Lovely recording as well.

ABoneChroneDrone
RealWorld (Caroline) 2356

This 1996 album is similar to *Quiet*, but the production is far more elaborate. Each of the six numbered drones here are soundscapes: extended vocal tones, punctuated by vocal percussion and some subtle instrument sounds (bagpipes on one track, a didgeridoo on another). The overall effect is ethereal and calming, with the feelings that might arise when walking down a windy shoreline or traveling through the sky in a glider. There are obvious similarities to new age music, but Chandra's scholarly understanding of vocal music and her past experiences in sculpting vocal sounds and drones suggest greater depth.

LINK➤ *Various Artists — Trance Planet: Volumes 1, 2, 3*
                Worldly Music (Triloka) 444-477-206, 7120, 4110
Mid-1990s collections of soundscapes with drones, repeating rhythms, synthesized textures, and some ecstatic vocals. Each volume mixes well-known names (Chandra, Zakir Hussain, Cesaria Evora, Oumou Sangare, Ali Akbar Khan, Mercedes Sosa) with less familiar artists.

The best-known of **Irish** traditional bands for several decades, the Chieftains started in Dublin in 1963. They were popular from the start; Paddy Moloney on the Uillean pipes (pronounced "ill-un," it's an Irish bagpipe) was a respected virtuoso, and he was a major draw; other musicians were also significant contributors in the traditional Irish subculture. The Chieftains were popular, but they performed and recorded on a part-time basis until the early 1970s. They gained momentum with a new generation of Irish Americans and reached an even larger audience on the soundtrack of Stanley Kubrick's film, *Barry Lyndon*. A tour and TV appearances followed, along with an Island Records contract. In time, this generated significantly more recording activity, involvement with rock stars (Van Morrison, for example), more film soundtracks, high-visibility work with orchestras, and celebrity status. (John Glatt's biography of the Chieftains was published by St. Martin's Press in 1997.)

The Chieftains 3 Shanachie 79023

Extremely precise renditions of traditional Irish reels, airs, jigs, and other music played with scholarly attention to detail. Museum-quality craftsmanship on numerous older compositions, such as classics by Gaelic harp composer Turlough O'Carolan, who worked around 1700 A.D., and another tune praising the head of a 16th century family. Even in 1971, the Chieftains were very sophisticated, as the variations within "The Trip to Sligo," suggest. Unfortunately, even opportunities for whimsy come off as a little cold. Despite the desire for more entertainment value (which comes later in their career), this is truly wonderful music, perfectly played. It's unfortunate that the quality of the recording is just adequate.

LINK➤ *Various Artists —*
Celtic Treasure: The Legacy of Turlough O'Carolan   *Narada 63925*
A carefully annotated collection of 18 songs associated with O'Carolan. Performances are uniformly splendid, but some artist names will be unfamiliar. (No problem: the liner notes include phone and fax numbers, e-mail and postal addresses, etc.) Superb string quartets on "Squire Parsons/James Betagh."

The Chieftains 4 Shanachie 79024

The breakthrough album, from 1973. It begins with the up-tempo "Drowsy Maggie," an ensemble number that breaks for solos from each member of the band. Then, there are the duets and solos: Seán Keane's fiddle adaptation of the challenging bagpipe song, "The Bucks of Oranmore," the harp and tin whistle duet of Derek Bell and Paddy Maloney on "The Tip of the Whistle." The group also plays a nice range of reels, jigs, airs, etc. The dramatic work, "The Battle of Aughrim," places Maloney's bagpipe on the battlefield as the pounding bodhrán details the skirmish, the bones count deaths, and a whistle sings its requiem.

LINK➤ *Derek Bell — Carolan's Favorite*   *Shanachie 79020*
Every once in a while, Bell records a solo album with the help of some other Chieftains. This one focuses on O'Carolan's compositions. Carolan's Receipt *(Shanachie 79013) is Bell doing O'Carolan with an orchestra; it's available only on cassette.*

The Chieftains 10: Cotton-Eyed Joe   Shanachie 79019

As the numbers suggest, Shanachie released lots of Chieftains albums (unless you're a big fan, they do resemble one another). Why is this one special? The title cut, for one thing: it's a country-and-western song played as if it were Irish! But that's just a gimmick. The heart of this album is extremely well-played reels, jigs, airs, and, best of all, a pair of harp compositions by Carolan. These works, composed around 1700, possess a classical formality and are treated as chamber music. Also special: "Manx Music," several traditional themes from the Isle of Man.

LINK➤ *Milladoiro — As Fadas de Estraño Nome*   *Green Linnet 3118*
Listen carefully for the connection between Celtic and Galician music (from Spain). Milladoiro has a long history, but little is available in the U.S.

The Bells of Dublin   RCA 60824

The Chieftains at their collaborative best—and one of the finest holiday albums of all time. These songs, recorded in 1991, are often played on the radio in December; many will sound familiar. Kate and Anna McGarrigle sing two French-Canadian songs related to Christmas: "Il Est Né/Ca Berger." Elvis Costello, who cowrote the funny "St. Stephen's Day Murders" with Paddy Maloney, sings lead. Jackson Browne's "The Rebel Jesus" reflects a true understanding of the rhythms of Irish music. Rickie Lee Jones's fragile "O Holy Night" is made richly reverent with the Chieftains' instrumentation. Marianne Faithull sings "I Saw Three Ships a Sailing."

LINK➤ *Maura O'Connell — Wandering Home*   *Hannibal (Rykodisc) 1410*
Former DeDannan lead singer who shares the broad view with the Chieftains: she's now based in Nashville, and often works with bluegrass musicians like Bela Fleck. And yet, most of these 1997 songs are either traditionally Irish or written in that style.

Irish Heartbeat   Polydor 834-496

Technically, Van Morrison gets top billing (it's by "Van Morrison & the Chieftains"), but this is an equal partnership, produced by Morrison and Maloney over the 1987-88 winter. Morrison is a spirited vocalist who's clearly enjoying this run through traditional songs that are close to his heart; he's loose, and his voice often sounds like a permanent resident of this distinguished Irish band. The Chieftains are having fun, too, sounding less stiff than usual. "Star of the County Down" is a rouser; so's "I'll Tell Me Ma" (great percussive bones on that one!). Fantastic arrangements throughout. Best is "Marie's Wedding," a dance.

LINK➤ *Van Morrison — Veedon Fleece*   *Warner Brothers (Not on CD)*
From 1974, an album that connects with the mysticism of his Irish roots. It's not available on CD (though CD availability seems to change daily), but some research in used LP stores and on the Internet should turn up a copy.

The Gaelic word for "family" is "clannad," an apt description of this **Irish** band's beginnings. Maire, Ciaran, and Pol Brennan (or, more traditionally, O Braonáin) started performing at their father's pub, along with two uncles. (Their father, tavernkeeper Leo O Braonáin, toured Ireland in the 1930s and 1940s playing American big band swing.) In 1970 Clannad won first prize at the Letterkenny Folk Festival, and for the next few years, built its audience through folk festival appearances. The group released a first album in 1973, and worked hard over ten years to gain recognition in the British and Irish pop music worlds. Eithne Brennan, who later became famous as new age singer Enya, worked with the band in the early 1980s. Success came with the hit recording of "Magical Ring," the theme to *Harry's Game*, a British TV thriller series that took place in Northern Island; additional TV work followed.

Clannad 2   Shanachie 79007

Early Clannad, in the days when the band was Maire Ni Bhraonáin backed up by simple acoustic instruments played by her two brothers and her two uncles. The hypnotic "Coinleach Ghlas an Fhómair" showcases the expressive power and depth in her voice; the mandolin, bass, and other string instruments play fascinating patterns that deserve as much attention as the vocal. The choice of material is excellent; the songs are varied, colorful, and melodic. They're easy to enjoy even if you don't understand Gaelic lyrics. Several group vocals are upbeat and entertaining ("Rince Philib a'Cheoil" is an especially good example).

LINK▶ The Pogues — Essential Pogues   *Island 510-610*
Most (but not all) of the best work from the alternative Gaelic-rock band popular in the 1970s. Next, track down Rum Sodomy & the Lash (MCA 732), whose contents are not included here.

Dúlamán   Shanachie 79008

Although later Clannad albums intermingle contemporary instrumentation with tradition, this 1976 album is recorded only with traditional instruments. Maire Ni Bhraonáin's voice centers the group's lively sound, with the other members providing backup vocals. This formula works especially well on "Two Sisters." The whole group creates a harmonic fabric on "Dúlamán" (the song is about seaweed, or more accurately, winning the hand of a seaweed harvester's lovely daughter). Experimentation with vocal harmonies is also the key to "dtigeas a Damhsa," a children's song. Instrumentals are refined and intriguing: "The Jug of Brown Ale" begins with a long instrumental setup, then invites some vocals as it becomes a dance.

LINK▶ Various Artists — The Celtic Lullaby   *Ellipsis Arts 4150*
Beyond the obvious calming effect, there are some artists here who should be explored further, notably Scottish harpist Alison Kinnaird, Scottish singer Jean Redpath, and Welsh carol group Plethyn.

Fuaim
Atlantic 82481

"Fuaim" (pronounced "foom") is the Gaelic word meaning "sound." The album was recorded in 1982, with Enya (her given name: Eithne Ní Bhraonáin, sister to Maire and Ciarán) a member from 1980-82. This pivotal work is filled with gorgeous melodies and quiet arrangements, wonderful textures and effortless beauty, in part created by electronic instruments. Enya sings lead on "An Túll" (performed with some urgency in the harmonies) and on "Buaire a dh An Phósta." Maire's graceful, dramatic voice outlines a much clearer picture on "Strayed Away," sung in English. "Na Buachchaillí Álainn" begins in a somewhat impressionistic way, but digs into a compelling melody, also sung by Maire.

LINK➤ *Enya — Watermark*   *Reprise 26774*
The Enya new age phenomenon took off in 1989 with these achingly beautiful songs: a musical journey through her soul, given flight by astonishing orchestral arrangements. "Orinoco Flow" was a major hit song in England.

Rogha: The Best of Clannad
RCA 66978

Clannad is a band with enormous range; some songs here are progressive rock with a big guitar and drum sound, and others are acoustic treatments of traditional Irish music. Even here, there is considerable variation. "The Fairy Queen" is delicate and lovely, while "Journey's End" is a boisterous march. "Theme from Harry's Game," the song that made them famous, is a slow choral work. The constant is the deep, rich, powerful lead voice of Maire Ni Bhraonáin. This CD doesn't cover Clannad's entire career, only 1983-87. *Pastpresent* (RCA 9912) is another anthology from the same period.

LINK➤ *Afro-Celt Sound System —*
Volume 1 Sound Magic   *RealWorld (Caroline) 2359*
With equal parts Celtic and African, this 1997 release was one of world music's most successful 1997 fusion projects. Studio technology enhances sound of traditional instruments.

Anam
Atlantic 82409

This 1992 album could be taken for contemporary rock. "In A Lifetime" is an enormous structure built of the latest in synthesized materials. The empassioned vocal duet is performed by Máire Brennan with Bono. Brennan's frail vocal lead into "Harry's Game" multiplies into a chorus with some effects, an eerie, soul-less theme for a zero-sum political confrontation. It's interesting to contrast these gigantic productions with Ciarán's delicate acoustic meditations, "Wilderness," and "Dohbar." Máire's voice also shines through synthesized haze on "Úirchill an Chreagáin," a lovely traditional song. On the title song, her vocal, the digital textures and the acoustic instruments join for something special.

LINK➤ *Wolfestone — Year of the Dog*   *Green Linnet 1145*
Rocked-out Scottish music with lots of bagpipes and attitude. Great party music from 1994. Try also 1991's Unleashed.

Clegg was born in Lancashire, England, and raised in Zimbabwe, Zambia, and **South Africa**. As a young teenager, Clegg became fascinated with Zulu culture. In the early 1970s, he befriended Zulu musician Sipho Mchunu. They formed Juluka, a band that played traditional Zulu music and English folk-rock. As Juluka gained renown, it was a magnet for rage. Imagine: a white English youth adopting Zulu ways, a white teen dancing Zulu war dances (in full costume), a group featuring a white musician and a black musician onstage together in South Africa during the reign of apartheid in the 1970s. There were bomb threats and danger everywhere. The group endured until 1986, when Mchunu left to buy a farm. Clegg then formed the more electric, and eclectic, Savuka. The group borrows from Celtic music and mbaqanga (African street rock, notable for its choruses and bass groaning), but Zulu dance routines remain an important part of the act.

In My African Dream: The Best of Johnny Clegg & Savuka
Rhythm Safari 253912

Although Savuka's indvidual albums were spotty, just about every song on this collection is powerful, meticulously produced, and totally engaging. Clegg sings lead, always passionate and articulate, but the instrumentation makes this work unique. There are strong similarities to Paul Simon's work on *Graceland*, particularly on the sudden percussion breaks, Zulu walking rhythm, accordion on "Great Heart," and the a capella vocals of "Asimbonanga." Clegg's talent for integrating of Western and African sounds exceeds Simon's, but he lacks the American songwriter's melodic sense and lyrical poetry. Still, this is a magnificent album filled with surprises, and it's enthusiastically recommended.

LINK➤ *Paul Simon — Graceland*   ***Warner Brothers 25447***
Essentially a slicked-up version of Johnny Clegg's Savuka music with less of an angry edge. Clegg receives "special thanks."

A Johnny Clegg and Juluka Collection   Putumayo 127

Juluka had a simpler, folkier sound than the later Savuka. This music was recorded by Clegg and Sipho Mchunu from 1979–83 and originally appeared on five successful (but now hard-to-find) albums. Earlier tracks, like "Africa" and "Deliwe" (both from 1979's *Universal Men*, their first album), feature Clegg's very Celtic-sounding lead vocal, Mchunu's choruses, a guitar, drums, and a whistle. Later tracks are more elaborate, as on "Two Humans on the Run" (from 1983's *Scatterlings*), with more commercial rock arrangements. A second collection, called *The Best of Juluka* (Rhythm Safari 57138), contains entirely different songs.

LINK➤ *Various Artists — Putumayo Presents the Best in the World: World Vocal Volume 1*   ***Rhino 71203***
One of the best world music compilations around. The perfect gift for a newcomer. Includes tracks by Clegg, Makeba, Ladysmith Black Mambazo, Gilberto Gil, Juan Luis Guerra, and many others.

At age 14, in 1962, James Chambers left his home in St. Catherine, **Jamaica**, hoping to become a singer in Kingston. Chambers had sung in front of an audience only once before. After winning a prize at a poultry contest, he jumped onstage and sang a Fats Domino song. Chambers moved to Kingston, started recording for other acts, and then scored a hit with his first single, "Hurricane Hattie," and his second, "Miss Jamaica." A few years later, Chambers, now called Jimmy Cliff, recorded his first album and a popular late-1960s protest song, "Vietnam." Now based in London, Cliff continued to write and record, but drifted (his song "Sitting in Limbo" describes the feeling), until he starred in *The Harder They Come*, a film that introduced reggae to a generation of college students. The movie made Cliff's music and Jamaican culture internationally popular. Cliff continues to record and perform and remains a popular attraction at music festivals.

The Harder They Come
Mango 539-202

This 1972 soundtrack album moved reggae from a small Jamaican style to a worldwide phenomenon. Cliff's voice is strong and inspiring; this is positive, forward-looking reggae at its motivational best. Some of his best songs are here: "You Can Get It If You Really Want It," "Many Rivers to Cross," "Sitting in Limbo," and the title cut. But half the tracks aren't Cliff's work—"Rivers of Babylon" is sung by the Melodions, "Shantytown" is by Desmond Dekker, and "Pressure Drop" is by the Maytals. Cliff stars in the movie—it's a terrific picture, but not often carried in neighborhood video stores.

LINK➤ *Various Artists – This is Reggae Music*   *Mango 539-251*
One of the best reggae samplers, it includes the Wailers' "I Shot the Sheriff," the Maytals' "Funky Kingston," the Heptones' "Book of Rules" and other hits. The first CD in a series of five.

Reggae Greats
Mango 539-794

A definitive Jimmy Cliff collection, covering mostly the late 1960s and early 1970s, when Cliff was at his best. Four of the 11 songs here are also on *The Harder They Come* soundtrack, but the other 7 are as good or better. "Vietnam" is a protest song that was, according to the liner notes, a favorite of Bob Dylan and a principal influence for Paul Simon's reggae flirtation, "Mother and Child Reunion." Cliff not only wrote the songs here, but also produced most of them, and there are gems: "Sufferin' in the Land," and "Struggling Man" among them.

LINK➤ *Freddie McGregor – Sings Jamaican Classics, Vol. 1, 2, 3*
VP 1200, 1276, 1472
Three collections by one of Jamaica's most popular singers, who, like Cliff, was comfortable in all of reggae's forms. Released in 1991, 1992, and 1996 respectively. In the U.S., he's not as well known as Cliff, but he's a favorite in Jamaica and worldwide.

A major innovator, producer, performer, trumpeter, trombone player, singer, and **Latin American** musical icon, Willie Colon was born in the Bronx, NYC, in 1950. By 16, he was recording hit songs. A year later, Colon was signed to Fania Records and leading his own band with singer Hector Lavoe (they worked together for more than a decade). Others on Colon's long list of collaborators include Rubén Blades (the two worked as a team for awhile), Celia Cruz, and many other stars, both Latino and non-Latino. Winner of poll after poll, Colon's most interesting work combines music from Brazil, Africa, Panama, Haiti, France, and the U.S. This fusion goes well beyond influences; when Colon becomes interested in a musical form, he integrates its sound so skillfully that an entirely new musical idea results. Still, with all the talent, awards, and popularity, his work is available almost exclusively through Latin record stores.

The Good-The Bad-The Ugly
Fania 484

One of the most important 1970s salsa albums, and one of Colon's best. The sound is distinguished by phenomenally tight twin lead trombones played by Colon and Eric Matos, and by three lead vocalists singing their best: Colon, Hector Lavoe, and Rubén Blades. The playing is tight, fast, and the arrangements (by Colon and Marty Sheller) make the most of the trombones and the varied Latin and Brazilian percussion section. With 18 band members, this is a recording filled with surprises—gliding from straight salsa to Brazilian rock to jazz/rock fusion then back to Latino, all in a single song. Made in NYC in 1975.

LINK➤ *Hector Lavoe — The Fania "Legends of Salsa" Collection, Vol. 1*   *Fania 700*
Puerto Rican singing superstar Lavoe recorded 58 albums for Fania, mostly with Colon and the Fania All-Stars. Many consider him to be one of the island's greatest talents. This 2-CD box contains his best work, plus extensive bios and photos.

Canciones del Solar de los Aburridos   Fania 597

Credited to Willie Colon and Rubén Blades, this is the best of many collaborations. On this album, made in NYC in 1981, both singers sound great, and they're working with superior material, plus a theme: searching for answers. Great songwriting from Blades. The album begins at a beach with seagulls and ocean sounds, then a radio tuning and finding the first song, "Tiburon." Fortune teller "Madame Kalalu" has no answers, despite the repeating "digame" ("tell me"). No answers by phone either, but telephone ringer in "El Telefonito" provides a nifty percussion device. "Y Deja" is a perfect Brazilian song showcasing Blades's vocal range.

LINK➤ *Orchestra Harlow —*
The Best of Orchestra Harlow & Ismael Miranda   *Fania 496*
Larry Harlow was another terrific salsa bandleader, and an imaginative arranger as well (he's in Willie Colon's league as an arranger). Every song is memorable; "Arsenio," "Tumba y Bongo," and "No Me Llores" are among the very best. Harlow also produced hundreds of Fania albums.

One of many well-known **Brazilian** musicians from the northern state of Bahia, Costa was born in the city of Salvador in 1945. After working in a record store, she met Caetano Veloso, recorded with him, sang his songs, and with his help, became one of Brazil's finest singers. She, too, was part of the Tropicálismo cultural movement of the late 1960s, a Brazilian renaissance that transformed and modernized popular culture. She became well-known as the leading interpreter of composers in trouble with the military government. João Gilberto called her "the greatest singer in Brazil"; Veloso called her voice "fantastically beautiful, heavenly...untouchable"; Jobim said she has "the greatest vocal chords in Brazil." Costa has recorded a very wide range of Brazilian music, including some work by earlier composers who had fallen out of favor. Her recording career spans over 25 years. She is a legend in Brazil.

Meu Nome é Gal (My Name Is Gal)   Verve 836-841

The voice of Gal Costa is outspoken, involved, passionate, and, according to Caetano Veloso, "untouchable." Hers was the voice Brazilians heard singing Veloso's songs during his exile—the voice that interpreted his lonely "London, London" anthem of dislocation. Costa also commercialized the Tropicálismo movement with meticulous vocals atop new kinds of instrument sounds and arrangements. Most songs in this retrospective come from the 1970s and early 1980s. The fine work of such MPB composers such as Veloso, Caymmi, and Djavan is a good match for Costa's expressive voice. Modern interpretations of older songs are also refreshing. "Teco Teco (The Sound of Marbles Colliding)" and "Canta Brasil" are two examples. Wonderfully varied music.

LINK➤ *Caetano Veloso & Gal Costa — Domingo (Sunday)*
Verve 838-555

This 1967 album by two of Brazil's most popular artists is gentle and innocent. It is influenced more by the bossa nova of their youth than the Tropicálismo instrumentation and lyrics that soon followed.

Gal Canta Caymmi   Verve 836-014

The title translates as "Gal Sings Caymmi," and this collection of ten songs by the talented Brazilian songwriter Dorival Caymmi is one of Costa's best CDs. These songs celebrate the lovely state of Bahia, Costa's home. "São Salvador" recalls the exciting capital city with lilting guitar and Brazilian percussion— and Costa's long, cool phrasing. The feverish dance song, "Dois de Fevereiro," will have you singing along, and, probably, swaying or dancing. There are songs about the fishing trade, a mermaid, the wind breezing through town, and the food ("Vatapá" refers to a fish and meat dish). From 1976, and it's still handsome and invigorating.

LINK➤ *Dorival Caymmi — Caymmi's Grandes Amigos*   *EMI 422-963*

Caymmi performs with his talented children, Dori (a performer with several albums available), Nana, and Danilo. Currently unavailable in the U.S.

One of **Cuba**'s greatest singers, Cruz has been an international star for several decades. Raised in Barrio Santra Suarez, a small town near Havana, in the 1930s, Cruz grew up at a time when Cuba was renowned for its nightlife. Serious about music, she attended the Conservatory of Music in 1947, started her career (unsuccessfully) singing protest songs, and switched to the more popular guaracha. She was hired by a famous Cuban band, Sonora Matancera, and together, they rode the wave of 1950s interest in Cuban entertainment. When Castro came to power, Cruz moved to the U.S., became a citizen, and gained fame as a mambo singer. As

salsa took shape in the late 1960s, she began working with Tito Puente, who became a long-time collaborator. By the early 1970s, Cruz was one of salsa's hottest performers, and she joined the Fania All-Stars. She continued to record and perform, often with other salsa stars, through the 1980s.

Cuba's Queen of Rhythm   Palladium (F.T.C.) 154
In 1950, Cruz joined Sonora Matancera, one of Cuba's top bands. This 1957 album (originally released on Seeco) captures more of the excitement of Cuban music circa 1957. Cruz's lead vocal on "Pa'La Paloma," the male chorus's answer to her lines, the conga solo, and the precise match of horns and rhythm are pure magic! The colors in Cruz's voice get proper showcasing in "My Voy a Pinar del Rio." The horns are so sweet on "El Lleva Y Trae," as is her interaction with the coro (male chorus). It's also interesting to hear a taste of Jerry Lee Lewis on the catchy (and otherwise, entirely Cuban) "Rock and Roll."

LINK➤ *Celia Cruz — 100% Azucar! The Best of Celia Cruz*
Con La Sonora Matancera   **Rhino 72816**
Rhino's compilations are exceptional. This one collects her work with the band from the early 1950s through the early 1960s.

Celia & Johnny   Vaya 31
One of the most successful salsa albums of all time, this 1974 release places Cruz in front of Johnny Pacheco's band. "Quimbara" is nothing short of phenomenal. Drums are heard, and Cruz uses her voice as percussion (almost an African call). Razor-sharp horns repeat the rhythm pattern, and Cruz sings with them as the drums keep the beat. After a horn break, the tempo starts to increase. Now things are really getting hot! Cruz and the chorus sing very fast and keep pace with the drums. Then there's a piano break, then horns, shouts, faster singing, and trumpets blasting up to the sky—it's all unbelievably exciting! Ready for more? Try 1978's *Eternos* (Vaya 80).

LINK➤ *Johnny Pacheco — La Perfecta Combinacion*
Fania 380
One of Pacheco's best salsa albums, recorded with singer Pete (Conde) Rodriguez.

Cruz & Colon: Only They Could Have Made This Album
Vaya 66

Cruz's work with Willie Colon is very different from that done with Johnny Pacheco. On "Usted Abuso," she's a lead vocalist accompanied by horns in a lush arrangement. Percussion and chorus are parts of an integrated whole. Acoustic guitars and quiet percussion provide a background evocative of old Cuba on "Plazos Traicioneros." A unique piano rhythm (unusual use of space and time) guides "Zambullete"; an electric guitar spices with some funk as Cruz comes in for the fast-singing close. In fact, "Professor Joe" Torres deserves special credit for clever piano work; he sets the pace on "Pun Pun Catalu" as Cruz again delivers a giant performance. (What a great singer!) From 1977.

LINK➤ *Wille Colon — The Big Break - La Gran Fuga*   **Fania 394**
The great Hector Lavoe sings lead on one of Colon's finest albums. From 1976.

Celia Cruz y La Sonora Ponceña
Vaya 84

A Latin music record producer once described La Sonora Ponceña as "the salsa band every other band wishes they could be." Leader Enrique (Quique) Lucca possesses three key assets: Papo Lucca on piano; the outstanding trumpeters Ramon A. Rodriguez, Delfin Perez, and Nelson Feliciano; and a fantastic group of percussionists. "Soy Antillana" makes sharp use of those cutting horns and exhilarating percussion during its instrumental portions. This group provides a whole lot more than your standard accompaniment. Listen to the tone of those horns on the first few bars of "Abreme La Puerta," or the way the whole band leaps forward on "Raices." Ultimately, the compositions on the Pacheco and Colon sets are better, but this band is truly phenomenal. From 1979.

LINK➤ *Sonora Ponceña — Thirty Years, Vol. 1, 2*   **Musica Latina 60, 61**
Each of these CDs was released in 1985. The first includes the hit "Fuego en El 23" and "Sancocho Prieto." The second begins with "El Pio Piao." Start with the group's excellent work with Cruz—recorded during a magical session.

La Candela
Fania 19

"La Candela" is a roving salsa festival, a song that captures the excitement of dancing in the streets. The chorus is catchy and very memorable, the kind of song that requires singing along. Production takes good advantage of multitracking and some studio enhancements—it's pure energy, transforming itself from one minute to the next. The carnival spirit continues with Johnny Pacheco's "El Guaba," another big studio production, and another in which Cruz sings faster than any human should be able to. For a wider-ranging rundown on Cruz's many hits, pick up *The Best* (Vaya 111) for "Quimbara," "Cucula," "Usted Abuso," and "Lo Tuyo es Mental." Next, move on to *The Best Vol. 2* (Vaya 112).

LINK➤ *La Lupe — Lo Mejor De La Lupe (The Best of La Lupe)*   **Tico 1318**
"Amor Gitano" is one of several songs that recall Edith Piaf. But then there's "Yo Soy Como Soy" that shows how close La Lupe could come to Cruz's approach. The brave boleros and other material on 1969's Definitivamente La Yi-Yi-Yi (Tico 1199) are also recommended.

With interest in **Cuba** escalating, it's no surprise this multigenerational Cuban dance band become so successful in the 1990s. Its work pays tribute to many Cuban dance styles, while maintaining very high standards for the musicians. The group is led by Jesús Alemañy, a trumpet player who started with a leading Cuban band at age 15. Pianist Alfredo Rodríguez is in his forties; he's been living in Paris since 1983, where he's highly regarded as a top Latin piano player (he's played with Celia Cruz, Sonora Mantancera, Johnny Pacheco, and many other top names). Manuel "El Guajiro" Mirabel and (Jesús's uncle) Luís Alemañy played together when Havana was a jazz center, and the Tropicana was one of the hot spots. Other members came from Irakere and NG La Banda, two of Cuba's top bands. The combination of youthful enthusiasm and long-term experience placed this band on top of U.S. and European world music charts.

Jesús Alemañy's ¡Cubanismo! featuring Alfredo Rodríguez
Hannibal (Rykodisc) 1390

This stunning debut album, recorded in Havana in 1995, gets off to a rousing start with "Descarga de Hoy (Jam Today)." This piece, a guaracha-son, climaxes with Rodríguez's rhythmic piano solo, then bursts out with a dialogue between Jesús on trumpet and Carlos Alvarez on trombone. "Mata y Guaguanaco," composed by Rodríguez, is a sensuous rumba (where the dancers are close, but never touch) with more reach-for-the-sky trumpeting from the group's leader. "Aprovecha" is a cha-cha. (The album, with its liner notes, is practically a textbook on Cuban dance forms.) "Ahora Me Voy (Here I Go)" is a conga—a finale for a street carnival that closes a spectacular album.

LINK➤ Ry Cooder (and others) — Buena Vista Social Club
World Circuit 50

This popular 1997 album explored another side of Cuban music: son (acoustic, mostly guitars). Cooder plays with the legends, including Ibrahim Ferrer and pianist Ruben Gonzalez. Don't miss this!

Malembe
Hannibal (Rykodisc) 1411

Sex and violence set the tone for "Mulence," the opener for this 1997 release (also recorded in Havana). It's a fight between two rumberos (masters of the rumba) from different regions of Cuba. The unusually complicated pilón rhythm of the 1960s is the basis of "¡Cubanismo!" which includes a terrific solo from former Irakere flute player Orlando "Maraca" Valle. Danzón combines European structure and harmony with syncopated African rhythm, and often includes brief quotations from other songs. "Danzón Duela," written for Jesús's daughter, modernizes the form and includes a brief bit from a string trio (played by members of Havana's symphony orchestra). This music is hot, danceable, and great fun.

LINK➤ Africando — Trovador   *Stern's Africa 1045*
A wonderful 1993 studio collaboration of Cuban and African (mostly Senegalese) musicians who grew up playing Cuban music. Try also the same recording sessions' Tierra Tradicional (Stern's 1054) and, best of all, 1995's Gomba Salsa (Stern's Africa 1071).

According to Henry Kaiser, who discovered the guitar player while recording the *A World Out of Time* compilations of **Madagascar**'s music, D'Gary is "one of the most amazing guitarists on the planet." D'Gary's given name is Ernest Randrianasolo. He was born in 1961 in Antananarivo, the capital city, but moved to the small, remote tribal village of Betroka at age 17. D'Gary is a member of the Bara tribal group, native to southern Madagascar. In Betroka, the many frustrations include corrupt officials who are paid off to condone the stealing of zebus, the humped ox that is his people's livelihood. D'Gary writes and sings about these conditions. He plays the kabosy (kin to a ukelele) and other traditional instruments in his music. His ability to imitate the sounds of traditional Malagasy instruments on acoustic guitar made a deep and lasting impression on Kaiser's partner, David Lindley, who produced D'Gary's first solo album.

Malagasy Guitar   Shanachie 65009

The first solo recording by D'Gary, this album was produced by Henry Kaiser and Dama Mahaleo in 1991. It's an intimate session—D'Gary insisted that the producers sit facing him, with their knees touching his. The album features steel string acoustic guitar, D'Gary's pleasant voice, and the most subtle percussive brushing from Pana (Panayotis Dourantonis). The modern 20-bit recording captures every nuance of D'Gary's guitar. Sit back and listen to the pure tone and virtuosity of his thumb and index finger as they pick the strings on "Anary Tany" and create subtle textures on "Tiambaly." Music doesn't get much better than this.

LINK➤ *Dama & D'Gary – The Long Way Home*   *Shanachie 64052*
Dama is Dama Mahaleo, a Malagasy superstar with a fine deep tenor voice that complements D'Gary's superb guitar, and sounds great in harmony with D'Gary's higher singing voice. Sharper, more melodic songwriting. Highlight: a fiery duet by D'Gary and fiddler Michael Doucet.

Horombe   Stern's Africa 9005

D'Gary's skillful arrangements and outstanding guitar work make this 1994 album by his new band, Jihé, a standout. The first four tracks are pure Afro-pop with a pumping accordion doing battle with guitar, and some really tuneful backup singers. It's dance music that's acoustic and easy. The six songs that complete the album return to straight acoustic guitar and vocals. "Lagnana" is an instrumental that tells the story of a river and the men who try to ford it (and never get across). "Malagasy Boxing" advises average people not to go into the boxing ring with Madagascar's boxing stars. ("Protect your nose!" "Duck!")

LINK➤ *Various Artists – The Moon and the Banana Tree: New Guitar Music from Madagascar*   *Shanachie 64074*
Besides D'Gary and Dama, this anthology features Madagascar's legendary Etienne Ramboatiana, old-style Malagasy theater music from Colbert, the "stuffed guitar" of Haja (who sounds like he's playing a harp), Johnny (who plays guitar for Tarika Sammy), and others.

Isaiah Kehinde Dairo was born to a **Nigerian** railway worker in 1931, the younger of twins (according to Yoruba tradition, the second born is considered the "elder," wise enough to send his sibling into the world as a scout). When his sibling died, I.K. exorcised remaining evil spirits by singing and dancing in the streets. During the late 1940s, he was apprenticed to a bandleader and worked as a musician. In the 1950s, Dairo formed the Morningstar Orchestra.

Later renamed the Blue Spots, it was his band for two decades. The band played high life and Dairo's signature juju music. His fame grew throughout Africa and to England, where Queen Elizabeth honored him as a Member of the British Empire (M.B.E.) for his musical contributions. For years, Dairo led Nigeria's musician's union and copyright society. He also owned hotels throughout Yoruba Africa, which he closed after finding that they were dens for thieves and prostitutes.

Definitive Dairo
Xenophile (Green Linnet) 4045

Producer Andy Frankel searched through the "purgatory" of Decca West Africa's tape archive and against reasonable odds, mastered an extraordinary 1971 session. This is Afro-pop before the endless electric instruments and overblown arrangements, when virtuoso drummers held close to Yoruba traditions, and the excitement was a lead vocalist's call-and-response with the chorus. The extended drum break on "Baba Ngbo Ti Wa (Father Hears Us)" is phenomenal. Extensive liner notes include English translations, so contemporary listeners can understand Dairo's reminder for temporary emigrants to bring their wealth and knowledge home on "Omo Owa o Ijesa," and can consider the importance of agriculture in a rapidly changing world on "Labondo."

LINK➤ E.T. Mensah — All for You   *Retroafric 1 CD*

Looking further back into the history of West African dance music, E.T. Mensah's early 1950s high-life recordings are essential. The sound is similar to big band music, but with an African rhythm pattern. The story continues through the early 1960s on Day by Day (Retroafric 3CD).

Ashiko
Xenophile (Green Linnet) 4018

The unusual relationship between Seattle producer Andy Frankel and African legend I.K. Dairo continued through two albums of new music (and revised versions of old hits). The first, *I Remember* (Music of the World 212), was recorded in Nigeria in 1990. This album was made in Seattle in 1992. The music is spare and clean, depending upon Dairo's talking drum and accordion, a few guitars, and African conga drums (called akuba). "Salome" was Dairo's biggest 1960s hit; listen for the call and response between the talking drum and male chorus. The accordion and drum interaction on "Mo Sorire (I have been blessed)" is charming.

LINK➤ King Sunny Adé — Juju Music   *Mango 9712*

Dairo, King Sunny Adé, and Chief Commander Ebenezer Obey have been three of Nigeria's most popular juju stars. This is probably Adé's best work.

The most popular singer in **Greece** for two decades, Dalaras was born in Nea Kokkinia, in Piraeus (Athens's port), in 1950. His father was a famous "rempete," a traditional Greek musician specializing in bouzouki. Dalaras released his first album in 1969; the music linked tradition and modern styles. In 1972, he worked with Apostolos Kaldaras on *Mikra Asia* (Asia Minor), a landmark retelling of 1922's miseries with Turkey. In 1974, he recorded an album of songs by Mikis Theodorakis to celebrate the fall of Greece's dictatorship. In addition to many collaborations with Greek artists, Dalaras has worked with Paco de Lucia, Al DiMeola, Jan Garbarek, and Argentinian composer Ariel Ramirez. With more than 40 albums and many more collaborations to his credit, even the 9-CD, 180-song *Music Box* collection tells only part of the story.

50 Hronia Rebetiko Tragoudi   Minos-EMI 38232

Rebetiko (also known as rembétika, or rebetika) is similar to U.S. blues. Sung by refugees in Athens and other large cities during the 1920s and 1930s, it was the music of the poor and oppressed. In time, as refugees aged and their children grew up, rebetika was discarded. It was revived in the 1960s and rejuvenated with albums like this 2-CD set from 1975. Dalaras's voice and careful arrangements are a good, if slightly sanitized, introduction to rebetika. Among the many other excellent Dalaras albums: 1971's *O Metikos* (Minos - EMI 302), 1987's *Latin* (with Al DiMeola) (15014), and *Mikra Asia* (with Apostolos Kaldaras and Haris Alexiou) (MCDPI-5001).

LINK▶ *Markos Vamvakaris, Startos Payiomtzis, Yiannis Papaioannou — Live Recording at Taverna*   *Lyra 4683*

The recording quality isn't perfect, but these 1972 rebetika songs are sung by masters of the form in an intimate setting. In short, this is the real thing. Liner notes (in English and in Greek) include an extensive interview, plus biographical material.

Kalos Tous (Welcome)   Minos-EMI 480439

This popular 1994 album is a good representation of Dalaras's current work—a fine dance record with expert bouzouki. "Let's Go Somewhere New" is about changing old habits, and it's accompanied by guitar, bouzouki, and a few wistful backup singers. "Mesogios" is the Greek word for the Mediterranean Sea. Small-time fishermen, working for dangerous clients, assist in the arms trade as they maneuver from rock to rock in the middle of an uncaring sea. One song's title translates in a rather messy way, something like: "You keep me between the 'why are you doing this to me' and the 'I've had enough.'" The principal songwriter is the popular Christos Nikolopoulous.

LINK▶ *Statmatis Kokotas — Ta Portreta Tis Minos*   Minos-EMI 424/5

Another of Greece's many popular singers, Kokotas was at his most influential when Dalaras was just starting his career. Notable for his work with composer Xarhakos, Kokotas was also known for his large sideburns.

De Dannan (sometimes: De Danann) started informally: a group of friends playing together on Sunday mornings at an **Irish** pub near Galway Bay. The band was formed during those sessions around 1972 by fiddler Frankie Gavin and bouzouki player Alec Finn. (Finn plays the six-string Greek bouzouki, not the eight-string model favored by other Irish players.) De Dannan's first album came out in 1975, and since that time the personnel has included singers Dolores Keane, Mary Black, and many other notable Irish musicians (De Dannan has always been a somewhat loose organization,

and musicians seem to come and go often, hence the long alumni list). The virtuoso Gavin also plays flute, viola, accordion, and other instruments, and he has worked with Elvis Costello, Keith Richards, Sir Yehudi Menuhin, Stephane Grappelli, and other artists. Gavin has also recorded several solo albums.

The Star Spangled Molly
Shanachie 79018

De Dannan had many female lead singers, but none as game as Maura O'Connell, who is ideal for this Irish-American vaudeville salute. Her best track, "My Irish Molly-O," was a popular barroom dance from the Flanagan Brothers. John McCormack's "Maggie" (which you might know as "When You and I Were Young, Maggie") is her tearjerker. Fiddler Frankie Gavin's emigration song, "I'm Leaving Tipperary" (and "I'm Bound for New York City, Boys, 3000 Miles Away!"), recaps Larry Griffin and the Shamrock Band's 1920s song. Jackie Kimmel made his own accordion to simulate the bagpipe-like instrument played by "The Irish Dutchman" (who was from Germany!) for "The Cuckoo's Nest."

LINK➤ *Dolores Keane and John Faulkner — Brokenhearted I'll Wander*
Green Linnet 3004

Keane is one of Ireland's strongest voices; her husband Faulkner is the string player. Try also Farewell to Eirinn, *a collection of Irish immigration songs (3003). Keane sings with De Dannan on 1987's* Ballroom *(3040).*

Song for Ireland
Sugar Hill 1130

Mary Black is the vocalist on this 1983 album (released by a label known mainly for bluegrass), and her handful of song tracks are terrific. Her version of "Hard Times," a folk classic, is deeply felt, as is the poetic "Song of Ireland." All told, this is an album that belongs to the instrumentalists, particularly fiddler Frankie Gavin, who also plays flute, whistle, viola, and piano. The clarity of this recording brings out the best in Johnny (Ringo) McDonagh's bodhrán (a hand drum), and Alec Finn's bouzouki (a stringed instrument) sounds too often drowned in the mix of Irish recordings. Try also *Hibernian Rhapsody* (Shanachie 78005) for some awesome fiddling.

LINK➤ *Mary Black — Best of Mary Black*
Curb 77718

Although rooted in Irish music, singer Mary Black is equally facile in other types of music. This sampler is a good place to start. Her newer album, Shine *(Curb 77888), emphasizes folk-rock, circa 1997. Also try* Babes in the Woods *(Gifthorse 77258) with collaborator Declan Sinnott (guitar, dobro, mandolin).*

Paco de Lucia was born Francisco Sánchez Gómez in 1947 in Algeciras, a southern port city in **Spain**. He learned the guitar from his father, his brother, and family friend Niño de Ricardo, a virtuoso. By age 7, de Lucia was playing flamenco guitar; by 12, he was recording. Before his teen years, he had won several guitar competitions. By 13, de Lucia was touring internationally with José Greco's flamenco show. He started composing and playing backup for various Spanish singers, notably the great Gypsy singer (or cantador) Camarón de la Isla, with whom de Lucia worked from the late 1960s until the early 1990s. In addition to leading his own group, de Lucia has collaborated on projects with John McLaughlin, Chick Corea, Al di Meola, and even Placido Domingo. De Lucia is widely regarded as the finest living flamenco guitarist—and one of several musicians who has modernized the classic Spanish form.

Dos Guitarras Flamencos en America Latina Philips 842-952

Many of the tunes on this 1967 album will sound familiar; they are the "standards" of Spanish guitar music that inform the stereotype. You might not know their names, but you'll sing or hum along with "Cielito Lindo," "Mañana de Carnaval," "El Jarabe Tapatio" (kids call this "Mexican Hat Dance"), and "Granada." There is classical flamenco here as well, music that brings to mind a gallant dancer, as in "A Pesar de Todo." As the title suggests, this is an album by two flamenco guitar players; Ramón de Algeciras became a long-term de Lucía collaborator. Remarkably clear recording. Start here.

LINK➤ *Various Artists — Duende: The Passion &*
Dazzling Virtuosity of Flamenco   *Ellipsis Arts 3350*
The ultimate flamenco collection. It's a 3-CD set with at least one performance from every major star: Camarón de la Isla, Gerardo Nuñez, Agustín Carbonell "Bola," Pepe Habichuela, Ramón Montoya, Ketama...the list goes on. A 48-page book explains it all.

Entre Dos Aguas   Philips 814-106

A more interesting release, filled mostly with extraordinary original de Lucía compositions from 1973 and 1976 (many earlier de Lucía albums contain tracks from other albums). Most tracks are again recorded with partner Ramón de Algeciras (who receives the tiniest possible credit despite huge contributions). This is the advanced class: de Lucía and de Algeciras anticipating and answering one another at astonishing speeds among consistently fascinating arrangements. "La Niña de Puerta Oscura" uses a dancer's stomps as the percussion track. Jazz guitar player Larry Coryell plays acoustic guitar on the most complex track, a rumba called "Convite."

LINK➤ *Pat Metheny — Bright Size Life*   *ECM 21073*
Both de Lucía's "Monasterio de Sal" and this Metheny album were released in 1976. They sound like work from the same session!

Live...One Summer Night   Philips 822-540

Here's the thrilling, no-holds-barred, blazing-guitar, high-energy concert re-
cording that caused many rock fans to pay attention to a flamenco guitar player.
Recorded by de Lucía's Sextet in 1983, it's terrific ensemble work with de
Algeciras, a flutist named Jorge Pardo, and an equally facile percussionist,
Rubem Dantas. John McLaughlin composed a pretty intro to "Alta Mar," and
"Chiquito" is dedicated to Chick Corea; listen for strong 1980s jazz/fusion influences in de Lucía's interplay with electric bassist Carlos Benavent, and the
flute and guitar arrangement that begins "Gitanos Andaluces." But it all comes
back to de Lucía's straight flamenco.

LINK➤ *El Camarón de la Isla — Autretrato*   *Philips Spain (Import)*
*Definite retrospective of one of the all-time great flamenco singers (and one of
the most vividly emotional singers of the century). Paco de Lucía was his close
musical collaborator.*

Siroco   Mercury 830-913

This 1987 album is de Lucía's virtuoso turn, a return to pure flamenco music.
Songs are all originals with strong Andalusian roots. This is solo work with
only minor accompaniment (second guitar [de Algeciras] on only a few tracks,
some handclaps, and other percussion). De Lucía shines. "Casilda" and "Callejón
del Muro" are representative: ornate mid-tempo guitar miniatures with strong,
if temporary, rhythms; small mandolin-style embellishments; single notes that
hang for an instant, then vanish; flourishes emphasized by the deep percussion of a dancer's stomping feet. Overall, his best recorded work. Great sound.
For traditional work in a sextet context (with some pyrotechnics), try *Live in
America* (Philips 518-809).

LINK➤ *Paco de Lucía — Antología Vol. 1, 2*   *Mercury 528-422, 3*
*These two CDs offer a random excursion through much of de Lucía's work,
notably Zyrab (with Chick Corea), Paco de Lucía Intrepeta a Manuel de Falla
(Spanish composer of El Amor Brujo, etc.), and various solo and quartet work.*

Guitar Trio   Verve 830-913

Credited to Paco de Lucía, Al DiMeola, and John McLaughlin, this pristine 1996
album picks up on an earlier collaboration: the three guitar players toured and
recorded as a trio in the early 1980s. Typically, the format here is ensemble
playing to set up one or two solos per song (no other accompaniment—just
very distinguished guitar playing). Luis Bonfá's Brazilian jazz standard "Manha
de Carnaval" includes an astonishing solo from DiMeola. McLaughlin's "Letter
from India" begins with a refined solo from de Lucía. Two compositions by de
Lucía are the best work on the album, and both stay close to flamenco roots:
"La Estiba" and "Cardeosa."

LINK➤ *Al DiMeola — Heart of the Immigrants*   *Mesa 79052*
*DiMeola's tribute to Astor Piazzolla. With Dino Saluzzi on bandoneon. DiMeola
performs on acoustic guitar accompanied by an interesting variety of background instruments.*

Toumani Diabate

In 1965, Diabate was born into one of **Mali**'s leading musical families. His father, Sidiki, was widely regarded as the "King of Kora" (a kora is a 21-string instrument that combines the concept of a harp and a lute). Diabate became known as the Prince. At age 5, he'd taught himself to play, and by age 13, he was performing in public. While a teenager, he joined the National Ensemble. From this traditional basis, Diabate has become well known not only as a kora virtuoso, but also as an accompanist to one of Mali's most popular singers, Kandia Kouyate. Intrigued by the acoustic guitar, Diabate often experimented with non-African music. In 1987, he met and played with Ketama, a Spanish flamenco group, and the combination of their guitars and his kora worked so well that two albums were recorded (as Songhai).

Kaira   Hannibal (Rykodisc) 1338

The classic kora album. Diabate creates magic on the 21-string West African kora, a cross between a harp and a lute. The kora typically accompanies a singer, but Diabate builds on influences from acoustic guitar, drums, and Western music, and this instrumental work more than stands on its own. Songs are kora classics. "Kaira (Peace)," written by his father in the 1940s, helped establish the kora as a solo instrument. "Alla L'Aa Ke (God's Work)" is 100 years old. The music follows no established rhythm, though the pace is relaxed and easy. Micro-melodies materialize and vanish, their places taken by new ideas.

LINK➤ *Alhaji Bai Konte — Kora Melodies from the Republic of the Gambia, West Africa* *Rounder 5001*

Same instrument in the hands of another remarkable master, recorded in 1973 in solo and accompaniment settings. A purist approach, without the range of Diabate's influences, and a rootsier sound.

Djelika   Hannibal (Rykodisc) 1380

Just as Toumani Diabate is a kora master, Keletigui Diabate is an expert on the balafon (a xylophone), and Basekou Kouyate is renowned on the ngoni (a lute). These instruments were played in the Mali Royal Court in the 12th century. This trio recording, made in 1994, isn't as exotic as it might seem. "Djelika," named for Toumani's young daughter, quotes the theme from *The Good, The Bad and The Ugly*, one of his favorite films, and "Tony Vander" celebrates their Belgian agent. Distinguishing between centuries-old melodies and new material requires a practiced ear. Warm, inviting sound.

LINK➤ *Songhai* *Hannibal (Rykodisc) 1323*

A surprising and effective combination of kora and flamenco guitar, recorded with the flamenco guitar group Ketama. See separate entry on Songhai.

Diblo Dibala (& Loketo)

About 200 miles up the Congo River from its Atlantic Ocean delta, there are two bustling river cities: Brazzaville, capital city of the Republic of Congo, and Kinshasa, capital of the **Democratic Republic of Congo (formerly Zaire)**. There, Cuban jazz, dance music from central Africa, and tribal rhythm blended to create soukous, dance music based on a chiming guitar. Franco's TPOK Jazz Band was the most popular jazz band, and when Dibala was 15, he was hired by Franco as lead guitarist. Dibala stayed from 1969 until 1979, when he was hired away by another local star, Kanda Bongo Man. Together they moved to Paris, where they recorded soukous amid a busy local scene and became stars. In 1986, Dibala left to formed Loketo with vocalist Aurlus Mabele. Loketo toured the U.S., helping to spread the popularity of soukous. In 1991, Dibala formed another group, Matchatcha.

Super Soukous   Shanachie 64016

Actually, this album was recorded by "Diblo with Loketo," a band Diblo Dibala formed with singer Aurelus Mabele. File this CD under "Diblo Dibala" or under "Loketo." Heavy on precision, rapid-fire, almost bell-like guitar playing, horns, and a strong beat, "Amour et Souvenir" is a big soukous dance number. But the album offers more than world-class dance music. The finest moments are Dibala's guitar solos. He masterfully builds a head of steam with a very long series of repeating patterns on "Kelele," a song about a mother raising twins. Seductive guitar and percussion make "Bolinga" great; it's Diblo's remembrance of a lover who inspired his music.

LINK➤ *The Four Brothers — Makorokoto* *Atomic Theory (Omnium) 1106*
Edward Matiyasi's ringing lead guitar is the connection between this Zimbabwe group from the 1980s and Dibala's Zairean soukous from the same era. Best-of, released 1990.

Extra Ball   Shanachie 64028

One of two albums released under the name of the band: Loketo. 1990s' *Soukous Trouble* (Shanachie 64025) is an interesting transition, but this confident, fun-loving production is better. It opens with the title track, named for the extra ball that rewards a skillful pinball player. The basic components remain, but the kinship between drummer Mack Macaire and Diblo Dibala on "Cyndi" is tremendous (the song was written for  Macaire's new baby daughter). The beat is terrific; the guitar work is complicated and fascinating, as well as absolutely precise and perfect. If your hips start swaying on "Techke Linha," blame the traditional Baluba rhythm. The steamy, sensual "Mondo Ry" is even more low down.

LINK➤ *Diblo Dibala & Matchatcha — Aimer La Dance Nyekessé*
Afric'Music (Stern's) 15
Stern's carries two Matchatcha albums, both exciting (though the Loketo work is more satisfying). The other is O.K. Madame (Afric'Music 15).

A major reggae star in **South Africa** and throughout the world, Dube grew up poor, raised by relatives around Johannesburg. (His name really is "Lucky"—his mother never thought she'd be able to have children.) Dube started performing as a child, earning enough to buy a guitar. He eventually joined a mbaqanga band (mbaqanga is homemade Zulu township rock) and launched a career as a solo mbaqanga singer. His heart, however, was with reggae: Jimmy Cliff, Peter Tosh, and Bob Marley were his heroes. It wasn't just the beat, it was the messages: black identity, and the struggle for freedom among them. He made the switch and became South Africa's first reggae star. Dube is a major concert draw, one of Africa's most popular performers and a consistently successful recording artist. Two of his albums, *Slave* and *Prisoner*, have sold more than a million copies in South Africa alone.

Prisoner   Shanachie 43073

Dube's voice is smooth and appealing, credible and sincere. When he sings on the title track, "but today, here I am in jail...I'm a prisoner, I am a prisoner!" the innocence in his voice suggests that this could happen to anyone. When he warns, against the hard edge of dance-hall horns and drums, that "False Prophets" sell nothing but "lies and illusions," his arguments resonate. The familiar reggae theme of fighting for freedom in a bewildering world is the basis of "War and Crime." Richard Siluma, who contributed several songs, wrote "Remember Me," a poignant call to a friend who hasn't been seen in years. Sung in English. From 1991.

LINK➤ *Aswad — Roots Rocking: The Island Anthology*
Island Jamaica 524-323

Not all reggae comes from Jamaica. Aswad has been one of England's best reggae groups for more than two decades. This 2-CD set tells the story; lots of dub additions to the basic pieces.

House of Exile   Shanachie 43094

A year later, Dube's sound is bigger and more expressive. His backup band is still the Slaves, featuring the superior drumming of Isaac Mtshali. Five female backup singers are also superb. Richard Siluma's production is extremely clean. Once again, Dube's credible, everyman voice is searing on tough topics. "Up with Hope (Down with Dope)" strikes out against the preacher he has known for years, the judge, the teacher, who are secretly doing cocaine, drinking alcohol, sniffing glue. "Hold On" is an emotional request to a mother; the boy singing can't believe that her dreadful man is really his father. Sung in English; lyrics included.

LINK➤ *Majek Fashek — The Best of Majek Fashek*
Flame Tree (Stern's) 524

Nigeria's reggae star. He sings protest songs in English. And his reggae is made distinctive through the (very effective) use of Yoruba talking drums. Fashek played lead guitar for the Mandators, a popular West African reggae group.

El Din was one of the first African musicians to become well known in the U.S. Born in a small village in northern **Sudan**, part of the area once known as Nubia (now submerged by the Aswan High Dam), he left to study engineering in Cairo. While in school, he took up the oud (an Arab lute) and changed his major to music. While studying in Rome, friends arranged for a U.S. visit, which led to a 1964 album for Vanguard. El Din stayed, supporting himself by performing and teaching. He also worked on film soundtracks, notably *The Black Stallion*. In 1980, El Din visited Japan to study the biwa (another lute-like instrument). Drawn to the culture, he often performed there and eventually made the country his home. He still tours internationally, spends much of his time in San Francisco, and often works with progressive artists like the Kronos Quartet and director Peter Sellars.

Music of Nubia Vanguard 79164

The sound of the ten-string Arab oud, which is played like a guitar, doesn't go quite as high, but possesses the deeper resonances of a cello. Remarkably, on "Fegir Nedan (Call to Worship)," El Din simultaneously plays melody on the higher strings and rhythm on the lower. Much of this is solo instrumental work, often on religious themes, but El Din's reedy voice also tells a good story. "Kuto Fa Pattaroni" is about children playing hide-and-seek; other songs celebrate Nubia, love, and remembering a lost son. Liner notes explain each song, but El Din is easily enjoyed on the basis of instrumental work alone. From 1964.

LINK➤ *Musicians of the Nile — From Luxor to Isna*
RealWorld (Caroline) 2307
Introduction to Egypt's native instruments: rababah (traditional fiddle), tablah (fish skin stretched over a clay pot), zumarin (oboes), arghul (double-reed clarinet), and some very intriguing music.

Song of the Nile JVC 5007

Nearly 20 years later, in 1990, a more complex approach to oud. This is immediately evident in "Oud Duo," a duet that El Din performs alone, playing both melody and rhythm. Overall, the recording quality is slightly clouded, and some of the oud's resonances are lost, but the additional richness in El Din's voice and his increased versatility more than compensate, as on "Anesigu," a marriage ceremony. El Din also plays the tar, a Nubian drum, on the chant-like "Hamalaya"; it's also heard deep in the background on "Hela Lisa," a song of faraway love, and on "El Hilwatu," another love song.

LINK➤ *Abdel Gadir Salim — Nujum Al-Lail / Stars of the Nigh*
Shanachie 64039
A popular Sudanese band leader, he has also blended in music from other cultures, from reggae to acoustic dances.

The Erguner family has long been associated with the classical Sufi music of **Turkey**, and with keeping an ancient culture alive (this music dates back to at least the 14th century). Erguner learned to play the ney (a long wooden flute) from his father, Ulvi Erguner, a master and himself a descendant in a long line of ney musicians. Their art is associated with the Melveli sect; together, father and son accompanied the sect's famous "whirling dervishes." Born in Istanbul in 1952, Erguner worked beside his father at Radio Istanbul, moved to Paris in 1975 to study architecture, but eventually opened a school for traditional Turkish music and became a musicologist. In 1988, Erguner started the Fasl Ensemble to play semiclassical Turkish music from the Ottoman period. His work has been heard on numerous film scores, including Peter Brooks's *The Mahabharata*.

Sufi Music of Turkey   CMP 3005
Hard to find, but worth the trouble, this 1990 album begins with a lengthy (12-minute) improvisation on the ney (a long wooden flute with a deep, dark, somewhat mysterious sound) by Kudsi and Süleyman Erguner. Jahahhi'ddin Roumi, who founded the Mevlevi order of Sufism, compared the sound of the reed flute to "the words of a wise man and a lover of God"; his words come to life when accompanied by the ritualistic sounds, the extended meditational lines that carry such great authority. The profound sonority of the frame-drum, also played by Kudsi, adds even more power.

LINK▶ *Erkose Ensemble — Tzigane*   *CMP 3010*
The folkloric side of Turkish music, or, plainly, music of Turkish gypsies. This is more fun than the Erguner material, akin to dances played by Muzsikás, maybe with some klezmer style and Arab rhythms. Interesting mix, but CMP's discs can be hard to find.

(Works of) Tatyos Efendi
Traditional Crossroads 4277
Scholarly liner notes explain the importance of composer Kemani Tatyos Efendi. A classicist, Tatyos wrote in the style of the Tulip Age (1718-30), a period when art and music flourished in the Ottoman Empire. Tatyos was born in the mid-1850s, and worked through the Empire's last decades, when Ottoman classical music was very popular. The Erguners make this music new again; the affection they feel for this work is palpable. Kudsi and Süleyman are featured on ney; the other seven players, on period strings and percussion, are meticulous, attentive, and artful. An ideal introduction to Turkish music. Made in 1996.

LINK▶ *Simon Shaheen — Turoth (Heritage)*   *CMP 3006*
A splendid 1992 recording of classical Middle Eastern music featuring solo improvisations and ensemble works by 19th and 20th century composers from Turkey and the Arab world. Features Simon Shaheen on the violin, lud, and bass lud.

Cape Verde is a group of islands a few hundred miles from Senegal. With few natural resources, the islands became a slave port and stopover for trade ships. Sailors from West Africa, Portugal, England, and Brazil brought their music along. In the 1800s, these influences became the morna, a distinctive melancholy song style perfected in Cape Verde. The best contemporary singer of mornas is Cesaria Evora. She started singing professionally as a teen in the early 1950s, and stuck with it for about 20 years—a star in her own poor country. Then, she dropped out. At 45, she tried again, this time traveling to Portugal to record a few tracks for a Cape Verde sampler. This time, she was noticed. By the late 1980s, Evora was recording albums in Paris and touring the world. Despite the hoopla, she remains close to her roots. For example, she always performs barefoot, recalling her country's poor.

Miss Perfumado Melodie 79540

Evora's breakthrough, recorded in Paris in 1992. Twin guitars of Paulino Vieira and Toy Vieira support the desperate loneliness of "Sodade," a "morna" (sentimental ballad). Paulino's piano, recalling a smoky Paris bar after the war, begins almost every song. But this is Evora's show. "Direito di Nasce (Birthright)" claims the right to live in happiness. The wistful "Luz Dum Estrela" hopes for better times. "Angola" is particularly effective with its hand-clap percussion and group singing, a refreshing change from her blues, even better in the dance remix that ends the album. The title cut is one of her best songs. *Mar Azul* (Melodie 79533) is similar, and equally good.

LINK➤ *Amália Rodrigues – Fados e Guitarradas*   *Accord 401132*
The great Amália Rodrigues sang these blues with an intensity and a voice that's among the century's finest. This CD comes from a French label. Or try also the 1960 At the Olympia (Monitor 442E—cassette only). Or, First Recordings (EPM Musique 995782).

Cesaria Evora Live à l'Olympia Melodie 79591

June, 1993. Headliner, Paris' Olympia Theater. The marquee shows Cesaria Evora's name in letters 3-feet high. Someone snaps her picture in front of the marquee. She's carrying her pocketbook. A world-class singer from the backwaters, Evora's live performance is a simple presentation with bluesy piano, clarinet, and guitars (album arrangements are typically more elaborate). The audience recognizes her songs; most are highlights from several popular albums: *Mar Azul* (Melodie 79533), *Miss Perfumado* (79540), *La Diva aux pieds nus* (82453). Evora sings of lovers lost to journeys, the expanse of the deep blue sea, and admiration for the troubled people of nearby Angola. Wandering, searching songs. Dark melodies nestle in the heart.

LINK➤ *Billie Holiday – Body and Soul*   *Mobile Fidelity 658*
Similar emotions resonate, focused by small and mellow accompaniment emphasizing piano, guitar, and quiet horns. The culture and the songs are vastly different, but the connection goes beyond slick songwriting and Lady Day's fancy gown and hat.

Cesaria Evora
Nonesuch 739379

The first song, "Petit Pays (Little Country)," establishes Evora's finest album. Crystalline sound articulates instrument sounds and vocal nuances. Guitars, not piano, dominate. Melodies are artfully shaped. The flute-like whistle comes in at just the right moments on "Xandinha." Harmonica, accordion, and echoing male chorus transform "Consedjo (Advice)" into an ideal choice for a wedding dance (lyrics: "You must work hard/So that tomorrow/You're not in need"). The guitars of "Nha cancera ka tem medida (My Fatigue Is Endless)" suggest kinship with Latin music. "Doce guerra (Sweet War)" is a guitar blues, a love song to Cape Verde. Superlative and magical. Recorded in 1995. Lyrics are translated into English.

LINK> *Mercedes Sosa — 30 Años* *Philips 518-789*
Exiled from Argentina in 1978, Sosa is another of the world's more remarkable female voices. Remarkable not only for her big voice and versatility, but also for her grace in lifting a song into a total emotional experience. Every collection should include at least one Sosa CD.

Cabo Verde
Nonesuch 79450

A more elaborate production adds some guest artists, notably James Carter on tenor sax, former band members Paulino and Toi Vieira, and cellist Vincent Segal. A morna, "Partida (Departure)," demonstrates how far she has come in a few years—and how much Segal's cello and the expansive artistry of her new pianist, Nando Andrade, contribute. The peppy "Beirona's Blood" is a coladeira, a dance with wry lyrics. The cavaquinho, a high-pitched Portuguese variation on the ukelele, is used to great effect on "Sabine largá'm (Sabino, Leave Me)." Song after song is a surprise and a delight. Once again, recording quality is excellent.

LINK> *Bana — Bana Chante La Magie du Cap-Vert*
Lusafrica (Stern's) 8630
Another Cape Verde singer with decades of experience, his warm voice possesses the same worldwise character as Evora's. He sings mostly mornas and caldeiras.

Various Artists: The Soul of Cape Verde
Tinder 42831732

Evora is one of more than a dozen artists from Cape Verde on this collection. Maria Alice, whose voice is higher than Evora's, performs a morna, "Falso Testemunho (False Witness)." The reed and vocal duet, performed by Voz de Cabo and Djosinha on "Partida" (sung by Evora on *Cabo Verde*) is magnificent. Saxophone player Luis Morais, a leading force in Cape Verde's music scene, solos on "Boas Festas." Bau, who played on several Evora albums, does a beautiful cavaquinho solo. The popular, deep voiced Bana contributes "Sina de Cabo Verde" and "Serpentina." Titina and Celinda Pereira, two popular female vocalists, are interesting to compare with Evora.

LINK> *Various Artists — Cape Verde: Anthology 1959-1992*
Buda 92614
This 2-CD is part of an extensive series from Buda that cover music from a particular country or culture. This one focuses on the development of Cape Verde's unique musical traditions, such as morna, coladeira, and funana.

The preeminent **British** folk rock band came together around 1967 with guitar players Richard Thompson, Ian Matthews, and Simon Nicol; bassist Ashley Hutchings; drummer Martin Lamble; and vocalist Judy Dyble. A year later, after the first album, Sandy Denny replaced Dyble, and the band took off with a much-loved combination of traditional folk songs and covers of 1960s folk songs (often obscure). Denny's soaring voice provided the magic. The year 1969 brought more personnel changes: Matthews left, and Lamble died in an accident; in came drummer Dave Mattacks and fiddler Dave Swarbrick. Within the year, Hutchings left for Steeleye Span and Denny for Fotheringay. Thompson left in 1970 and eventually became a very popular solo artist. The last original, Nicol, was gone a year later. Fairport continued, encouraged by an undying fan base, but there were many more personnel changes, and the magic never returned.

What We Did on Our Holidays   Hannibal (Rykodisc) 4430

1968's first Fairport album, *Unhalfbricking* (Hannibal 4418) contains classics like "Who Knows Where the Time Goes" and "A Sailor's Life." This is their second: lead singer Sandy Denny's debut. This is a late 1968 amalgam of folk ("Fotheringay"), folk-rock a la the Mamas & the Papas ("Mr. Lacey") or the Byrds ("Book Song"), and a nexus for traditional British folk and psychedelia ("She Moves Through the Fair"). It's the transition from tradition to something new and fresh, beautifully done with strong contributions from lead guitarist and singer Richard Thompson, singer Ian Matthews, and bassist Ashley ("Tiger") Hutchings. Denny and Thompson's compositions stand strong alongside songs from Bob Dylan and Joni Mitchell.

LINK➤ *Sandy Denny — Who Knows Where the Time Goes?*
                                                        Hannibal (Rykodisc) 5301
3-CD set samples various solo albums, work with Fairport Convention and Fotheringay, plus demos and unreleased tracks. Splendid interpretations, intelligently selected material. The 1-CD The Best of Sandy Denny *(Hannibal 1328) contains only the well-known songs.*

Liege and Lief   A&M 4257

Their best, Denny's final album with the group (aside from reunions, etc.). "Come All Ye" is the rousing invitation to the fair, and the feeling of Olde England is maintained throughout. Denny was versatile, but her best work was in story songs. "Matty Groves" is the cinematic tale of a crazed British lord who eventually murders both his wife's lover and his wife. "Tam Lin" is no less a dark epic, this time invoking mythology. At about 8 minutes each, there's time enough for a well-told tale. Very strong arrangements artfully combine rock and old British folk. Recorded in 1968.

LINK➤ *Fotheringay*   *Hannibal (Rykodisc) 4426*
Some of this material is on the Sandy Denny box, Who Knows Where the Time Goes. *The focus is on Denny as very nearly a solo artist. She sings story songs, ballads, some Dylan. A good addition after purchasing the two Fairport Convention albums.*

For more than 1,000 years, the Pueblo villages in what is now New Mexico and Arizona have been home to **Native Americans** (or, if you prefer, American Indians). There are about 30 small settlements in all. People live in buildings constructed of adobe blocks and wood. Each settlement includes a kiva, a sacred private space where hunting and agriculture ceremonies are performed. Dance and music are central to these events; songs and steps are passed on from one generation to the next, and new ones are created as well. The Garcia Brothers are sons of White Leaf (Gaa Ts'an), a noted singer and composer (there were 12 children; 6 became singers, and when these recordings were made, 4 were still alive). Through decades of touring (first in the U.S., then in Canada and Europe), Peter Garcia has become well known as a teacher, composer, and singer. Peter and Cip Garcia are the song leaders at San Juan Pueblo.

Songs of My People
Music of the World 133

The album is credited to Peter Garcia and the Garcia Brothers. "Tsaay Shadei (Eagle Dance)" accompanies pairs of dancers, each wearing an eagle headdress and a row of eagle feathers on the arms and shoulders, simulating wings. Peter Garcia sings solo (one of his several on this CD) and is accompanied by a single drum and jingling metal bells. Changes in rhythm encourage the dancers to more accurately depict eagle flight. All four Garcia Brothers perform "Pogon Shadei (Cloud Dance)," composed by their father. As the tempo increases, the dance encourages rainfall. Peter Garcia does one version of "Turtle Dance Song" as a solo, and another with his brothers.

LINK➤ *Honor the Earth Powwow: Songs of the Great Lakes Indians*
Rykodisc 10199
Mickey Hart made these field recordings in the early 1990s. Expert engineering brings out the voices and the drums. Outstanding groups include Little Otter Singers and the LCO Soldier's Drum.

Various Artists — Talking Spirits   Music of the World 126

On this 1992 compilation, the Garcia Brothers represent the San Juan Pueblo with "San Juan Turtle Dance" and "San Juan Green Corn Dance." Chester Mahooty performs "Zuni Sunrise Song"; it's a work composed about a century ago that has remained one of the best-known Native American songs. It's performed here with a hopeful voice accompanied by the quiet beat of a single drum. Roger Mase and the Singers from the Second Mesa contribute a third of the album's songs, including two associated with autumn: "Hopi Corn Dance" and "Hopi Rainbow Dance." The same group's "Hopi Comanche Dance" celebrates the vigorous warriors of the Plains. An excellent introduction to this neglected music.

LINK➤ *Jerry Alfred & The Medicine Beat —*
Etsi Shon (Grandfather Song)   *Red House 93*
By combining traditional drumming and chant-like vocals with electronic keyboards and a jazz-like ensemble, Alfred very successfully creates an appealing synthesis. From 1994.

The place: Sundsvall, 200 miles north of Stockholm, **Sweden**. The time: January 1990. Violinist Stefan Brisland-Ferner and guitarist Rickard Westman attended a performance of Shakespeare's *Hamlet* whose dreary mood was set with ancient Swedish music. Intrigued, they sought out old songs and old instruments. With lute and bowed harp player Gotte Ringqvist, they formed a trio and started to perform on the festival circuit. They added drummer Jens Höglin just before Hultsfreds-festivalen, an important rock festival. In 1993, they recorded an EP with guest vocalist Emma Härdelin; she eventually joined as a full-time member. The group's name means "keepers of the gates of hell," and, according to Swedish mythology, refers specifically to a pair of dogs that guard those gates. Garmarna sings in Swedish, and many of its darkest songs are based on music from the Middle Ages and Dark Ages.

Vittrad   Omnium 2008

The title translates from the Swedish as "Crumbling Away." The music, released in the U.S. in 1994, is full-bodied folk that's enhanced by modern instruments to intensify the bottom end. "Nämndemans-Ola (Commissioner Ola)" is one of several instrumentals; it's performed on a hurdy-gurdy with a Jew's harp, then joined by flute and percussion. The sharpness of Emma Härdelin's voice and Jens Höglin's overwhelming rushes of percussion offer dark counsel to "Straffad Moder & Dotter (Mother and Daughter Punished)." It's a violent tale of a mother's two children, transformed with her consent into a fox and wolf, who return home to murder their mother and sister. English lyrics are provided.

LINK▶ *Hedningarna — Hippjokk*   *NorthSide 6003*
Industrial-strength Swedish folk music. Greater emphasis on instrumental work than Garmarna, but similar themes: "Drafur & Gildur" is a bloody medieval ballad. Includes a few original compositions and some reels from Sweden and Norway.

God's Musicians   Omnium 2014

Released in Sweden as Guds Spelemän (God's Musicians), this 1996 album begins with "Vänner och Fränder (Friends and Kin)," a ballad that predates most medieval songs. It sounds new because of modern percussion, Härdelin's vocals, and a skillful balance between folk tradition and modern rock. A mountain troll falls in love with "Sir Mannelig," offering otherworldly gifts, but the knight turns her down. The texture is ominous,

but the song ends without incident. "Varulven (Werewolf)" is, of course, another story, a sad and violent one at that. It rocks. "Hilla Lilla" tells her story to the Queen: her fiancé died, her mother died, and now, she dies in the lap of the Queen.

LINK▶ *Hoven Droven — Groove*   *NorthSide 6002*
A rocking sextet from Sweden that drives hard with fiddle and guitar, and also with congas, saxophones, fluegelhorn and trumpet. For more about this whole scene, visit Northside's Web site: www.noside.com.

The dudek is an Eastern European reed instrument, similar to the oboe, and Djivan Gasparyan is a master, one of **Armenia**'s finest musicians. He was born in Solag, near Armenia's capital city of Yerevan, in 1928. Listening to the old dudek masters, Gasparyan was able to teach himself the instrument. At age 20, he was soloing with the Yerevan Philharmonic Orchestra and playing with a national ensemble. Playing mostly Armenian instrumental folk music, Gasparyan has toured the world and has won four Gold Medals in competitions organized by UNESCO. In 1973, he was awarded the honorary title, People's Artist of Armenia, the only musician ever so honored. Gasparyan has also worked on Western projects; his music is part of the soundtrack of *The Last Temptation of Christ*, a Peter Gabriel project. Gasparyan has performed with the Kronos Quartet and with the Los Angeles Orchestra.

I Will Not Be Sad in This World   Warner Bros. 25885

Slow-moving, mournful music from an Armenian master. There are two instrument sounds here: the dudek, played by Garsparyan, and the drone dudek, played by Vachagan Avakian. The drone is background sound—long, deep notes that sometimes harmonize with Gasparyan's melody line. Gasparyan's room-filling sound is warm and easy, relaxing and pensive. Because the tempos are similar, each song sounds much like the one before, but patient listening brings out the beauty of the work. First released in Russia in 1983. Superb sound. Later collaborative work, emphasizing the ambient aspects of this music, was collected by producer Michael Brook for *Moon Shines at Night* (Caroline 6604).

LINK➤ *Hossein Alizadeh — Neynava, Song of Compassion*
Kereshmeh 103
Djamshid Andalibi performs the solos in "Neynava: Concerto for Ney and String Orchestra." It's a very appealing Persian classical work for Western orchestra. The second piece, a requiem for earthquake victims, is played on Iranian folk instruments.

Apricots from Eden
Traditional Crossroads 4276

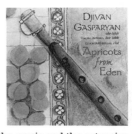

The solo dudek is always played with a second droning dudek (dam) and on folk music, it's often accompanied by the d'hol (a double-headed drum). Vachik Avakian is back on dam dudek, and Levon Ashakung plays d'hol. This is Armenian folk music gathered from a variety of sources. There are love songs, wedding songs, even a song of divination (to accompany the young girls who tell fortunes by the village fountain). Start here for both the music and the extensive liner notes that explain each song. Released in 1996. The earlier *Ask Me No Questions* (Traditional Crossroads 4268) is an excellent recording that brings out tonal nuances.

LINK➤ *Muradian Ensemble — Hayastan*   *Van Geel (Import)*
Excellent, but hard-to-find collection of Armenian folk music. Van Geel is a Dutch label.

Gil was born in 1942 in Salvador, Bahia, in **Brazil**. At dance parties (forros), he played accordion and guitar. By the early 1960s, the career-minded Gil was busily studying business administration, writing jingles for radio commercials, and performing. His breakthrough came in 1965: Elis Regina recorded one of his songs. He also moved to São Paolo and, with Caetano Veloso, led a radical musical and political movement called Tropicálismo (also called Tropicália; parallel to 1960s U.S. activism, but dangerous because of Brazil's right-wing military government). Gil was jailed and exiled for several years. He returned in 1972 and became a major star. His repertoire now included African music and reggae (his cover of "No Woman No Cry" was a huge hit). Gil's activism eventually led to membership in Salvador's city council. Busy, he has not neglected music: a free Copacabana concert that drew over 80,000 fans and his *MTV Unplugged* appearance were both extraordinarily popular.

Mina História Philips 510-477

Gil recorded for Philips from 1966 until 1978, and several collections are available. This one, part of a 1993 anthology series (CDs by famous Brazilian artists, each one titled Mina História), is just 48 minutes long, but it's an excellent introduction to a fabulously versatile musician. Some songs are typically Brazilian, heavy on percussion with either guitar or horns accompanying poetic lyrics, as on "Esses Moços." The 1969 party single, "Aquele Abraço," celebrates friends Caetano Veloso and João Gilberto, and life in Rio. "Maracatu Atomico," from 1973, borrows heavily from Santana. Wonderful sound quality on most tracks. Great music (but nonexistent liner notes).

LINK➤ *Elis Regina — A Arte De Elis Regina* *Verve 836-250*

Brazilian singer Elis Regina helped to start Gil's career by recording his song "Louvação," which is included on this best-of album. Regina was one of Brazil's finest interpreters (and biggest musical stars), and many of her hits are included here.

Realce WEA Brasil 382

This CD is more closely aligned with 1979 rock and dance music than with Brazilian traditions. The title cut, which translates as "Shine On," soars with a strong rock drum beat, female backup vocalists, powerful lead and rhythm guitars, and Brazilian horns. This being the disco era, Gil sings in a falsetto for part of the song. There's some traditional acoustic work with guitar and Brazilian rhythm, as on "Rebento," but American rock has more to do with the style of "Tradição (Tradition)" than traditional Brazilian music. The two ideas, rock and Brazilian style, come together on "Marina," and several other songs.

LINK➤ *Jorge Ben — Personalidade* *Verve 832-806*

A best-of album by Jorge Ben (a.k.a. Jorge Ben Jor), who combined samba from his native Rio de Janeiro with African music and R&B. In 1975, the two musicians recorded a great acoustic album called Gil Jorge *(Verve 512-067).*

Raça Humana
WEA Brasil 21222

Most of Gil's 36 albums are special and unique in their own way. This 1984 record, for example, features Gil with a powerful drum track (on most cuts, from Téo Lima), electric guitars (Liminha), electronic keyboards (Jorjão Barreto), and backing vocals. The Wailers join the band for "Vamos Fugir," a reggae song that fits seamlessly into the Brazilian music. "Indigo Blue," "A Mão da Limpeza," "Tempo Rei (King Time)," and several other songs are standouts— very commercial records with international appeal. Songs are consistently bouncy and fun, and Gil sounds like he's having the time of his life.

LINK▶ *Milton Nascimento — Sentinela*   *Verve 813-357*
The magnetic forces of Brazilian folk culture, the voices of Mercedes Sosa and Nana Cammyi, and superior songwriting result in a very special recording.

Acoustic
Atlantic 82564

Released in the U.S. as *Acoustic*, you'll find this album as *Gilberto Gil Unplugged* in Brazil and elsewhere. Consistent with MTV's *Unplugged* format, Gil appears with an acoustic band and sings many of his popular songs. It's delightful to hear "Realce" in such a simple arrangement. With so many of Gil's albums hard to find in the U.S., it's wonderful to have "Espresso 2222," "Parabolicamará," "Tempo Rei," "Sampa," and other Gil songs on a single CD (with English translations of the lyrics). Arrangements are usually guitar and voice, sometimes with flute and subtle percussion. Very laid back, but filled with quiet energy.

LINK▶ *Caetano Veloso & Gilberto Gil — Tropicália 2*   *Nonesuch 79339*
Inspired by the 25-year anniversary of Tropicália, the two friends created a new album of contemporary music together. Beautifully sung with inspired accompaniment by musicians Carlinhos Brown and Liminha (who co-produced). Enthusiastically recommended!

Quanta
WEA Brasil 86442

Gil has always been socially conscious, but few musicians have covered the territory that he so artfully transverses here. This 1997 two-CD set considers quantum mechanics ("Quanta"), quarks and other subatomic particles ("Átimo de pó"), Internet communications ("Pela Internet [Through the Internet]"), and metaphysical philosophy ("Pop we wei," a salute to Chinese philosopher Wu Wei). There are also considerations of religion ("Dança de Shiva," about Hindu divinity) and even garlic pills ("Pílula de alho"). Gil has transformed all of this into pop music; as always, his voice sounds terrific, and the arrangements are lively and entertaining. His Web page: http://www.gilbertogil.com.br.

LINK▶ *Arto Lindsay — Mundo Civilizado*   *Bar None 82*
A noted producer of Brazilian fusion, Lindsay (whose heritage is U.S. and Brazil) plays both ends of the spectrum: sweet bossa nova and edgy material akin to Gil's current thinking. With Don Byron (clarinet) and Bernie Worrell (organ).

Born in 1932 in **Brazil**'s northeasten state of Bahia, Gilberto became famous as the man who developed and perfected the bossa nova. A guitar player and vocalist, Gilberto essentially reduced the polyrhythms and the raucous style of samba to a calm, peaceful syncopation. His breakthrough came about with the 1958 Brazilian release of *Chega de Saudade*, an album currently unavailable in the U.S. Through his early recordings, Gilberto was closely associated with Antonio Carlos Jobim, whose compositions were ideal bossa nova material. HIs most famous recordings were made with his then-wife Astrud Gilberto and jazz saxophone player Stan Getz. From the liner notes of *The Legendary João Gilberto*, a quote from Brazilian musician Caetano Veloso: "João Gilberto is the starting place for understanding Brazilina music. He gave me a complete idea of what music could be, what art could be, of what beauty could be."

The Legendary João Gilberto
World Pacific 93891

With 38 tracks on one CD, this immersion in Gilberto's early work and entry into bossa nova (1958-61) could hardly be more complete. Many of these songs were covered by Sergio Mendez and Brasil 66, and played on U.S. radio: Jobim's "Desafinado (Out of Tune)" and "Sambo de una Nota Só (One Note Samba)," Gilberto's "Bim-Bom," and the often-recorded Luis Bonfá tune, "Manhã de Carnaval (Carnival Morning)." Some of the best work here is also the simplest: Gilberto's beautiful tenor accompanied by his own guitar, though many songs are more elaborately arranged. Superb interpretations throughout, and an excellent recording as well.

LINK▶ *Sergio Mendes and Brasil 66 — Foursider*   A&M 216-012
Mendes deserves credit for introducing many Brazilian songs, by some of Brazil's finest songwriters, to U.S. audiences. Pretty arrangements. Material includes not only "Mas Que Nada," "Bim Bom," and Jobim's "Wave," but also covers of "Fool on the Hill" and other pop.

Getz/Gilberto   Verve 810-048

Listed as a Stan Getz album, Gilberto sings all but two of the songs and strongly influences Getz's approach (Getz's sax imitates Gilberto's voice on "O Grande Amor"). Getz contributes several extended solos that combine contemporary jazz with Brazilian style. Jobim, who plays piano, wrote "The Girl from Ipanema," "Desafinado," "So Danco Samba (I Only Dance Samba)," and "O Grande Amor." Recorded with considerable skill by Phil Ramone in 1963, this is the ultimate bossa nova album. João's then-wife, Astrud Gilberto, was not yet a professional singer, but her English section of "The Girl from Ipanema" and her naive rendition of "Corcovado (Quiet Nights)" are highlights.

LINK▶ *Stan Getz — The Girl from Ipanema: The Bossa Nova Years*
Verve 823-611
This set includes Getz/Gilberto plus all of the other bossa nova music recorded by Getz in the 1960s: big band, small groups, etc. There's enough to fill four CDs with few alternate takes. The concept (almost) never grows thin.

They're not real gypsies. They're the sons and nephews of flamenco musician Jose Reyes, a straightforward flamenco group that started in Arles, a small city in **Southern France** in the 1970s, earning money by performing at weddings and parties, and as a street band. (They claimed to live like gypsies, hence the name change from the original Los Reyes). Producer Claude Martinez added influences from North Africa and the Middle East, encouraged more of a pop music philosophy, and started making hit records first in France, then throughout Europe, then the U.S. By the early 1990s, they were deep into show business culture, associating with Elton John, Eric Clapton, and other pop stars. Their first U.S. album went gold; the Gipsy Kings are world music stars. And often, they're criticized for being the tourist version of a real flamenco band. But their music belies the criticism.

Gipsy Kings   Nonesuch 60845
Their first album, released in 1988, remained on the charts for much of the year and eventually went gold. The varied program borrows liberally from many Spanish styles, but the rich sound of multiple Spanish guitars gives this music heart and soul. "Djobi, Djoba" opens with a Nicholas Reyes's quick, subtly hoarse vocal, very fast guitars, and invigorating drums. It's one of the group's best songs. "Un Amor" is slow and breezy, similar to Brazilian music, but the hefty sound of multiple guitars adds a symphonic quality. "Moorea" is a more traditional flamenco dance, enriched by folk harmonies. Listen for those amazing riffs on "Quiero Saber."

LINK➤ *Jesse Cook — Gravity*   *Narada 63037*
Cook (a Canadian who has lived in Spain) takes a entirely modern approach to flamenco, and adds a subtle new age texture with Andean flutes and African drums. From 1995.

Este Mundo   Elektra 61179
The accordion, fast danceable rhythm, and vocal tradition on the Gipsy Kings' original "Baila me" links directly to "Iko Iko" and other songs sung in New Orleans clubs. It's an exciting lead into an varied album where everything comes together. There's high drama here: Nicholas Reyes's big vocal on "Sin Ella," and "Habla Me." The big production number is "Oy," with trombone, trumpets, and saxophones—a cross between flamenco and NYC Latino music. "Ternuras" is a great instrumental with hand-clap percussion. "Lagrimas," another instrumental, spotlights guitar player Tonido Baliardo with simple, lilting percussion, and synthesizer accompaniment. "No Volvere" is accompanied by a lush string orchestra. From 1991.

LINK➤ *Clifton Chenier — Zydeco Dynamite*   *Rhino 71194*
Though the connection is stronger on some songs than others, the soul that infuses Chenier's accordion is akin to the soul within the Gipsy Kings' music.

Love & Liberté   Elektra 61599

A more elaborate electronic production enhanced by drum machines and digital keyboards, released in 1993. "Escucha Me" typifies a new style: gone are the clustered guitars, sensitive guitar solos, and peasant vocals. "Navidad" pushes further into contemporary dance music. "Ritmo de la Noche" is an old-fashioned flamenco guitar number, one with a very strong percussion track. "Madre Mia" also follows tradition, but it's a more complicated production with a prominent digital bass and keyboards. In contrast, "Montaña," with Canut Reyes singing lead vocal, is one of the group's prouder accomplishments; it uses electronic instruments only to add majesty to the basic flamenco sound.

LINK➤ *Various Artists — Gypsy Passion: New Flamenco*   Narada 63931
Purists may question how much flamenco resides in the heart of the Gipsy Kings, but whatever it is that they're doing, other artists are doing, too. On this compliation: Strunz & Farah, Willie & Lobo, Jesse Cook, Ottmar Liebert, and others.

Best of the Gipsy Kings   Nonesuch 79358

Four Gipsy Kings albums are well represented here. Six tracks come from the first album, *Gipsy Kings* (Elektra 60845), four from *Mosaïque* (60892), two from *Gipsy Kings Live* (61390), three from *Love & Liberté* (61599), and one from *Este Mundo* (61179). The big decision is whether to start here or with the first album; neither *Mosaïque* nor the live album is essential. There is a version of "Volaré" here (from *Mosaïque*), but the song has been so overexposed that not even the Gipsy Kings' virtuosity and enthusiasm can save it. Still, the closing medley, which includes five of their best songs, is worth the price of this CD.

LINK➤ *Fania All Stars — Bamboleo*   Fania 650
Four of the six songs on this album are Gipsy Kings classics: the title cut, "Siento," "Quiero Saber," "Djobi, Djoba." The result is powerful salsa. The other two tracks are "Smooth Operator" and Stevie Wonder's "Don't You Worry About a Thing."

Tierra Gitana   Nonesuch 79399

A return to acoustic instruments and a cleaner overall sound, released in 1996. A dream CD for lovers of Spanish guitar, "Estellas" is one of the group's best instrumentals. The church bells that begin and punctuate "Los Peces en el Rio" signal their most passionate work: very fast guitars, hand-claps, and other rapid-fire percussion, as well as splendid group vocals. A string quartet accompanies the Gipsy Kings on "Mi Corazon." The cello and the lower ranges of guitar sound warm and wonderful together, and the violin and viola lift the music into the heavenly realm. This is beautiful music-making, some of the Gipsy Kings' finest work.

LINK➤ *Ginesa Ortega — Siento*   Harmonia Mundi France 987011
A 1997 album of authenic Spanish flamenco from a husky-voiced modernist. This is roots music that carries on the tradition without bowing to the commercial concerns, raw and empassioned—and more akin to North African music than to the Gipsy Kings.

Grayhorse Singers

The Grayhorse Singers are led by legendary Jack Anquoe. He and his performing family are members of the **Kiowa** nation, located in what is now Oklahoma. Anquoe's family have been making music for generations, and he has been performing since childhood, a tradition he continued with his own children (Redcloud, Jim, Rick, Warren and Jimmy Anquoe comprise half the group). Jack has been making music for more than 30 years; his life is singing the traditional songs, and telling stories of his people (he is nearly as famous for his storytelling as for his music). They travel the Pow Wow Highway, playing small, medium, and large Pow Wow competitions throughout North America, and consistently winning top prizes. In short, the Grayhorse Singers are one of world music's most successful Pow Wow groups.

Gourd Talkers   SOAR 143

This 1991 album is filled with gourd dances. The term requires some explanation. A sundance is a sacred ceremony that can last for days, and in which singing, dancing, and the piercing of skin offer spiritual thanks to Wakan Tanka (the Creator). The U.S. Government banned the sundance in the 1800s, but the Kiowa (and other tribes) got around the rule by substituting the gourd song and dance. These celebratory songs are performed, as on "Old Kiowa Gourd Song," by a group blending (frequently ecstatic) song with chant, accompanied by a loud drum. The album contains 13 gourd songs, plus several other songs related to ritual.

LINK➤ *Cornel Pewewardy — Spirit Journey*   SOAR 140
Dr. Pewewardy, a full-blood Comanche/Kiowa (also from Oklahoma), was 1991's Indian Educator of the Year. Here, his music blends natural sounds with a lighter, easier approach to several gourd songs. A recommended starting place.

Spirits Who Dance   SOAR 177

Far better recording brings out the excitement of the drum and the robust singing voices. "Missing Warrior," composed by Jeanette Mopope in 1942, rationalizes fighting for the U.S. and remaining a member of the nation. Mopope also wrote "Warrior's Song" to celebrate World War II Commander Gus Palmer, a Kiowa. "Come Out Grass Dancers," "Oklahoma Snake Dance," and the Buffalo song, "Dance for Those Who Cannot," are quite different in rhythm and feeling from one another—a good response to those who (ridiculously) believe that all of this music sounds the same. "Dance for Those Who Cannot" includes some fast, thrilling drumming and very spirited vocals. Another excellent starting place for a Native American library.

LINK➤ *Eastern Eagle Singers — Traditionally Yours*   SOAR 178
One of the youngest groups on the Pow Wow circuit, it is led by Brian Knockwood of the Mi-Kmaq nation and they come from Nova Scotia, Canada. Energetic, and extremely well recorded.

As a girl, Griffiths sang in church and in school and imitated Aretha Franklin, Dionne Warwick, and other U.S. singers. Her career began with a **Jamaican** TV appearance, which led to a Studio One recording contract and a series of hit records with Jamaican cover versions, British and U.S. pop tunes, and original material written by Bob Andy (the two performed as Bob & Marcia and had some hits together). An early 1970 cover of "Young Gifted & Black" reached number 5 on the U.K. charts, and the followup "Pied Piper" cover reached Number 11. Griffiths became Jamaica's top female singer. In the early 1970s, she formed the I-Threes with two of Jamaica's popular female vocalists, Judy Mowatt and Rita Marley. From 1974 until 1981, the I Threes toured and recorded as part of Bob Marley's organization, but Griffiths also recorded as a solo. After Marley's death, Griffiths resumed her solo career, but without the previous momentum.

Steppin'   Shanachie 44007

This solo album was recorded in 1978, while Griffiths was working with Bob Marley. It's filled with great singing and great songs. Griffiths is especially convincing on a reggae anthem, "Steppin' into Babylon," as full of the righteous spirit as anything she recorded with Marley. Griffiths's long experience as a solo hitmaker comes to play in her handling of "Peaceful Woman." The song is magnificent pop because she so totally believes in the lyrics: "I'm a peaceful woman; I don't believe in doing wrong." She easily maneuvers between rhythmic singing and long moaning notes. Griffiths's voice is nicely complemented by Sonia Pottinger, Jamaica's only significant female producer at the time.

LINK➤ *Rita Marley — We Must Carry On*   *Shanachie 43082*

A very spirited album with terrific songs and exciting arrangements. Marley shares more of the clear-voiced pop spirit with Griffiths; Mowatt's work is more serious, her arrangements more sophisticated.

Naturally   Shanachie 44014

Griffiths possesses one of those amazing pop voices that makes every song sound like a major hit. A strong reggae beat plays perfectly against her treatment of Bunny Wailer's optimistic "Dreamland" to open this 1979 album. Great harmonies (against her own voice), too. Pottinger is again the producer, but this time, Sly Dunbar's drums seem more prominent (he also played on *Steppin'*), and the horns are more clearly articu-

lated. The result is a more precise production that elevates Griffiths's voice on the pop love song, "Tell Me Now," and other songs. Marley's "Lonesome Feeling" is framed by insistent percussion and detailed with ethereal background vocals.

LINK➤ *Marcia Griffiths — Put a Little Love in Your Heart*   *Trojan 325*

Greatest hits from 1969 to 1974, many (like "Young, Gifted & Black") recorded with Bob Andy as Bob & Marcia. Other covers include "Pied Piper," the title song, and "Band of Gold."

In the **Dominican Republic**, the popular music is merengue—but don't confuse the term with the music popular in other Caribbean countries (the instruments are different). Dominican merengue thrived in the '30s, '40s, and '50s encouraged by President Trujillo, who spent serious money to establish a Dominican musical tradition. Johnny Ventura, Willie Vargas, and Cuco Valoy were major 1980s merengue stars, but a new form, bacháta, took shape in poor neighborhoods. Guerra combined merengue with bacháta, and in time, became Latin music's biggest star. Born in 1957 (the son of a professional baseball player), Guerra studied arts and philosophy at the National Conservatory and music theory at Berklee College of Music. In the mid-1980s, Guerra made his first album. By slowing down merengue, adding bacháta, infusing jazz, and concentrating on melody, Guerra appealed to upscale Latin urban professionals. His band, 440, is named for 440Hz, the frequency of the A note.

Grandes Exitos de Juan Luis Guerra /440   Karen 29418

Guerra is one of contemporary Latin music's more inventive talents, and it's a kick to follow his growth on this greatest hits album ("exito" means "success" or "hit"). Half of this music comes from *Bachata Rosa* (Karen 136). Two songs come from *Mientras más lo pienso...tú* (105). Both "Me enamoro de ella" and "Guavaberry" are dance songs with snappy beats, Guerra's fast-paced lead vocals, and a chorus. Several tracks from *Ojalá que llueva café* (126) shape the same components in a smarter, more modern way. "El costa de la vida," one of his best songs, comes from *Areito* (146).

LINK➤ *Various Artists – Merengue: Dominican Music and Dominican Identity*   **Rounder 1130**
A history of Dominican merengue produced in association with Temple University Press, publisher of a book with the same title in 1996. The liner notes provide far more than the usual historical and cultural details.

Ojalá que llueva café   Karen 126

One of the best-selling albums in the history of Latin music, and the title cut (which translates as "I hope it rains coffee [in the fields]") is a good reason why. A delightful fantasy with an extremely appealing rhythm track; Guerra's warm and gentle lead vocal; images of butter and honey mountains; strings, horns, and sound effects in just the right places...it's a wonderful song. "Visa para un sueña" is a poem whose lyrics visit a dream in the early morning, set to an urban dance beat. "Woman del Callao" is Guerra's style of merengue: danceable with a male lead vocal and a slick female chorus.

LINK➤ *Caetano Veloso – Circuladô*   **Nonesuch 79277**
Guerra shares some of Veloso's gift for poetic images, and for arrangements that enhance those visual ideas. This 1991 album is probably as close as the two artists get to one another.

Bachata Rosa
Karen 136

His best; the album that won Guerra his first Grammy. His songwriting has matured; "Estrellitas y Duendes" is a charming dream song. The title cut, "Bachata Rosa," is a love song with an unusual rhythm; Guerra's influences are widening, with touches of Africa informing the fast dance "A Pedir su Mano." A very tightly arranged coro (vocal chorus) and a stunning female lead vocal on "Reforestame" are an entrancing combination. As Guerra moves beyond dance music, "Acompañeme Civil" raises the notion of social awareness that will soon become central to his career. Even here, production is clever with a danceable beat.

LINK➤ *Oscar D'Leon — Oro Salsero - 20 Exitos* *Rovden (UNI) 3115*
Like Guerra, Venezuela's Oscar D'Leon pioneered a modern form of danceable music from his country's older forms. An exciting salsa performer, much of his influence comes from Cuba.

Areito
Karen 3456

Guerra heard Zairean guitar player Diblo Dibala performing "El Costo de la Vida (The Cost of Living)" in S.O.B.'s, a NYC nightclub, and deftly added lyrics whose subtle humor stirred up emotions in fellow Dominicans. The airtight arrangement runs with a neat dance beat, but this song is full of surprises: a call-and-respond chorus, tiny references to "The Lion Sleeps Tonight," and other pop culture. It's a message song presented as fun. "Ayer (Yesterday)" is another superb production, one that benefits from Guerra's early influence from the Manhattan Transfer (interestingly, the influence is more often heard in the horns than in the group vocals). From 1993.

LINK➤ *Joe Arroyo — Grandes Exitos* *Discos Fuentes 10150*
Arroyo is Colombia's leading salsa singer, but his unique approach combines not only salsa, but music from the Dominican Republic, Haiti, and throughout the tropics.

Fogaraté!
Karen 21110

Guerra performs one song by Papa Wemba and two by Diblo Dibala, whose distinctive ringing guitar adds just the right touch throughout this 1995 album. The blend of soukous from Zaire and quieter bachata merengue from the Dominican Republic is enormously appealing. It's a mesmerizing combination on Wemba's mellow "Viviré." Two up-tempo dance numbers, Dibala's "Los Mangos Bajitos" and Guerra's "El Farolito," spin the brain around: is this Dominican soukous or African merengue? The charming "Los Pajaritos" is presented as a slick, old-fashioned Latino song with small horns, primitive percussion, and small unison chorus. Francisco Ulloa's accordion solo on "Canto de hacha" is amazing.

LINK➤ *Isaac Delgado — Con Ganas* *Qbadisc 9012*
In addition to the obvious joy of Isaac Delgado's voice, producer Gonzalo Rubalcaba's smooth production makes this album a delight. Released in 1994.

When Guo Yue's was a young boy in **China**, his father, a respected musician, died. His mother was sent away, the result of the Cultural Revolution. Guo Yue and his brother, Guo Yi, grew up in a Beijing ghetto, a musicians' compound where they learned to play a variety of musical instruments. Yue gravitated toward the flute, and Yi became expert with the ancient sheng (a handheld mouth organ). As a teen, Yue worked with China's Army Orchestra, often performing in remote areas. Yi became involved with film, eventually composing hundreds of soundtracks. In the mid-1980s, the Guo Brothers' band was based in London. In 1989, Guo Yue began a solo career, collaborating with the Chieftains, Sinéad O'Connor, Peter Gabriel, and others. This led to the formation of Trisan with Joji Hirota and former Clannad member Paul Brennan. Guo Yue's work can also be heard on the soundtrack to *The Last Emperor*.

Yuan
RealWorld (Caroline) 2310

Clannad founder Pól Brennan produced this 1990 album of acoustic Chinese folk music. He also performs. Guo Yue plays Chinese bamboo flute, with his brother Guo Yi on sheng (mouth organ), and Shung Tian on Chinese oboe; they are four of eight musicians. A blend of modern and traditional songs, the music is classical in tone, peaceful, and very imaginative. In "Fishing by Lamplight," the simplicity of the yan qin (dulcimer) simulates flickering lamps on the lake surface. New villages are celebrated with folk dances on "Soldiers of the Long March," but as they reenter the endless road, the music becomes weary.

LINK➤ *Fong Naam — The Sleeping Angel*   *Nimbus 5319*
Nine-piece classical orchestra from Thailand plays two suites and several other ensemble pieces with gongs, xylophones, and percussion. Superbly played, and very special. Highest recommendation!

Red Ribbon
Shanachie 64059

This time, Guo Yue is paired with Japanese percussionist Joji Hirota, well-known as a music director for dance. Their formal relationship began in 1991 with the formation of Trisan, a trio with Paul (a.k.a. Pól) Brennan. Hirota's percussion can be subtle, as on "Goodbye Again" (in Chinese, the word for "goodbye" also means "see you again"). Hirota is more aggressive and versatile in "The Beginning," but his chimes and Guo Yue's whistles on "Little Bird" paint a fragile image. Similarly, the picture of a flowing "Red Ribbon" is effortlessly envisioned by simply listening to the long flute lines and the subtle folds in the percussion. Magnificent.

LINK➤ *Tadashi Tajima — Shingetsu*   *Music of the World 124*
Tajima is a master of the Japanese flute known as the shakuhachi. Made of bamboo, the flute has a reedy, rustic presence. Music evokes a leaf falling without restraints, encourages the overcoming of difficulties, guides the safe passage of a soul.

Morocco's Gnawa people have evolved a variety of arts and rituals; some are quite spectacular (involving acrobatic dancing and huge drums). They're the central attraction at Marrakech's thrilling Jmaa el-Fna entertainment square. Born in Marrakech in 1963, Hakmoun started learning Gnawa traditions early. Hakmoun's mother, a shuwafa (healer) led ceremonies involving ancient ritual songs. As a teenager, he developed skills on the sintir (the Gnawi lute, which is a wooden box covered with camel skin) and on various percussion instruments. Hakmoun left home and school at age 14, traveled to France and Spain, then returned to Marrakech as a street musician at Jmaa el-Fna, performing popular Berber and Arab songs. Working locally with his band, Zahar, Hakmoun moved toward fusion music. By the 1990s, his work was well known within the world music community (his album *Zahar* was released by the Knitting Factory, a cutting-edge NYC venue and label).

Gift of the Gnawa   Flying Fish (Rounder) 70571

Adam Rudolph, who produced this 1991 album in NYC and plays percussion (notably tabla), recorded as a member of the Mandingo Griot Society with Foday Muso Sosa in 1978. Hakmoun plays sintir and sings, Richard Horowitz plays the ney (a Turkish clarinet), and Don Cherry plays pocket trumpet (Cherry is also a world fusion veteran). This is an album of contrasts: trance and lively rhythm, for example. Cherry's horn easily glides along the gray area between North African ritual and jazz. It's easy to get lost inside the music and to wonder how jazz and this percussive music can sound so similar. Cherry, by the way, is superb. Credited to Hakmoun and Rudolph.

LINK➤ *Adam Rudolph & Yusef Lateef — The World at Peace*
YAL / Meta 753

Ambitious ensemble work for 12 musicians made possible by two lifetimes of interest and experimentation with world music. Very difficult to classify as jazz, world music, or something entirely new. Released in 1997 on two CDs.

The Fire Within: Gnawa Music of Morocco   Music of the World 135

A best-selling 1995 album of traditional Gnawa music from the ceremony known as derdeba—a way to purge or placate evil spirits to enhance a relationship with a happy spirit. "Sala 'Alik Dima Dima," performed on sintir with overdubbed percussion, is one of several pieces that accompany the devotees' entrance into the ceremony. "Bu Derbala" is a solo related to the dedication of ceremonial robes. "Layali," another piece in which Hakmoun's various instruments simulate a group via multitracking, invokes the spirit of a saint summoned in desperate situations. And while these topics may seem exotic, the music is both accessible and sufficiently intricate to justify repeat listening.

LINK➤ *Hassan Hakmoun & Zahar — Trance*   Caroline / RealWorld 2334
Zahar is Hakmoun's band, a rocking ensemble that maps Anthony Michael Peterson's electric guitar alongside Hakmoun's sintir for patterns that straddle rock and Gnawa. Note also Hossam Ramzy's Egyptian percussion. From 1992.

Most of **Nubia** no longer exists; it was submerged by Lake Nasser, the result of the construction of the Aswan High Dam. But the spirit of Nubia, one of the world's oldest continuous civilizations, remains vibrant due in part to its music. Hassan grew up in a small Nubian village near Aswan. He has since become one of Egypt's greatest stars and most prosperous record producers. In the late 1940s, Hassan moved with his family to Cairo where he learned to play the clarinet. He formed a band in the mid-1950s and for decades, played weddings and other celebrations. His band was a showcase for upcoming Egyptian stars, whom Hassan often produced. The band also brought music from other cultures into Egypt, notably Cuban music (hence the nickname Kuban). And this is not just one band—it's an organization employing more than 50 musicians who can cover up to seven simultaneous jobs.

Nubian Magic   Mercator (Caroline) 7003

Hassan's skill in blending Western-style instrumentation with adaptations of ancient Nubian rhythms is just part of the story. He also has a knack for songwriting that invites the audience to sing along (even CD listeners are likely to sing along—even though the lyrics are in Arabic or Kenuz! Instrumentation is often Western-style: bongos, saxophones, accordions (with some Arabic instruments, like the tabla). Mostly love songs, this music is most often performed at weddings. The two best songs are "Samiry," a Nubian samba, and "Mabrouk Wo Arisna," Sudanese reggae. From 1994. Try also *From Nubia to Cairo* (Shanachie 64036), a greatest hits collection of wedding dance music from 1991.

LINK➤ *Salamat – Nubiana*   *Piranha (Stern's) 1044*

Salamat represents the younger generation of Nubia (born after the Nubia was submerged). This is his third album—a rousing affair with aggressive percussion and superb musicianship from Les Musiciens de Nil. Salam Delta (Piranha 936) is also recommended.

Walk Like a Nubian   Piranha (Stern's) 43

Don't be misled by the cover photo. Hassan, an older musician, is pictured as a folksinger with a lute-like tar. This is totally modern electric dance music performed by a steaming hot band. The electric bass, horns, and fast tempo of "Om Sha'ar Asmar Medaffar (The beauty with the black plaits)" outshines the folksy version on *From Nubia to Cairo*. Hassan again embraces foreign sounds— "Habibi" ("My darling, my medicine") is performed with a jerk rhythm. Cascading horns and accordion on "Al Ghazal (The gazelle)" capture the romping animal; this song would be a hit at any Western wedding. World-class arrangements and recording quality. A terrific album!

LINK➤ *Mahmoud Fadl – Music of the Nile*   *Piranha (Stern's) 1147*

Drumming journey from the Nubian desert to Mohamed Ali Street in Cairo. Very wide range of stories and settings: a bride's chamber, angry street noise, women who sing by the banks of the river. A festival of instruments: duff, darabuka, oud, djembe, plus more familiar accordion, conga, etc.

Ofra Haza

A modern **Israeli** singer with strong roots to tradition, Haza was born in Yemen in 1957. Her family trekked on foot to immigrate to Tel Aviv, where she was raised in the poor, tough Yemeni district. At age 13, she became a singer with the Hatikva community theater, the first step to club performances and records. As a teenager, Haza became a very popular singer with many gold and platinum albums to her credit. She has stayed close to her roots as a Yemenite Jew. Over the course of nearly 20 years in show business, she has worked closely with producer and manager Bazalel Aloni. Haza has, however, played an important role in the growth and popularity of the world music phenomenon; her music is heard in many countries' dance clubs, and she has worked closely with producer Don Was.

The Fifty Gates of Wisdom: Yemenite Songs
Shanachie 64002

After recording several popular Israeli albums, Haza returned to her roots in Yemen for this 1988 release. With producer Bezalel Aloni, Haza reworked traditional Yemenite Jewish music, added contemporary instrumentation and a beat, and, remarkably, came up with a song played in many dance clubs worldwide ("Galbi"). Many of these songs are based on the poetry of Rabbi Shalom Shabazi, a Spanish Jew who wrote about God, country, and love in the 16th century. The combination of Haza's powerful voice, percussion played on oil cans (in memory of a Muslim ban on musical instruments), and such modern instruments as conga, double bass, bassoon, clarinet, and strings weave a mighty spell.

LINK➤ *Natacha Atlas — Diaspora*   *Nation 47*
Haza began the world dance fusion phenomenon with her 1988 album. Atlas and her band, Transglobal Underground, built on the trend. This is her first solo album, notable for Egyptian composer Essam Rashad's work with 13-piece Arab orchestra performing "Feres."

Desert Wind
Sire 25976

As Haza's chic contemporary dress in her cover portrait suggests, this is modern dance music, circa 1989. The producer is Arif Mardin. Haza's big voice reigns over endlessly dynamic electronic percussion, but the heart of this album is "Ya Ba Ye," which attempts to reconcile a mother's old-style values with the freedom of her daughter. Political statements burst through the dance beat: "Middle East," about peace, and "Mm'mma," about Jews unable to migrate from Yemen and Ethiopia. "Kaddish" (a Jewish prayer for the dead), with its sampling, drum machine, and modern vocals, is a big a step into the future. Which is precisely what Haza, and this album, are about.

LINK➤ *Yosefa*   *Worldy Dance (Triloka) 320-201*
Popular dance music from an Israeli singer of Moroccan and Yemeni descent. Very representative of 1993 discos.

Huun-Huur-Tu

The term "Huun-Huur-Tu" refers to the countryside in **Tuva** in southern Siberia. More specifically, it refers to the perfect way in which rays of light are broken by blades of grass at sunrise and sunset. In 1992, Sayan Bapa, his brother Sasha, and two other musicians, Kaigalool Khovalyg and Albert Kuzevin, adopted the name for their new ensemble, one that would sing the extraordinary traditional Tuvan folk music. Kaigal-ool has a marvelous voice and a talent for singing not one, but several notes at a time; this is called Tuvan throat-singing; it is only a small part of a huge musicial heritage lovingly presented by a remarkable group of musicians. Huun-Huur-Tu has been exceedingly successful. Their unusual sounds, supported by unfamiliar instruments (one is a rattle made from the kneebones of a sheep and the scrotum of a bull) and their entirely authentic presentation have attracted considerable attention in the U.S. and elsewhere.

The Orphan's Lament   Shanachie 64058

In Tuva, where family relationships are central to existence, the orphan is a symbol of disastrous misfortune, hence the lament. "Kaldak Khamar" tells of building a mountain road—the trip up on horseback, and return down in a "hard iron machine," an automobile. Other songs are about a girlfriend, not understanding someone's jokes, and the loss of a mother. Clearly, there's more happening than unusual polyphonic throat singing and rustic Asian instruments. Stop to marvel at Kaigal-ool's deep voice, but also read the liner notes. They make sense of sounds that can be rough on Western ears. From 1994.

LINK▶ *Various Artists — Deep in the Heart of Tuva*   *Ellipsis Arts 4080*
A 64-page book describes the former Tannu Tuva, years under Russian rule, and 1992 emergence as a new republic. Colorful articles explain Tibetan Buddhism, shamans, the national obsession with wrestling, games played with sheep-knuckle bones, Tuvan food, and the variety of Tuvan music on this CD.

If I'd Been Born an Eagle   Shanachie 64080

Recorded in the Netherlands in 1996, this is a friendlier introduction to challenging music. Kaigal-ool again does his masterful polyphonic vocal solo, but here it's an artful imitation of an owl's song. Avid Tuvan music collectors, Huun-Huur-Tu's connection to Russian music is emphasized; Russian folk musician Sergei Starosin guests. Still, daily Tuvan life and music are inseparable. "Dadyr-Todur" derives its rhythm from a horse's trot (percussion instruments include two dried horse hooves). Kaigal-ool's most expressive "Song of a Lonely Man" bemoans separation from family to the igil's sad drone. (An igil is a 2-stringed fiddle with a carved horse's head on top.)

LINK▶ *The Gyoto Monks — Freedom Chants from the Roof of the World*
                                              Rykodisc 20113
Ritual polyphonic chanting—each monk sings two or three tones simultaneously. They've been making this music for half a millenium. Includes an interesting response from Philip Glass, Kitaro, Jerry Garcia, and Mickey Hart.

A group of students at the Technical University of Santiago, **Chile** formed Inti-Illimani in 1967. They wrote and played in the Nueva Canción style (the term translates into "new song," an update on older formulas with greater social awareness). The group gained a following but was exiled by the government in 1973. The members persevered, touring and recording regularly; during the 1980s, several of their albums were released by RCA Italy. In 1988, Inti-Illimani returned from Italy and became deeply involved in Chile's traditional music scene. The group has often performed with popular artists and was part of Amnesty International's concerts with Bruce Springsteen, Tracy Chapman, Peter Gabriel, and others. Each of Inti-Illimani's eight musicians plays multiple instruments; altogether, the group members play more than 30 wind, string, and percussion instruments. Horacio Salinas is Inti-Illimani's artistic director and principal composer. The group is once again based in Santiago.

Andadas   Xenophile (Green Linnet) 4009

Translated, the title of this album is "Wanderings." Recorded in Santiago, Chile, in 1992, the album begins with "Angelo," a lilting instrumental played mainly on a wooden flute. The second track is a dramatic choral number with poetic lyrics called "El Equipaje del Desteirro (The Luggage of the Banished)." Musicianship is extraordinary. Each song presents a different combination of beautiful vocals, South American percussion, guitars, and flutes. Several earlier albums are also worth the search: *Fragments of a Dream (Fragmento de un Sueno)* (CBS 44574) with guitar players John Williams and Paco Peña, and some 1980s Redwood and Monitor releases.

LINK➤ *Various Artists — Andean Legacy*   *Narada 63927*
A broad-based collection of contemporary South American music. Artists include Sukay, Inti-Illimani, Savia Andina, and others who are not as well known in the U.S. Liner notes provide interesting background on each of the artists.

Arriesgaré la Piel - I Will Risk My Skin
Xenophile (Green Linnet) 4049

Fine recording quality, some excellent lyrics, and superb arrangements make this 1996 album—the group's 25th—the place to start. "Medianoche (Midnight)" borrows a tango mood for two lovers saying goodbye. The destruction of South America's forests is a story eloquently told by metaphor in "El Hacha (The Axe)." "Entre Nosotros (Between Us)" features a magnificently recorded male chorus, accompanied by guitar. The title track is a passionate vocal, also with a guitar accompaniment. "Kalimba," named for the African thumb piano, is a lovely piece; it's played on piano and South American percussion instruments. "Cumpleanõs 80 de Nicanor (Nicanor's 80th Birthday)" celebrates a beloved Chilean poet.

LINK➤ *Various Artists — Mountain Music of Peru*
Smithsonian Folkways 40020
One of the best South American ethnomusicology collections, recorded over 30 years ago but still sounding fresh and new. And don't let the "enthno" label frighten you away. This is invigorating music, very well played.

Early in the 1970s, members of **Cuba**'s top big band, Orquesta Cubana de Música Moderna, decided to form their own band. By 1972, pianist Chucho Valdés and saxman Paquito D'Rivera were driving the organization, with former

Orquesta bandmate Arturo Sandoval's outstanding trumpet a key asset. They started with infectious dance music but quickly matured. Their break came with a 1977 goodwill visit by some well-known U.S. jazz musicians and outspoken jazz journalists. Columbia records then sponsored "Havana Jam," a concert featuring U.S. and Cuban jazz performers, notably its newly signed act,

Irakere. The honeymoon lasted two years until U.S.-Cuban relations fell apart, preventing some recording sessions and causing U.S. executives to lose interest. In 1980, D'Rivera defected to the U.S., followed by Sandoval in 1981. Valdez kept the band alive, recording and performing worldwide (but not in the U.S.). Sandoval and D'Rivera have built successful jazz solo careers.

Irakere, Vol. 1: Seleccion de Exitos (1973-1978)

Habacan 2403

Absolutely brilliant Cuban jazz: gutsy and streetwise. This music's hot, but it's also imaginative, cutting-edge, and smart. "La Comparsa" is set up by keyboards over rolling percussion, accented by an electric guitar's wah-wah, then Arturo Sandoval soars above with a winsome trumpet solo, and Pacquito D'Rivera's sax joins him as the rhythm gets funky. Heavy drums, heavier horns, big electric guitar solo, and everything gets real steamy real fast. Filled with twists and unexpected turns—quiet flute or vibe melodies accented by gigantic horns, sudden tempo changes, Chucho Valdés's seemingly child-like melodies that ignite and fly off like rockets. Hard to find; worth the effort.

LINK➤ *Arturo Sandoval — I Remember Clifford*   *GRP 96682*

Sandoval's tribute to jazz trumpeter Clifford Brown provides the opportunity for pyrotechnics: very fast playing, amazing high notes, and so on. It's straight jazz, not Latino.

The Best of Irakere

Columbia 57719

Big band Cuban jazz, slicker and less carefree because it was recorded for a major label, but still among the best. Trumpet and keyboard solos by Sandoval and Valdés on "Claudia" are backed by a (handsome) string orchestra. "Gira Gira" is a fast number with thrilling interplay between horns and percussion, some bluesy guitar, a bit of flute, and drumming that recalls footsteps of slaves. "Ilya" gets the juices flowing with call-and-response between the vocalist and the drummers, then whips up a frenzy with electric guitars and a sizzling horn section. Classier work, like "Adagio on a Mozart Theme" and the original "Misa Negra" show future direction. Recorded 1979-80.

LINK➤ *Irakere — Misa Negra*   *Messidor (Rounder) 15972*

Produced in Germany in 1986, this digital recording includes the definitive version of Valdés's African Mass, which celebrates Yoruba culture and religion, brought by slaves to Cuba. The influence of Ellington is evident.

One of reggae's long-time favorites, Isaacs was born in 1951 in Kingston, **Jamaica**, and came up through talent competitions. His professional start came with the Concordes, and by the early 1970s, Isaacs was recording with Jamaica's top producers and labels. In 1973, to gain more creative control, he founded the African Museum record label (he later formed Frontline, a second label). Nicknamed the "Cool Ruler" for his easy style and his leadership position, he was a top reggae star by the early 1980s. A few years later, a combination of legal and personal problems found Isaacs in jail; in need of cash, he recorded a vast numbers of sides, somehow maintaining a high standard of quality on as many as six new discs per week. His act changed with the music in the late 1980s, as he worked with a new range of producers, and fixed his street-smart, rude-boy image.

Night Nurse   Mango 539-721

Recorded at Tuff Gong Studios in Jamaica, this 1982 album is Isaacs's very best. The six-man Roots Radics is totally attentive. They add just the right spice: miniature percussion running in-between Isaacs's relaxed phrases; the electronic splash of a synthesizer, a tiny wah-wah, and a recapped phrase on piano ("Steelie" Johnson deserves extra credit for his keyboard work). The songwriting, by Isaacs and Sylvester Weise, is especially well-suited to his singing style. The vocal cascades built into "Night Nurse" are graceful and unique, but even standard reggae love songs, like "Objection Overruled" and "Sad to Know (You're Leaving)," are delivered with elegant charm.

LINK▶ *Various Artists — Reggae Jamdown: The RAS Tapes*
                                                        Rykodisc 20151
This 1990 sampler of RAS productions' first decade places Isaacs in context with contemporary reggae vocalists, including Ini Kamoze, Sugar Minott, Dennis Brown, Freddie McGregor, Jacob Miller, and Charlie Chaplin.

The Best of, Volumes One and Two   Heartbeat (Rounder) 97

An excellent sampling of Isaacs from the late 1980s covering his two favorite themes: love and freedom. The mid-tempo "Special Guest" is upbeat by Isaacs's standards. With the gentlest possible voice, he sings against the sweet melody of the organ, a reggae beat kept by bass, drums, and subtle horns. "My Number One" is one of Isaacs's best-known songs, made lively with some doubletracking and a comparatively memorable melody. "Cool You," with its understated vocal and minimalist melody, is vintage Isaacs. Even "A Riot" doesn't move much faster. With Isaacs, passion is about seething, not shouting. Sound quality is excellent; be wary of other (often unauthorized) Isaacs collections.

LINK▶ *Dennis Brown — Words of Wisdom*   *Shanachie 44004*
Brown's voice soulful and expressive on themes so overwhelmingly positive, they naturally lend themselves to winning melodies. Highlights include "Black Liberation," "Rasta Children." Terrific rhythm section, great organ, too. Try also 1979's Visions *(Shanachie 44002).*

Antonio Carlos Jobim

As a composer, Jobim created many of **Brazil**'s most popular songs. Born in Rio de Janiero in 1927, he originally planned a career in architecture, but piano gigs in Rio's nightclubs drew him into the 1950s scene. In 1956, he became known as the composer of the play, *Orfeo do Carnaval* (the basis for the popular Brazilian film *Black Orpheus*). In 1958, singer and guitar player João Gilberto recorded some of Jobim's songs. Gilberto's gentle, breezy approach became known as bossa nova (new wave). The form intrigued U.S. jazzmen Donald Byrd and Stan Getz. Getz's hit recording of Jobim's "Desafinado" started a bossa nova craze (Getz rode this wave for several years). When things calmed down, Jobim focused on TV and film scores. When Brazilian music became popular again in the 1980s, Jobim played Carnegie Hall and other major venues. He died in NYC in 1994.

The Man from Ipanema
Verve 525-880

An unusual 3-CD set in a double spiral-bound book. One spiral holds a 60-page book filled with a bio, interviews, and photos. The other holds cut-paper CD sleeves resembling a blue fish, a pink shell, and a green leaf. More important than the striking visual presentation, this is precisely the right collection of Jobim songs, performed by the composer and by artists who made his work famous: U.S. jazzman Stan Getz, Astrud Gilberto, top Brazilian vocalist Elis Regina, arranger Claus Ogerman and others. The most engaging vocal interpretations come from *Elis & Tom* (Verve 824-418), which dominates the first CD. Getz and João Gilberto are an ideal combination to present "Só Danço Samba;" Gilberto's gentle voice and Getz's sympathetic tenor sax evoke the most beautiful images of Brazil. Astrud Gilberto's "Amor em Paz (Once I Loved)" features Jobim on guitar, and an interesting arrangement with Bud Shank on flute. Jobim sings "Luiza," and his style points up the one failing of this set: he does not sing often enough! The second CD begins with a warm and lovely jazz arrangement of "Wave" (more than 20 musicians sound like a small, cozy group). Various string arrangements by Ogerman are attractive (some have a 1960s movie soundtrack feeling, others are stunning), but none is prettier than the version of "Desafinado" that begins the third CD. Two other versions of the same song follow, one with Stan Getz and Astrud Gilberto, and another with jazzmen Joe Henderson, Charlie Haden, and Al Foster. Several versions of "The Girl from Ipanema" are done by the same sets of musicians. Altogether, the slant is more toward the Verve and A&M catalogs (both owned by PolyGram), and with too much jazz and not enough interpretations by João Gilberto and other Brazilian singers. Still, this is a splendid collection, lovingly produced.

LINK➤ *João Gilberto — The Legendary João Gilberto*
World Pacific 93891

Excellent interpretations of songs by Jobim and other Brazilian songwriters. Every bit as essential as the Jobim collection.

A leader in popularizing African music in the world marketplace, Kanda Bongo Man came to international prominence in Paris in the 1980s. Born in 1957 in Belgian Congo (subsequently, **Zaire**, now Democratic Republic of Congo), the young musician got his career started with the help of his uncle, soukous singer Jean Bokelo. He formed Orchestre Belle Mambo (later called Orchestre Bella Bella) in the early 1970s and toured extensively with other bands. But he had international stardom in mind, and in 1977, this larger-than-life character moved to Paris. Life wasn't easy. He spent two years earning money as a manual laborer, but by 1981, the first Parisian albums were released; by 1983 he was starring at the WOMAD festival. A year later, Kanda Bongo Man had his own record label, distribution deals for international exploitation, and stardom. The evolution of his music has moved from modernized traditional dance music through some experimentation with Latin and zouk sounds.

Amour Fou/Crazy Love   Hannibal (Rykodisc) 1337

In 1988, when this album was released, soukous was the hottest dance in Paris, and Kanda Bongo Man was the hottest soukous act. Diblo Dibala's stinging electric guitar sets up "Ekipe" and Ringo Star (no, not the same one) keeps the dance floor moving with his rhythm guitar. The beat just keeps rolling on while Kanda Bongo Man sings with his pleasant high tenor. There is great consistency (some would say similarity) not only on this album's songs, but also on *Kwassa Kwassa* (Hannibal 1343), released the same year. Marvel at Diblo's licks, get into the groove, and while away the night. It's delightful music.

LINK➤ *Diblo Dibala — Super Soukous*   *Shanachie 64016*

More of a rock-and-roll sound, but that same distinctive rhythm guitar. See also his work as a leader of the Loketo band.

Soukous in Central Park   Hannibal (Rykodisc) 1374

This 1993 album gives a pretty good indication of what the excitement is all about. Guitar player Nene Tshakou provides a relentless lead on "Liza," a song that can't help but make folks get up and dance. Tshakou takes charge of the song and just as things begin to settle into a groove, he makes a change that ignites the whole thing all over again. "Bedy" and "J.T." depend more upon a slower rhythm accented by lead guitar. The slow rhumba "Luta" simmers on this NYC afternoon. The showstopper is "Lela Lela," precisely the sort of high-energy soukous that made Kanda Bongo Man vastly popular in the clubs. Great fun!

LINK➤ *Tshala Muana — Soukous Siren*   *Shanachie 64031*

Best-of collection by one of the most popular 1980s female soukous singers. Muana started in Zaire, then moved to West Africa, where the entertainment industry offered more promise. 1996's Mutuahsi *(Stern's Africa 1069) borrows more heavily from Cuban influences.*

From the early 1200s until the late 1400s, the Manding Empire was the major force in Western Africa. The Empire's founder, Sunjata Keita, is still a hero for descendants living in today's Guinea, Mali, Senegal, Gambia, and Guinea-Bissau. The Keita name is revered; Salif's mother and father are both of Keita descent. This high birth all but prevented him from a career as a public entertainer. Poor eyesight limited his options, so he started singing traditional music on the streets of Bamako, **Mali**'s capital city. In the early 1970s, he joined the Rail Band, sponsored by Mali's government to play Manding music at Bamako's railway station restaurant/bar, an unconventional wel-

come to Mali. About a year later, Keita switched to a rival band, Les Ambassadeurs du Motel. He remained with this popular band for a decade, then left for Paris to start a solo career, ultimately recording in the U.S.

The Mansa of Mali...A Retrospective   Mango 539-937

Glimmering sax and electric guitar solos on "Mandjou," the 12-minute title track from a 1978 album, are definitely jazz, but the rhythms and Keita's cry-ing, skipping vocals are resolutely African. Keita's first Mango album, *Soro* (539-808), is best represented by "Sanni Kegniba (Sanni the Beautiful)," a lush arrangement of electronic instruments that tells the story of a tribal chief who must sacrifice his beautiful daughter. "Nou Pas Bouger (Don't Move Us)," from *Ko-Yan* (539-836), swings with a catchy melody with a serious concern: the possibility of losing one's home country. With several fine songs from *L'Enfant Lion*, a movie soundtrack (unavailable in U.S.).

LINK➤ *Kante Manfila – Ni Kanu*   EMI 32865
Manfila played lead guitar for Les Ambassadeurs. He also wrote many of the group's hits. A griot, he stopped singing because Keita's voice was so extraor-dinary. Here, he's back singing and playing Manding guitar. Recorded in 1994 with three bonus tracks from a 1990 album called Diniya.

Amen   Mango 539-910

All three Keita albums are worth owning, but jazz musician Joe Zawinul's elaborate production makes this the first choice. In 1991, Paris was a hotbed for African musicians, and Keita surrounded himself with the best, notably arranger Cheik Tidiane Seck (keyboards) and Kante Manfila (guitar). Before the final mix, Zawinul flew the master tapes to L.A. for additional material from Wayne Shorter (sax), Carlos Santana (guitar), and the wonderfully inven-tive Bill Summers (percussion). Zawinul pushed the 48-track studio to its ab-solute limit, adding density that makes "Waraya" and other songs fill the room with excitement. To hear everything Keita and Zawinul had in mind, listen on a superior stereo system.

LINK➤ *Mory Kante – Akwaba Beach*   Barclay (Import)
Kante replaced Keita in the Rail Band. This CD contains the huge 1988 smash "Yeke Yeke" and provides a good sense of Kante's hyperactive "electro-griot" sound. He moves further in this direction with 1997's Tatebola (Misslin 18).

Continuing a generations-old tradition, Pepe Habichuela became famous playing flamenco guitar accompaniment to well-known cantadores (singers) such as Camarón de la Isla and Enrique Morente. Three of his nephews, Juan, Antonio, and José Miguel Carmona, formed Ketama in the early 1980s with José Soto, who was also related to a great flamenco guitar player, El Sordera. Ketama's idea: update Madrid's traditional gypsy flamenco music and fuse it with modern **Spanish** urban music. The group's personnel has changed over time, but the original mission remains. Ketama has played with salsa musician Ray Barretto, African kora virtuoso Toumani Diabate (in a conglomeration called Songhai that recorded two albums), and with jazz player Don Cherry. Ketama has been recording roughly one album per year since 1985, but Spain's Nuevos Medios label is not generally distributed in the U.S. (If a relative, friend, or business associate visits Madrid, request a special shopping trip.)

Ketama   Hannibal (Rykodisc) 1336

A 1987 album licensed from Nuevos Medios featuring a three-man Ketama. José Soto's grainy voice sings lead; he also plays guitar and contributes hand claps. Juan Carmona plays guitar, and brother Antonio Carmona is the percussionist, both on drums and hands. Why the emphasis on hand claps? They're the primary percussion sound—fast, furious, and artful. Pepe Habichuela also plays some guitar. Other musicians subtly round out the sound with flute, electric bass, piano, etc., but the primary sound is two lead guitars, male vocals, and hand claps. "No Sé Si Vivo o Sueño" adds a gurgling new jazz bass line to traditional flamenco; it's one of several songs with subtle fusion.

LINK➤ *Songhai*   *Hannibal (Rykodisc) 1323*
Fusion of flamenco and North African music with former Steeleye Span bassist Danny Thompson. Very popular.

De Aki a Ketama   Mercury 528-183

A live recording from 1995, again with a three-member group. This time, it's the three Carmona brothers, plus a larger, more prominent backup band. "No Estamos Lokos (Kalikeno)," written by the brothers with José Soto, shows how far they've come. Borrowing heavily from big band Latin jazz, Ketama's sound is dense with rhythm instruments, more passionate pop vocals, and carefully selected spots for superior guitar solos. The music is meticulously arranged (by Ketama), resulting in a more coherent, exciting presentation. Song after song borrows from flamenco tradition, but adds a modern feeling with background vocalists, contemporary Latin percussion, and on "Acaba de Nacer," Latin horns.

LINK➤ *Various Artists — Flamenco: Fire and Grace*   *Narada 63924*
Very flashy collection featuring Tomatito (who played with Paco de Lucía and Camarón de La Isla), singer Enrique Morente, and flamenco fusionist Jesse Cook.

Algerian culture is based on rigid Arab traditions and effusive French influences. Younger people found little excitement in the older style classical music and gravitated toward a more honest (and, at first, clandestine) musical style called rai. The word "rai" abbreviates "ya rai" (this roughly translates into "tell it like it is") and is shouted by excited audience members. In time, rai added a dance beat. As teenage society came out from under the heft of Arab tradition in the early 1980s, the new style became popular. In 1985, Cheb Khaled won a national festival, in which he was awarded the title "King of Rai" (the word "Cheb" means "kid"). This led to more acclaim, a recording contract with a PolyGram company, and first album sales topping 100,000 units. With maturity, Khaled dropped the "Cheb" prefix. He now lives in France. At home, his lifestyle would draw criticism and worse for himself and his family.

Kutché
Stern's 1026

Algerian pop music, circa 1988, from one of the country's most magnetic personalities. Khaled weaves his sexy tenor through rocking Algerian rhythms; he also plays accordion, synthesizer, and bendir (North African frame drum). Creative partner Safy Boutella, who gets joint billing, is the synthesizer wizard responsible for the colorful textures that surround Khaled's voice. Boutella also produced the album (with Martin Meissonnier).

"Chebba" benefits from a rolling percussion track, violins, and a great guitar opening. "Hana-Hana" hits hard with a big dance beat; Khaled skillfully sings a second rhythm, but the sweat really starts rolling off with Alan Hoist's sax solo. Take this to your next party!

LINK➤ *Various Artists — Pop-Rai and the Rachid Style:*
Rai Rebels, Volume 2 Earthworks (Stern's) 15
A 1990 collection of rai music from the same period. Cheb Khaled contributes "Maghbound (Desperate)." Other artists who are Westernizing rai include Cheb Mamid, Chaba Zahouania, and Cheb Zahouani.

N'ssi N'ssi
Cohiba (Mango) 124-012

Don Was produced four of these tracks, so it's no surprise that "Serbi Serbi" gets started with a piercing percussion. Electric guitars, synthesizer, and the huge saxophone unify every beat; Khaled's instinctive rhythmic phrasing is perfectly surrounded. Was has skillfully maintained the Arab sound, as on "Kebou," but he has transformed Khaled's sound into international dance music. (Compare the version of "Chebba" here with the one on the Stern's release!) That said, "Kebou," produced by Philippe Eidel, is even more powerful—a frenzied vortex with guitars and a gigantic string sound. (Play it loud!) Recorded in 1993.

LINK➤ *Fadela & Sahrawi — Walli* Rounder 5076
1997 album by the Chaba Fadela (Chaba is a female Cheb), and Cheb Sahrawi with a stronger connection to Algeria and rai's roots. Songs are catchy with interesting arrangements. Liner notes explain Algeria's musical traditions and recommend additional CDs for each type of music. Terrific performers, super package.

Khan traces his family back to the court of Emperor Akbar. The son of master musician Allauddin Khan, Ali Akbar was born in East Bengal (now **Bangladesh**) in 1922. For 20 years, he studied the sarode for 18 hours a day. He first performed in public at 13, became a court musician for the Maharja of Jodphur at 22, and earned the title Ustad ("master musician"). Classical violinist Yehudi Menuhin invited Khan to the U.S. in 1955, which resulted in the first Western album of Indian music. Khan founded a music college in 1956 in India. In 1968, he founded the Ali Akbar College of Music near San Francisco, where he teaches nine months a year; he spends the remaining months at a branch of his college in Switzerland. Among his many honors, he has twice won the President of India award (the highest recognition given to an Indian artist), and in 1991, a MacArthur Foundation Fellowship.

Then and Now
AMMP 9507

In 1955, Ali Akbar Khan recorded the first long-playing (LP) album of classical Indian music. After a spoken introduction explaining the scale played on Khan's sarod and the rhythm played on Chatur Lal's tabla, the two perform "Rag Sindhu Bhairavi," a morning raga. Their performance of an evening raga is preceded by a similar explanation. Both ragas are beautifully presented and nicely recorded. A tabla is played by Zakir Hussain on CD2, which also contains a springtime raga called "Rag Hemant" and an evening melody called "Rag Hindol-Hem." On the second disc, recorded at a San Francisco concert in 1994, the recording is a bit distant, and the program, subtle and sophisticated.

LINK▶ *George Harrison – Concert for Bangla Desh*   *Capitol 93265*
Ali Akbar Khan and Ravi Shankar were among the Indian classical musicians who performed on this 1972 consciousness-raiser. With Dylan, Clapton, etc.

Signature Series, Vol. 1 - 4
AMMP 9001, 9002, 9404, 9405

The Connoisseur Society produced Khan with the utmost care. These astonishing recordings were made with custom-built tube electronics on 1960s state-of-the-art equipment. As Khan performs, every nuance of his sarod can be heard with proper resonance. The weight and impact of Pandit Mahapurush Misra's tabla on *Volume 1*'s "Rag Chandranandan" move beyond the intellectual stimulation associated with Indian classical music and into the visceral thrills of rock music. *Volume 2* is more restrained. The slide notes that begin the alap on *Volume 3* 's "Rag Marwa" are masterful. Each of the first three volumes contains three ragas, and the fourth contains two. Misra plays tabla on most ragas.

LINK▶ *Lakshmi Shankar – Les Heures et Les Saisons*
Ocora (Harmonia Mundi) 558615
One of the finest singers of classical and devotional music from northern India. The sophistication in her voice is a powerful force.

Journey
Worldly Music (Triloka) 7184

A comfortable starting point for listeners whose primary exposure to Indian music has been the Beatles, this selection of larger group songs are generally upbeat and melodic. The melody line on "Fantasy," for example, is so firmly established that it's nearly impossible not to hum along. The flourishes on sitar (played by James Pomerantz) and soft synthesizer fill from producer Jai Uttal drift close to a pop music sensibility. A joy-filled eight-piece band generates a big sound produced by a combination of Indian instruments (sarod, tabla, sitar) and Western instruments (conga, guitar, keyboards, guitar). Recorded in Hollywood, California, in 1990.

LINK➤ *Salamat Ali Khan — Ragas Gunkali, Saraswati, Durga*
Nimbus 5307

Vocals are also an important part of classical music in northern India. Salamat Ali Khan (no relation to Ali Akbar Khan) performs with his two sons (Sharafat and Shafqat Ali Khan), with tabla accompaniment.

Plays Alap: A Sarod Solo
AMMP 9303

Alap is the introductory portion of a raga; it's performed without percussion. Because the alap sets the mood and quality of the raga, it must be presented with a deep understanding of the raga's meaning. This understanding requires study, maturity, and wisdom. This 1992 recording includes three works. "Shri Rag" is associated with twilight, and its flattened intonations will seem unfamiliar to Western listeners. "Pilu Baroowa" is more accessible. A light, classical piece for late afternoon or evening, it touches on joy and sadness. A popular piece, it will be familiar to those who regularly enjoy Indian music. "Ragini Iman Kalyan" is an evening raga. This state-of-the-art recording was made on Cello, Ltd., equipment.

LINK➤ *Shivkumar Sharma & Zakir Hussain —*
Raga Madhuvanti, Raga Misra Tilang
Nimbus 5110

Sharma's mastery was responsible for the acceptance of the santoor (derived from a Persian zither of the same name) in Indian classical music. On this exquisite 1987 recording, Hussain provides accompaniment on tabla.

Legacy
Worldly Music (Triloka) 7216

The title of this 1995 work is not to be taken lightly. Ali Akbar Khan learned these songs from his father, Allaudin Khan, who in turn learned them from his guru, Mohammed Wazir Khan, and so on through history, back to the 16th century. This is very traditional Indian classical music performed by Ali Akbar Khan on sarod (a lute used in Indian classical music) as soloist and accompaniment to Indian vocalist Asha Bhosle. She's in remarkable voice: clear and fresh, experienced and strong. These two musicians dominate, but others on cello, tabla, sitar, harmonium, and various percussion instruments enrich the soundscape. A masterful recording, made at Skywalker Ranch.

LINK➤ *Karnataka College Of Percussion — River Yamuna*
Music of the World 197

Classical music from southern India played on a variety of percussion instruments (including the human voice). Excellent liner notes.

Nusrat Fateh Ali Khan

Qawwali is devotional music associated with the Sufi sect of Islam, and it's most often heard in Pakistan and India. Qawwali has also become a popular music, heard in its frenetic splendor in Indian films and nightclubs. One who performs qawwali is called a qawwal. Nusrat Fateh Ali Kahn was the best-known qawwal. Born in 1948 in Punjab, a province in **Pakistan**, he was the son of famous singer and teacher Ustad Fateh Ali Khan, and the nephew of another well-known musician, Mubarak Ali Khan. In the late 1960s, Nusrat started singing with his uncle's party (a qawwali musical ensemble is called a party), and with his uncle's death in 1971, he took over, mimicking his elders' recordings and gradually becoming a great artist. In the next two decades, he recorded dozens of albums; his international fame grew through the efforts of WOMAD, a leading promoter of world music. Nusrat Fateh Ali Khan died in 1997 of a heart attack.

Devotional and Love Songs   RealWorld (Caroline) 2300

This 1985 album is a good place to start. Songs are traditional. Each song begins differently, often with a slow or medium tempo, but the same basic format evolves: Fateh Ali Khan sings lead, a male chorus repeats and chants, and a combination of tabla and hand claps creates a rhythm track based on the singers' chants. A mandolin opens the songs, then becomes a prominent rhythm instrument. Subtle differences between the devotional "Haq Ali Ali Haq" and a ghazal, or love song with contemporary lyrics, such as "Mast Nazroom Se Allah Bachnae," might not be easy for Western ears to comprehend. Fateh Ali Khan's soaring vocals and changes in tempo are fascinating.

LINK➤ *Various Artists — The Kings & Queen of Qawwali*
Shanachie 64832

Good sampler. One song from Nusrat Fateh Ali Khan, two from leading female artist Abida Parveen, one from Aziz Main, and one from the Sabri Brothers.

Shahen-Shah   RealWorld (Caroline) 2302

Three years later, the music on this 1988 album is somewhat less exotic. Passion can be felt in the most direct way in "Shamas-Ud-Doha, Badar-Ud-Doja," as Fateh Ali Khan and his party sing with fervent energy. The arrangements are not quite as dense, and the mix is more favorable to individual voices and instrument sounds. Tempos also vary: "Allah, Mohammed, Char, Yaar" is a devotional chant to four saints; the music suggests ceremonial worship. The clarity of the hand claps and harmonium on "Kali Kali Zulfon Ke Phande Nah Dalo," a ghazal, helps to focus attention on the nuances of the vocals.

LINK➤ *Nusrat Fateh Ali Khan & Bally Sagoo — Magic Touch*
Oriental Star (Import)

A collaboration of modern Western Sagoo-style dance tracks with Nusrat Fateh Ali Khan singing pop vocals. Recorded in the late 1980s. Fascinating combination of styles, very danceable. Lots of familiar riffs, too. Import only.

Shahbaaz
RealWorld (Caroline) 2315

Fateh Ali Khan's vocal talents are many, and this 1991 CD is his best showcase. Like a jazz scat singer, but many times faster, he is capable of uttering near-nonsensical syllables that transform themselves into lyrics. He can sing for very long periods without seeming to take a breath. He can mimic remarkably complicated percussion tracks. And all of this happens on the first track, called "Ben Haadh Ramza Dhasdha (He manifests himself in many forms)." An incredible Fateh Ali Khan solo—some of the most astonishing vocal work on record anywhere—is central to "Dhyahar-Eh-Ishq Meh (The Realm of Love)."

LINK➤ *Sabri Brothers — Ya Habib*   RealWorld (Caroline) 2311
The best-known work from another leading qawwali party, released in 1990.

The Last Prophet
RealWorld (Caroline) 2341

Recorded in 1993, the music is more refined. The voice of Fateh Ali Khan's younger brother, Farrukh Fateh Ali Khan, is prominent in "Maki Madni," the devotional song to the prophet Muhammed (Farrukh has been recording with Fateh Ali Khan for years, but this song is performed as a kind of duet). Extensive liner notes explain aspects of the Islamic culture so central to this music. "Sahib Teri Bandi," for example, describes a path to inner knowledge through a spiritual leader. Most of Fateh Ali Khan's albums combine sacred and secular themes. "Sochan Dongian" beseeches a boyfriend to return; his girlfriend desperately needs to know what she has done to make him unhappy.

LINK➤ *Nusrat Fateh Ali Khan and Michael Brook — Night Song*
Real World (Caroline) 2354

A breathtaking mixture of the old and the new, this 1995 recording combines Fateh Ali Khan's stirring vocals with Michael Brook's ambient guitar work, plus accompanying musicians from the Middle East and the U.K.

Intoxicated Spirit
Shanachie 64066

Instruments provide subtle textures on the opening vocal duet, "Yeh Jo Halka Halka." For the first time, liner notes contain a complete translation of a song in English (no lyrics for the other four songs). Intoxication is the theme, and the lyrics provide cultural insight: "O' holy man don't scoff at my apparent irreligiosity, I am the one who with his knack of chit-chat coaxed the divinity in granting me permission to drink." The song goes on to describe intoxication with a woman who is uninterested, invoking religious images and complicated wordplay, so central to qawwali music, and so completely lost on Western audiences who understand neither the words nor the underlying emotional contexts.

LINK➤ *Abida Parveen — Best of Abida Parveen*   Shanachie 64086
For those who find Fateh Ali Khan's voice too harsh, Abida Parveen's is sweeter and prettier. She's a major singing star in Pakistan, popular for her ghazals, but also sings the more chant-like qawwali music. Ten songs are highlights from 20 years of recording.

A true international star, Kidjo grew up in Ouidah, **Benin** (a small country on the Atlantic coast), in a household and community where artistic ideas were nurtured. Born in 1960, she listened to music her brothers liked—including the Beatles, Santana, and James Brown. Kidjo started singing in church, then moved to pop, joined a band (Sphinx, which was locally popular), and at age 20, traveled to Paris for formal classical and jazz training. She started recording and touring soon afterward, sometimes as an opening act for South African singer Miriam Makeba. This exposure led to a contract with Island/Mango, and the company hired top producers and sidemen to build Kidjo's career. She sings in Fon, her native language. Her style tends toward cutting-edge and dance music. Having recorded in Paris, Miami, and London, and played in clubs worldwide, Kidjo is very much the 1990s international star.

Logozo
Mango 539-918

The liner notes show a dancer with close-cropped black hair, dramatic eye makeup, a skin-tight shirt patterned like an animal's skin, and running shoes. This is party music, from Kidjo's first enormous vocal to the driving beat, to the sharp accents of the backup vocalists. The first song, "Batonga," establishes the mood: "Beautiful child, you are so poor but you dance like a princess and you do as you please." The saxophone solo on "Tché-Tché" and "Logozo" come from Branford Marsalis; the latter tells listeners not to behave like tortoises—to get out of their shells and live their lives. (Hey, it's dance music, not poetry.)

LINK➤ *Various Artists — Yoruba Drums from Benin, West Africa*
Smithsonian Folkways 40440
From a very different part of Benin's culture, an important roots collection. Two types of drum ensembles (bata, dundun) demonstrate rhythms used in religious ceremonies. The drum sound is the foundation of African-Cuban music.

Ayé
Mango 539-934

It's 1994. Kidjo has matured. The album opens with spectacular African drumming at the heart of an articulate "Agolo (Please)," in which Kidjo sings about God, love, and Mother Earth. "Azan Nan Kpé (A Day Will Come)" is one of five songs recorded at Paisley Park in Minnesota. Lush with synthesizers, the song allows Kidjo to relax and remove herself from piercing dance music (in which she admittedly excels). Her remarkable voice gets the showcase it deserves. "Djan Djan (Sound of a Rhythm)" is accompanied by a single acoustic guitar (and some miscellaneous background percussion). Kidjo's voice is rich with meaning ("my helplessness drives me crazy"). Start here.

LINK➤ *Angelique Kidjo — Fifa*
Mango 531-039
Very much a contemporary dance record with big vocals and heavy digitalia, but the base tracks were laid by traditional instrument players in Benin.

In the early years of this century, Manhattan's Lower East Side was one of NYC's largest **Jewish** ghettos; it was here that the Gershwin brothers and Irving Berlin grew up. In 1986, a group of adventurous young musicians from the Lower East Side formed the Klezmatics. Informed by scholarship and Jewish mysticism, and inspired by modern music and contemporary ideas, they created a post-modern form of klezmer. This refreshing approach has resulted in an astonishing range of projects. Some examples: the Klezmatics scored Tony Kushner's two-part Broadway show *Angels in America*; appeared with classical violinist Itzhak Perlman on Great Performances: *In the Fiddler's House*; and worked with Allen Ginsberg, John Zorn, and the Master Musicians of Jajouka. Through the 1990s, the Klezmatics have been the most popular klezmer act on the world music scene. Longtime members include David Licht (drums, percussion), Alicia Svigals (violin), Frank London (horns), and Lorin Sklamberg (lead vocals, accordion).

Shvaygn = Toyt
Piranha (Stern's) 20

The title, translated from Yiddish, means "Silence Equals Death." The album begins with the sentimental "Ershter Vals (First Waltz)" from Russia." Dave Harris's arrangement of the slow Hassidic dance "A Glezele Vayn (A Glass of Wine)," features additional horns from Les Miserables Brass Band (heard on a few other tracks, too). Trumpeter Frank London's arrangement of "Bilovi (In My Heart)" was inspired by post-modern jazzman Charlie Haden's Liberation Orchestra. It's one of several songs that set the Klezmatics apart from other klezmer groups. "Czernowitzer Bulgar" is Jewish party music. From 1989.

LINK▶ *Flying Bulgar Klezmer Band — Flying Bulgar Klezmer Band*
Dorian 80106

1990 debut recording by Toronto's leading klezmer group. Superior recording quality. Highlights include two tributes to flamboyant klezmer clarinet player and entertainer Naftule Brandwein (he wore an American flag suit made of Christmas lights), and a traditional dance copied from a scratchy old 78 disc: Kandel's Hora.

Jews with Horns
Xenophile (Green Linnet) 4032

Moxy Fr**üvous sings backup in the unbelievably fast "Man in a Hat," a song whose lyrical wordplay is enhanced by quick-tongued lead vocals. The alternative band BETTY plays on "Fisherlid," a slow dance featuring Alicia Svigal's desperate, cutting-edge fiddle. "In Kami" is an 1889 protest song from the Yiddish labor movement. Lorin Sklamberg's accordion accompanies his vocal reveling on the soulful "Nign." The band breaks out on "Honga," an instrumental dominated by Frank London's horns, David Krakauer's clarinets, and Svigal's fiddle. The album's title is a pun on an old anti-Semitic supersition: Jews had horns on their heads.

LINK▶ *Itzhak Perlman — Live in the Fiddler's House*   *Angel 56209*
Live 1996 performance with the classical violinist. The Klezmatics perform 5 numbers. Try also Perlman's In the Fiddler's House (Angel 55555).

Rhythm and Jews
Flying Fish (Rounder) 70591

This 1992 release is the group's most traditional klezmer album. Mahmoud Fald's percussion dominates "Fun Tashlikh"; vocal chants and moaning lead into a stop-time dance by Frank London (cornet) and David Krakauer (clarinet). London's cornet solo is just this side of free jazz. "NY Psycho Freylekhs" is a fast dance with a very familiar Yiddish theme; it features Alan Bern's accordion. There are special pieces for clarinet ("Clarinet Yontev") and violin ("Violin Doyna"). "Honizaft (Honeyjuice)" is a love song with a beat. "Klezmatic Fantasy: A Suite Mostly in D" combines folk tradition and classical formality.

LINK▶ *Andy Statman — Between Heaven and Earth*   **Shanachie 64079**
On this 1997 CD, clarinetist Statman concentrates on Judaism's mystical side. Basing his jazz improvisations on works that are centuries old, Statman stands out as a modernist with deep roots. Very easy to enjoy.

Possessed
Xenophile (Green Linnet) 4050

This 1997 album rocks out with "Moroccan Game." Guest John Medeski's Hammond organ centers a swirling, nearly mystical klezmer-rock fusion with David Licht, who drives hard on his drum kit, while Matt Darriau's clarinet updates the centuries. This absolutely thrilling music is the group's best to date. The old gypsy song "Shprayz Ikh Mir" is a fast dance. Medeski returns on the traditional moaner "Shvarts un Ways (Black and White)," which features a Jewish blues vocal and Darriau's astonishing bass clarinet. Half of this album comes from The Klezmatics' score for Tony Kushner's *A Dybbuk: Between Two Worlds*; it's good theater music, but the rest is more intense, and more fun.

LINK▶ *The Klezmorim — Jazz-Babies of the Ukraine*
Flying Fish (Rounder) 70465
Totally crazed klezmer music with hints of circus and showbiz shtick, "Digga Digga Doo," Cab Calloway's hit "Minnie the Moocher," other neat stuff. Endlessly inventive, tremendous fun. From 1987. Also: First Recordings 1976–78 combines two seminal LPs that sparked the new klezmer movement: East Side Wedding, and Streets of Gold. R.Crumb drew the cover.

Klezmer for the New Millennium
Shanachie 67072

The Klezmatics contribute one track to this 1997 collection—one of their more adventuresome pieces called "Khsidim Tants." Frank London goes well past his Liberation Orchestra orientation for a free jazz approach on "V'erestikh Li," linking klezmer to Ornette Coleman, Albert Ayler, and other jazz experimenters. The Paradox Trio features Matt Darriau's clarinet on "Als Far Gelt," which again straddles the line between klezmer and cutting-edge jazz. Kelye's swinging "Two Cents Plain" is big band jazz. The Godchildren of Soul's a capella vocals smash against hard street funk and rap on "Crown Heights Affair," with klezmer in there somewhere, too.

LINK▶ *Various Artists — Klezmer 1993 NYC*   **Knitting Factory 5650**
One of the first releases from members of what has been called the "Radical Jewish Culture" movement in NYC, this 1993 recording includes tracks from John's Zorn's Masada, the New Klezmer Trio, and the Klezmatics, as well as others less nationally known.

The word "klezmer" comes from two Hebrew words: kley and zmer, meaning "vessel of song." In the old country, in Eastern Europe, a klezmer was a village musician, often one who played the fiddle or the clarinet. When European **Jews** immigrated to the U.S., they not only brought their music, but also blended it with American popular music. By 1942, more than 700 klezmer records had been released. With the new generation after World War II, interest faded. Hankus Netsky, whose older family members were klezmer musicians, started a new klezmer band in Boston in 1980, playing klezmer standards with his own 13-piece big band. The music swings, and it became popular in and around Boston. The Klezmer Conservatory Band tends to be somewhat scholarly and traditional; other klezmer bands, like Toronto's Flying Bulgar Klezmer Band and the Klezmorim, are more liberal with the music. But this band plays it straight.

Yiddishe Renaissance   Vanguard 79450

"Lebedik un Freyekh (Lively and Happy)" came from a 1920s Yiddish theater hit. Judy Bressler, who comes from a Yiddish theater family, sings a European cabaret vocal on "Papirson (Cigarettes)" about a poor boy selling cigarettes and matches in the freezing rain. Klezmer often absorbed other popular music: "Yiddish Blues" is a ragtime (other albums include a Jewish Charleston and a Jewish rhumba). Don Byron's squawking clarinet sings lead in "A Rumenisher Doyne"; it's based on a 1920s song. The best-known song is the upbeat "Rumenye, Rumenye," danced at so many traditional Jewish weddings. Rousing clarinets, fiddles, and just the right amount of schmaltz. From 1981.

LINK➤ *Various Artists — Klezmer Music: A Marriage of Heaven & Earth*
**   *Ellipsis Arts 4090***
This 64-page illustrated hardcover book explains the history of klezmer, but it's hip enough to include newer work. Featured artists include Klezmatics, Alicia Svigals, the Flying Bulgar Klezmer Band, Andy Statman, and Brave New World. Essential for any world music library.

Klez! Vanguard 79449

On this 1984 album, Judy Bressler opens with a mid-tempo dance from the 1920s Yiddish theater: "In Ades (In Odessa)." Don Byron's clarinet ignites the big band arrangement on "Sirba Popilar (The Popular Serba)." This time, the tearjerker is "Yingele, Nit Veyn (My Little Boy, Don't Cry)." It's sung by Bressler, but Alan Bern's accordion will make you cry. Bressler sings beautifully on the well-known "Yidl mit'n Fidl (Yidl with his Fiddle)," easily the most satisfying number on this lovely album. "Skrip, Lezmerl, Skripe (Play, Musician, Play)" is the most fun, unless it's compared with "Bay a Glezele Mashke (Over a Glass of Whiskey)." Extremely well executed.

LINK➤ *Don Byron — Don Byron Plays the Music of Mickey Katz*
**   *Nonesuch 79163***
On another KCB album, violinist Marvin Weinberger and Don Byron stand out on the Yiddish big band number "Mazeltov Dances," a tribute to klezmer bandleader and Mickey Katz. In 1993, after leaving KCB, Byron recorded an intense and provocative set of Katz tunes.

Sado is an island in the Sea of Japan where performing and visual artists have flourished. Through the 1970s, musicians gathered on Sado to study taiko, a Japanese drum. In 1981, these musicians formed Kodo, a communal approach to living, learning, and music. The musicians lived together in a converted schoolhouse, and, in 1987, opened Kodo Village. The village includes an office building, a community kitchen, a world music library, a rehearsal hall, and a recording studio. Since 1985, Kodo has performed a December Concert in Japan's major cities. Gathering, performed with artists from other genres (orchestras, instrumentalists, etc.) is another annual concert series. For a decade, Kodo Village has hosted Earth Celebration; participants have included jazz drummer Elvin Jones, Nubian superstar Hamza El Din, African drummer Babatunde Olatunji, the Drummers of Burundi, various puppet troupes, and many Japanese artists. Kodo's time is divided equally between touring internationally, touring in Japan, and time in Sado.

Best of Kodo   Tristar 57776

In Japan, the music played by Kodo is considered folkloric—interesting as a kind of living museum and treasure, but hardly popular music. This 1988–1992 sampler is a good place to begin. The title track from 1990's *Irodori* (Alex 5647) contains the thick, resonant drumming that made Kodo famous. The larger drum anchors; the smaller ones provide dark rhythm. A flute plays a repeating melody line. From 1989's *Blessing of the Earth* (TriStar 80830) comes "Zoku." It features a ferociously large drum capable of shaking knickknacks off any nearby shelves (play it loud!). 1992's Kaiki provides "Yu-Karak II" with far more subtle percussion patterns whose intensity grows as the number progresses.

LINK➤ *Mickey Hart (& others) — Planet Drum*   Rykodisc 10206
Hart works with percussionists from around the world and creates an enormously exciting conglomeration. Musicians include Zakir Hussain, Babatunde Olatunji, Airto Moreira, and others who are not as well known. Flora Purim sings and co-produced. From 1991.

Ibuki   Tristar 36852

While 1985's *Heartbeat Drummers of Japan* (Sheffield Lab 12222) was an audiophile favorite for bass loudspeaker tests, the recorded bass on this 1997 album is both deeper and clearer. Producer Bill Laswell has done an excellent job with the recording, capturing Kodo's raging stage energy. "Nobi (Fires on the Plain)" recreates the frightful fascination of watching an enormous blaze by pacing higher and lower percussion and altering tempos. Everything in the room vibrates when the subtle background drums play on "Akabanah"; an innocent-sounding flute melody considers the ebb and flow of tides. "Ibuki" celebrates the breathing of animals and the wind; it resembles Native American song. The connections among sound, magic, and nature are powerful.

LINK➤ *Soloists of the Ensemble Nipponia —*
Japan: Traditional Vocal & Instrumental Music   Nonesuch 72072
A shamisen (three-stringed instrument, kin to banjo) performs pieces from Kabuki. The biwa (lute) performs "Ogi no Mato," based on a William Tell-like legend (involving a fan in place of the apple). The shakuhachi (flute) is part of several ensemble pieces. Stillness and depth.

Abeokuta, not far from Lagos, **Nigeria**, has long been known as a creative center, a place where radical ideas grow. Here, Kuti was born in 1938 to the distinguished Ransome family in the Yoruba tribe (his full name: Fela Anikulapo Ransome-Kuti). Kuti attended London's Trinity College of Music in the 1950s, studying trumpet and composition. He developed his Afro–Beat style, formed a band in Nigeria, and in 1969 moved to the U.S., where he became involved with the Black Panthers. A few years later, Kuti was back in Nigeria singing radical lyrics that attacked poverty, politics, and the military. His group, with a 20-piece band called Africa 70 (with female chorus, horns, and James Brown's influence), became fantastically popular (it was subsequently expanded to 30 pieces, and renamed Egypt 80). Relentless radicalism resulted in jail time and constant trouble. His son, Femi Kuti, is less radical and leads his own band, Positive Force. Fela Kuti died in 1997.

Beasts of No Nation
Shanachie 43070

Radical messages, but generally pleasant jazz accompaniment. There are two long songs. The first is "Just Like That." It begins with a cool, detached, relaxed style. Horns come in to shake things up, then the chorus and the acid messages. Kuti wonders how Kainja Dam is built, but 12 years pass without electricity. He wonders about local politicians and their corruption. And in the midst of all this, a winsome sax solo. "Beasts of No Nation" is mostly sung and spoken in English by Kuti with a responding chorus; he comes down hard on Botha, Thatcher, Reagan, and abuse of human rights. Printed lyrics in liner notes. Made with Egypt 80.

LINK➤ *Fela Ransome Kuti and The Africa '70 — Open & Close*
Stern's Africa 3010

The first seven minutes of the title song, "Open & Close," are 1970s big band jazz: tight horns and funky rhythm by a top-notch 12-piece ensemble, playing hard against Kuti's chanting and scatting vocals. From 1975.

Original Sufferhead
Shanachie 44010

Kuti's Egypt 80's sound is dominated by an electronic keyboard, guitars, and the kind of fermenting rhythm track Miles Davis used on *Bitches Brew*. Much of the 21-minute "Original Sufferhead" sounds like 1960s free jazz, including trumpet solos that strain to try new sounds, and small solos that float in and back out again. Halfway through, Kuti makes a quiet comment, scats some, runs some call-and-response with mostly female backup singers, and moves from jazz to African song. Other songs follow a similar format, although some become angry. "Colonial Mentality" and particularly "ITT" show Fela Kuti at his relentless best. 1990's *ODOO* (Shanachie 43078) is also recommended.

LINK➤ *Miles Davis — Bitches Brew*
Columbia 40577

The 1969 album that defined jazz fusion and set the course for 1970s jazz (and beyond). Listening to this, and to Kuti, suggests an interchange between continents that actually occurred to a very small degree.

Ladysmith Black Mambazo

In the 1920s and 1930s, many Zulu men in **South Africa** moved from their rural homes to work in mines and factories. They lived in hostels, where one popular leisure activity was a capella singing. By the late 1930s, there were competitions between hostel groups and even a hit record, "Mbube" (the basis for "The Lion Sleeps Tonight"). The style became known as "Mbube" and remained popular until the mid-1950s. It was reborn in the mid-1960s on a Radio Zulu program, but a lack of good recorded material forced the program to record new music. Many groups were recorded, but Ladysmith Black Mambazo embodied the spirit, sound, and religious orientation of the earlier music. The style, now known as "iscathamiya" ("to stalk or step softly"), became famous when Paul Simon recorded and toured with the group; he also arranged for many TV appearances. FYI: Black Mambazo, which means "Black Axe," refers to the group's strength in singing competitions.

Best of Ladysmith Black Mambazo
Shanachie 43098

Rich harmonies are the calling card, but complex vocal arrangements adjust the rhythm and pace of 16 songs that sound very different from one another. On "Uphi Umhlobo," a pair of small groups carries the melody, tongue clicks punctuate each line, and Joseph Shambala generally sings along or repeats lyrics as a chorus. Individual vocalists weave a complex texture, and on a good stereo system each voice can be distinguished clearly. "Pauline" is one of the group's better known songs (it's in English and includes the lyrics, "kiss-kiss and touch-touch"). "Yimani" is the best of several majestic songs with the signature sound of big group harmony.

LINK➤ *Various Artists — Mbube Roots: Zulu Choral Music from South Africa, 1930s–1960s*   **Rounder 5025**
Where it all began. Highlights include Solomon Linda's Original Evening Birds singing "Mbube" in 1939. Some work is loose and rough (and recordings scratchy), but it's interesting just the same.

Shaka Zulu   Warner Bros. 25585

After the group's mutual success with the *Graceland* project, Paul Simon arranged for the vocal group to sign with Warner Brothers, and produced this 1987 album with his longtime engineer, Roy Halee, in charge of sound. Sound quality is superb. The best songs are sung in Zulu: "Unomathemba (a girl's name)" is a charmer, in part because of the group's playful kissing sounds and laughter. English-language translations make sense of the Zulu (most Ladysmith albums are not released with any printed lyrics, so much of their message is lost). "Lomhlaba Kawunoni (The Earth Never Gets Fat)" is also lovely. Start here.

LINK➤ *Paul Simon — Graceland*   **Warner Bros. 25447**
A decade after this album made African pop music trendy, the hits ("You Can Call Me Al," "Diamonds on the Soles of Her Shoes," etc.) sound dated. But the songs that were not played as often, like "Under African Skies," are still very special.

Le Mystère des Voix Bulgares

Some clarification. The official name of the group is the Bulgarian State Radio and Television Female Vocal Choir. The "Mystère" name was dreamed up to sell records. And that word, mystère, does not mean "mystery." It comes from "mysterium," a guild of craftsmen who passed on secret skills from one generation to the next. And this is not, as frequently suggested, **Bulgarian** folk music. Instead, the music of this choir is a sophisticated modern style with some roots in rural female group singing.The polyphony, the unusual harmonies, the ways in which the unexpected resonances and reflections as this music interacts with the listening environment—all of these are rooted in folk traditions. The 28 women in the choir became well known with a series of 1980s recordings, released and heavily promoted by Elektra/Nonesuch, under the direction of ethnomusicologist Marcel Cellier. Previously, the choir's music was available on poorly distributed cassettes, of interest mainly to collectors.

Le Mystère des Voix Bulgares   Nonesuch 979165

At their best, the Bulgarian Women's Choir sings resplendent, dazzling, almost otherworldly choral music. "Svatba (The Wedding)" is one of the more Western-sounding arrangements; "Polegnala e Todora (Harvest Song from Thrace)" is another. The expressiveness of Yanka Roupkina's solo on "Kalimankou Denkou (The Evening Gathering)" is greatly enhanced by her vibrato, one of several traditions upheld. Another is diaphonic singing (to increase carrying power outdoors, two voices sing together, but not in perfect unison). The result is sometimes acerbic (an acquired taste); "Schopska Pesen" is a good example of this tradition. For more, there's *Volume 2* (Nonesuch 79201); both volumes are included in a 3-CD box (79374) with the less intriguing *Ritual*.

LINK> *Trio Bulgarika — The Forest Is Crying*   Rykodisc 1342

Three of the choir's heavenly voices—Eva Georgieva, Yanka Rupkina, and Stoyanka Boneva—also performed as a vocal trio. The same magic, less overwhelming, more likely to stand up to repeat listening. With some traditional instrumental accompaniment. From 1988.

Tour '93   Mesa 79069

Credited to the (easier to pronounce) Bulgarian Women's Choir, this is the same group performing in an idyllic setting: the Nidaros Cathedral in Trondheim, Norway, in 1993. The Cathedral's acoustics work in favor of the group's harmonies, and the Cathedral's eerie silence enhances the quieter vocal passages. This live album recaps some of the choir's best work. It begins with a magnificent version of "Polegnala e Toudora (Todora's Dream)," arranged by the choir's pioneering founder, Philip Koutev. The rhythms are jazzy and fun on "Tapan bie (Beating the Drum)"—the singers simulate a Hungarian drum. On "S'gaida na horo," they simulate a bagpipe. For sheer variety, start here.

LINK> *Dzintars — Songs of Amber*   Rykodisc 10130

Mickey Hart and Jerry Garcia produced the perfect voices of the Latvian Women's Choir for this 1990 release. Choral arrangements of Latvian folk songs fill most of the album; two Yiddish folk songs and some material by contemporary composer complete it. Beautiful work, not at all discordant. Recorded at Skywalker Ranch.

Tired of hearing only zouk dance music, Jean-Marie Ahanda, arts critic at *The Cameroon Tribune*, put together a new group whose rhythms were based on the Bikutsi music of the Beti people. This group worked out at the Chacal Bar in Yaounde, **Cameroon**'s biggest city, and debuted on TV in 1987. Unlike the popular clean-cut music stars, this wild new band painted their bodies, donned torn clothes (a reminder of a poor rural past), and wore backpacks painted in fluorescent colors (peasants can carry everything they own in a backpack). A year later, Les Têtes Brûlées recorded its first album in Paris. Back in Yaounde, lead guitarist Théodore "Zanzibar" Epeme committed suicide (a very unusual act in Cameroon). After auditions for a new guitarist proved futile, Ahanda kept the band alive and brought in George Essono, a local band leader, to play lead on keyboards. A world tour and second album followed, with Roger Bekongo on lead guitar.

Hot Heads
Shanachie 64030

If there is anything like a typical song for this band, "Naoum Wom" might be a candidate. It includes a rough-hewn lead vocal and big bright choruses, a driving rhythm that periodically stops for the sound of a bell or the end of a vocal line, plus ringing guitars and horns. Pure energy. It's the story of a man who can't satisfy his lady love's lavish lifestyle. Drummer André Afata's beat powers the band's anthem, "Ma Musique â Moi," a dance song. This music is a trip! The rhythms are so complicated and so completely intertwined that complexity becomes as strong a selling point as the beat!

LINK➤ *Various Artists — Makossa Connection, Vol. 1* TJR (Stern's) 107
Makossa is Cameroon's dance music, and this is one of four CDs presenting the country's biggest makossa stars. Start here for Charlotte Mbango and Moni Bilé, then go on to Volumes 2 *(108),* 3 *(109), and* 4 *(110). All available from Stern's catalog in NYC.*

Bikutsi Rock
Shanachie 64042

More carefully produced and therefore lacking in the feeling of a bumpy but colorful African bus ride, this 1991 record was made in Paris (the previous one was made in Boulogne with far less fanfare). Guest stars abound: Manu Dibango, Charlotte M'bango, and the horn section from the Mory Kante group. "Nkulnnam" is typical—a guitar and percussion rhythm track, proceeding at a singular tempo, supports a commercial horn section. Male vocals, previously woven through-out the songs, are isolated as brief a capella interludes between tracks. The jazz-rock fusion song, "Bikutsi Rock," might have been played by Herbie Hancock's Headhunters band.

LINK➤ *Bell'a Njoh — Ça Fait Mal L'Amour* Septocam (Stern's) 83201
Makossa and bikutsi from a popular musician in Cameroon. Find this (and lots of other interesting African music) in the Stern's catalog.

Kinshasa is one of Africa's bustling river cities, and for years it's been one of the continent's busiest music centers. The **Congo** music scene took shape in the 1930s: dance music inspired by local folk music and by imported Cuban 78s brought in by Greek traders. Pascal Tabu, nicknamed Rochereau (he got the nickname because he knew the names of Napoleon's generals in a French history class; the nickname stuck, and he eventually adopted it as a stage name), wrote his first hit song at age 14, then joined Le Grande Kalle, a leading bandleader, in Le L'African Jazz (Manu Dibango played keyboards). In 1965, Tabu Ley and another band member, Docteur Nico, formed Africa Fiesta, a new band. He has since written over 2,000 songs and has won fame for his commanding stage presence and his major musical innovations, thus securing a place as one of Africa's greatest stars.

Tabu Ley   Shanachie 43017

Tabu Ley's best work was recorded before he was discovered by world music labels, but it's available on import: *Merveilles due Passé* 1971–1977 (Sonodisc 36542) and 1973–1976 (36544), and 1985's *Sarah* (Génidia 1032). This 1987 album contains tracks recorded with his Sarah partner, female vocalist M'bilia Bel. They perform "Loyenghe" with a rolling percussion line, sharp guitar work, and yearning vocals. An old-fashioned French chorus, honking horns, and one of Tabu Ley's memorable lines makes "Gagner, Gagner" a standout (and a terrific introduction to his work). The faster "En Amour Ya Pas de Calcul" moves on a bass groove and features dazzling guitars and horns. Orchestra Afrisa International is a top-notch outfit.

LINK▶ *M'Bilia Bel – Phénomene (New Look)*   IMA (Stern's) 1002
Formerly a vocalist with Tabu Ley's band, Bel scored big with this album in 1988. Try also her 1985 duet album with Tabu Ley called Keyna & Cadence Mudanda *(Génidia 1014). These, plus the above albums, are available from Stern's Music.*

Omona Wapi   Shanachie 43024

This outstanding 1983 collaboration is credited to Franco and Rochereau. Like Tabu Ley, Franco was a Zairean superstar. His band, OK Jazz (also known as TPOK) recorded more than 80 albums, but unlike Tabu Ley, Franco remained in Africa (which is why he's not as well-known in the U.S.). Their distinctive voices are clearly differentiated on "Ngungi"—Franco with his higher, slightly hoarse lyricism flitting like an electric guitar, and

Tabu Ley with his rock-solid low tenor. The instrumentation fades to the background when these two giants are onstage! "Omona Wapi" has its vocal duet, but the comparison between guitar styles is more interesting. "Kabassele in Memorium" is an homage to Le Grand Kalle.

LINK▶ *Franco – 20ème Anniversaire Vol. 1*   Sonodisc (Stern's) 50382
Six extraordinary tracks with TPOK jazz. Franco's vocals are sweet and low, the guitars and horns get into stunning slow grooves. Very sensuous party music. Essential. And the Stern's catalog lists dozens more by Franco.

Babeti Soukous

RealWorld (Caroline) 91302

This is show biz, African style! Recorded with a live audience at RealWorld Studios, England, in 1989, this album is a real crowd-pleaser. Four horns (two trumpets, two saxophones) punch out with fierce energy and razor-sharp precision on "Kinshasa." "Sorozo" features guitars upfront, a commanding lead vocal from Tabu Ley, and four background singers. "Pitié," a "slow," recaps his sensational 1970 Paris appearance. "Mosolo (Money)" was one of the first soukous hits (circa 1968): the percussion runs deep, the horns are super-hot, and the chanting spreads above a call-and-response between Tabu Ley and the chorus. "Linga Ngai (Love Me)" was a 1985 hit in the kwassa-kwassa style. A good place to begin a collection.

LINK▶ *Orchestra Marrabenta Star de Moçambique — Marrabenta Piquenique*   **Piranha (Stern's) 1043**
The "marrabenta" is a searing version of soukous from Mozambique (on Africa's southeast coast). Extremely tasty guitars and drums, fresh rhythms, and a gutsy band that plays super-tight. Among the best African dance music currently available. Great sound, too. Buy this!

Muzina

Rounder 5059

This 1994 recording is crystal clear recording, but sometimes lacks the peak energy of Tabu Ley's earlier work. With worshipful lyrics, "Muzina" sings to God with a small gospel choir, and a keyboard and percussion groove accented by Huit Kilol's electric guitar. "Bania Irene" begins as a relaxed rhumba, but a crackling snare drum changes the song's direction to a power-packed call-and-response between drummer and chorus (it's the most exciting piece on the album). Female vocalist Kizital Yal sings about an Alonzo, a deceptive man who pretends to have money while courting a mate. The song borrows from Cuban attitude and style. "Requisitoire" urged Zaire's leaders (notably Mobutu Sese Seko) to clean up their act.

LINK▶ *Various Artists — Cuban Gold: Que Se Sepa, ¡Yo Soy de La Habana!*   **Qbadisc 9006**
Cuban dance music from the 1970s and 1980s, the kind of music that affected Tabu Ley's development. With Los Van Van, Ritmo Oriental, Conjunto Rumbavana, others.

Africa Worldwide: 35th Anniversary Album   Rounder 5039

Same 1994 sessions as *Muzina*, recorded in the same Louisiana studio, but with a different emphasis. "Sala Noki Pascal (Get a Move On, Pascal) goes back to 1961. It's a rollicking conversation between chorus and guitar inspired by Tabu Ley's wife-to-be as he postponed marriage. (The two were married for 31 years; Georgina Mowana died in 1991.) "Cafe Rica" has a nostalgic connection to a Kinshasa nightclub; Tabu Ley's vocal is both commanding and sentimental. In time, this all feels like a huge celebration of a man's wonderful career. It climaxes with "Africa Mokili Mobimba," which embraces not only African unity, but also the many who have left Africa, but keep it in their hearts.

LINK▶ *Grand Kallé & L'African Jazz — Merveilles du Passé: 1961-1962*   **Sonodisc (Stern's) 36536**
Where it all began for Ley. Includes Dr. Nico (guitar) and Manu Dibango (sax).

Lo was born in 1956 in Niger, but his family moved to Rufisque, near Dakar, in **Senegal**, where he grew up. Lo made his own guitars from oil cans and fishing wire, and his drums from cardboard, pots, and saucepan lids. His first "tour" was done on top of a bush taxi driven around town by his brother. By age 15, Lo was appearing on TV and in public concerts. In 1979, he joined Super Diamono, the hard-driving m'balax band from Gambia, and became famous in West Africa. By the mid-1980s, Lo was leading his own band; he recorded his first album in 1989 under the supervision of top African producer Ibrahima Sylla. Lo's 1991 album for the French Barclay label pointed the way toward worldwide success. His 1994 album Iso (now part of the Triloka release, below) was made with the help of Baaba Maal and Youssou N'Dour.

Ismaël Lo   Mango 539-919

Fans might begin with *Diawar* (Stern's Africa 1027), which collects material from the 1980s. This 1991 album benefits from superior recording quality, prettier arrangements, and slicker production. "Tajabone" is a delightful folk song with accompaniment by Doudou Konare's acoustic guitar and Cheik Ba's harmonica-like keyboards. "Raciste" is ever-so-slightly funky with a dominant electric bass and horns that punch through; however, it's all kept very low-key and easy. "Jiggenu NDakaru, " with its rapid vocals, stinging guitars, and more aggressive percussion, is stronger, but still very much within the tradition. Lo is best at building a superstructure of horns, rhythm, synthesizers, and background vocals atop simple folk melodies (a bit like what Paul Simon does).

LINK➤ *Touré Kunda — The Touré Kunda Collection*   Putumayo 121
Bouncy Senegalese pop music, mostly from the French album Sili Bento. Seek out Natalia (released on Celluloid in France), which is more sophisticated. Excellent band.

Jammu Africa   Triloka 534-233

A very successful 1997 album that is, in fact, a repackaging and remixing of five songs released earlier: two are from Lo's 1991 album, and eight are from 1996. Stomping percussion, background guitars that blur the distinction between flamenco and West African music, and an earnest vocal make "Jammu Africa" the album's best. Lo's harmonica sets up a dance mix on "Dibi Dibi Rek." "Without Blame," a duet with Marianne Faithfull, goes even further into a pop direction. Lo returns to Afro-jazz roots for "Raciste," an interesting blend of big band horns and electric guitar distortion in a folk-rock context. This fun, accessible music is the stuff recording stars are made of.

LINK➤ *Wasis Diop — No Sant*   Worldly Music (Triloka) 697-124-1082
Elaborate vocal interweaving, wonderful songwriting, and clever use of jazz instruments result in one of 1996's best albums. More new Paris than old Senegal.

Los Van Van is one of **Cuba**'s top dance bands. It was formed in 1969 by Juan Formell, whose story is key to understanding the band's development. Formell was born in Havana in 1942. In 1959, Cuba's revolutionary government drafted him to play in the National Police Band, with which he performed a variety of Cuban dance styles. The island's musicians were essentially isolated from non-Cuban sounds, but Formell was one of several important innovators who began to add electric instrumentation to Cuban dance music. Shortly after Formell joined Orquesta Revé in 1967, he electrified some of the instruments, updated the band's sound, and drew enormous crowds in Cuba's dance halls. Two years later, Formell founded Los Van Van (the name means "The Go-Go's"). The band's notable performers include pianist César Pedroso (who expanded to synthesizers), percussionist José Luis Quintana (known as "Changuito"), and longtime singer Pedro Calvo.

Dancing Wet   World Pacific 80600

A collection of 1980s hits by a top Cuban band. The music shines through mediocre fidelity. César Pedroso captures the essence of Havana neighborhood interaction in "El Buena Gente (The Good Guy)." Formelli's "El Negro No Tiene Na' (Nothing Wrong with El Negro)" told fans he was okay after a fire; the phrase came to mean "hey, I'm okay," and was emblazoned on Havana trucks. This is good time music (with a great lead singer in Pedro Calvo) with bristling horns and cooking percussion. The best cut was recorded live (and sounds fine): "Aquí El Que Baila Gana (The Best Dancer Wins)."

LINK▶ *Orquesta Revé — La Explosion del Momento!*
RealWorld (Caroline) 2303
Formell came from Orquesta Revé, a popular band that mixes an older vocal style with Yoruba percussion and a streetwise urban style. Highly recommended 1989 recap of three 1980s albums.

Lo Ultimo en Vivo   Qbadisc 9020

El Salón Rosado de La Tropical is Havana's favorite dance hall, home to Los Van Van for three decades. This 1993 session was recorded properly. Arrangements are tight, but they're also varied with three trombones, two violins, a synthesizer, Cuban percussion, and excellent lead vocals by Pedro Calvo and Mario Rivera. Formell's "¡Que Sopreso! (What a Surprise!)" is expressed with a snide attitude by Rivera; the up-tempo second half of the song is a classic montuno (can't help but dancing). "Soy Normal, Natural" is another way to say "Hey, I'm cool!" In "Un Socio," a local businessman is searching for a partner. Everyday life in Havana as presented by a hot band.

LINK▶ *N.G. La Banda — En La Calle*   **Qbadisc 9002**
One of Cuba's most popular 1990s bands is led by José Luis Cortés (formerly of Los Van Van, Irakere). Lead singers are Isaac Delgado (now a big star) and Tony Calá (formerly of Ritmo Oriental). Fantastic!

Jepther McClymont was born to a musical family in Manchester, England (specifically, in the Davey Town parish), in the early 1970s. His father built guitars and taught him to play. Some time singing in church and setting up sound systems provided the necessary background. By 1992, he was recording his own music as Luciano. (The name is derived from the Latin for "light and knowledge.") His first single was a cover version of the Stevie Wonder–Paul McCartney song, "Ebony and Ivory." More cover versions followed, which led to a relationship with reggae singer and producer Freddie McGregor and a hit record with "Shake It Up Tonight." Luciano then worked in Kingston, **Jamaica**, with other producers, including Sly and Robbie, and found a soulmate in producer Philip "Fatis" Burrell. A series of reggae hits followed, including a reworking of Bob Marley's "Chant Down Babylon," and a duet with deejay Beenie Man on "Crazy Baldheads."

One Way Ticket   VP 1386
A talented singer brings the spirit of Jimmy Cliff, Dennis Brown, and other reggae singers into 1994. Luciano's voice is sweet and earnest on "Black Survivor" and "Chant Down Babylon." Philip "Fattis" Burrell's production choices are perfect: rhythm, horns, and the spare use of background singers are all set to emphasize Luciano's expressive vocals. Three songs are performed with guests. "Bounty Lover" is lovers' rock with some pillow talk, accented by Lady G's brief comments. "Jah is Alive" is handled as a Rasta anthem with Charlie Chaplin; it's produced with a solid hook, more elaborate percussion and effects than the other songs. "Mr. Governor" features Cocoa Tea.

LINK➤ *Beres Hammond — Sweetness*   VP 1330
Well known for decades in Jamaica, Hammond broke through in the 1990s. Soulful voice, tender material, simple and effective arrangements. An old pro. Recommended.

Messenger   Island Jamaica 524-624
A continuation of work begun on 1995's *Where There Is Life* (Island Jamaica 539-957), affected by Luciano's months away at a religious retreat. His songwriting has matured considerably. Both in style and content, "Life" borrows from gospel and R&B (it's also similar to the Neville Brothers' more reverential material). Luciano contemplates the role of Jah (God) in daily proceedings. He also sings, with utter seriousness and compassion, a dedication called "Mama," another theme often found in soul music. "Never Give Up My Pride" recalls the best Bob Marley songs: it's upbeat, positive, and forward-thinking. Once again, very high marks to producer Burrell for his restraint and excellent taste.

LINK➤ *Sanchez — One in a Million: The Best of Sanchez*   VP 1483
Sanchez came to reggae from gospel. His fine style is youthful and soulful. Hits include "Give It a Chance," "Soon As I Get Home," and "I Can't Wait." Much fine work, but some lackluster songwriting and overdone production.

Maal grew up in the 1960s in Podor, a village of 6,000 people on the **Senegal** River. His father worked in the fields, but also called people to worship at the mosque. Contrary to local tradition, which denied music education to anyone but griot children, the school's headmaster encouraged students to learn kora, riti (violin), and hoddu (seven-string guitar). Maal learned songs and dances from his mother, who sang at weddings. He lived in nearby St. Louis (the colonial capital city) for a while before studying at the university in Dakar (the present capital). There he joined Asly Fouta, an arts group of 70 musicians. Maal moved to Paris for post-graduate studies at the École Des Beaux Arts, then traveled to southern Senegal with friend

(and griot) Mansour Seck to collect songs. In Dakar, Maal formed Daande Lenol ("the voice of the race"); the band released its first album in 1985.

Djam Leelii
Mango 9840

Credited to Baaba Maal and Mansour Seck, this 1984 recording was released about five years later. Their talents as vocalists and acoustic guitarists pleasantly complement one another. On the up-tempo "Loodo," one guitar is tuned higher to carry the melody, and the other is lower for a drum-like rhythm. "Muudo Hormo" meanders like a lazy river on a hot day; Maal calls out amidst the wooden block rhythm of a balaphon (xylophone) and is soon joined by Seck on vocal harmony. "Bibbe Leddy" is a snappy guitar duet that settles into a repeated melody pattern beneath Seck's more nasal vocal. Generally, this is acoustic work with some electric guitar fill.

LINK▶ *Mansour Seck – N'der Fouta Tooro, Vol. 1*   *Stern's Africa 1061*
A 1994 release with Mauritanian guitar player and singer Ousmane Hamady Diop (who sings lead on four songs) and Maal (who guests on two more). Vol. 2 (1073), from 1996, followed a solo European tour, and also features Diop. Both are acoustic albums similar to Djam Leelii.

Firin' in Fouta
Mango 539-944

Maal formed Dande Lelol (Voice of the Race), his modern electric band, in 1985. For this 1994 album, Dande Lelol is joined by such notables as Donal Lunny (bodhrán, bouzouki, etc.), Michael Brooke (infinite guitar), Jah Wobble (bass), and, on two songs, The Kicking Horns. "African Women" is an Afro-Cuban dance song with a pumping bass line, a good drum solo and a horn arrangement that might have been done by Tower of Power. "Nijlou" starts with a full-scale ethereal synthesizer treatment (plus drum machine), then settles into commentary about African currency's plight in the world market. Tight, ultramodern production emphasizes the right rhythms and Maal's fine voice, but it's sometimes overblown.

LINK▶ *Mansour Seck – Yelayo*   *Stern's Africa 1075*
Seck's best to date, from 1997. He sings lead for a larger (albeit acoustic) band and plays some dazzling guitar. His voice is also recorded with greater precision. Kora, guitar, and hoddu (lute), with two female backup singers.

Mahlathini (& Mahotella Queens)

In the 1950s, producer Rupert Bopape developed a **South African** group called Black Mambazo, whose sound was based first on the pennywhistle (a flute) and then on group vocals. Vocals became Bopape's specialty; his female vocal group, Dark City Sisters, were big 1960s stars. As pennywhistles gave way to saxophones, the mbaqanga was born, eventually spinning off a vocal style ("vocal jive"), which employs unorthodox harmonies and a male "groaner." Bass singer Simon "Mahlathini" Nkabinde became a popular groaner ("mahlathini" means "bush on the head"), and in 1964, Bopape brought Mahlathini together with a female vocal group, the Mahotella Queens, and an electric band. They've been popular ever since, evolving their mqashiyo sound (groaner plus harmonizing girl group plus electric band) to a full-scale stage show, complete with dance routines. Note, however, that recordings made in the 1970s were not the same Queens; the originals took eight years off to raise children.

The Lion of Soweto
Earthworks (Stern's) 2404

Mahlathini gets credit for this album as a solo. He's backed by the Makgona Tshole Band and the Queens (not the Mahotella Queens, with whom he recorded at other times). He's the growling lead singer, moving the instrumentalists and backup singers through guitar-based dance music. Nothing too elaborate: no horns or big drums or overpowering electricity. "Kudala Besifuna" is the kind of tight, jumpy song that Mahlathini does so well, a prime example of his streetwise brand of mbaqanga called mgqashiyo. He trades off with a ringing lead guitar (talented, but uncredited) and sometimes sings along with the Queens while drums keep the beat.

LINK➤ *Various Artists — The Indestructable Beat of Soweto*
Shanachie 43033

An essential CD for any world music library, this 1987 album introduced many listeners to African music. There's a song from Ladysmith Black Mambazo, two from Mahlathini backed by the Makgona Tshole Band, and plenty more from artists who never became famous (but should have!).

The Lion Roars
Shanachie 43081

Mahlathini reunited with the original Mahotella Queens in 1985, and this album was put together a short time later. In fact, this is more of a reunion, bringing together the mbaqanga jive rhythms and electric guitar of the Makgona Tsohle band and its talented leader, producer West Nkosi. The real fun here is the interaction among Mahlathini's growling vocals, the bouncy percussion track, and the Mahotella Queens' choruses. The combination is highly dependent upon good songwriting, and there's an abundance of entertaining material here, made better with superior guitar riffs, including "Seipati (Hidden Woman)," "Thuto Ke Senotlolo (Education Is the Key)," and "Khubetswana Yeso (Light-Skinned Woman)."

LINK➤ *Dark City Sisters and Flying Jazz Queens*
Earthworks (Stern's) 31

These are two distinct groups. The Dark City Sisters recorded from the mid-1950s until the mid-1960s. Mahlathini's older brother plays sax. The Flying Jazz Queens sing just 2 of the 14 songs. A significant source of the Mahlathini and Mahotella sound.

Izbani Zomgqashiyo   Shanachie 43036

To confuse matters, this a terrific album featuring neither the original Mahotella Queens nor Mahlathini. These Queens are Emily Zwane, Thandi Radebe, Beatrice Ngcobo, Thandi Nkosi, and Caroline Karpentar, all from South Africa, and all good singers. They're backed by the Makhona Zonke Band, and they generally sing with a male groaner. These songs feature unusually peppy interaction between the Queens and the groaner. On various tracks, the groaner is Potatoes Mazambane, Joseph Mthimkhulu, or Robert Mbazo Mkhize. The best song is the first one, "Zibuyile Nonyaka (The Girls Are Back This Year)." Recorded in 1986.

LINK➤ *Dalom Kids & Splash — Collection*   Putumayo 122
Pop music from South Africa. Splash, consisting of several male singers, is produced by Daniel Tshanda. The Dalom Kids are three female backup singers, originally brought to the studio for work with Splash, who became successful as a Tshana-produced act on its own.

Rhythm and Art   Shanachie 43068

The real thing. Simon "Mahlathini" Nkabinde sings, mumbles, and grumbles through his vocal lead. The bona-fide Mahotella Queens—Nobesuthu Shawe, Hilda Tloubatla, and Mildred Mangxola—harmonize like no other backup group. Fabulous production! When this comes together, as it does on "I'm in Love with a Rastaman," it's tough not to smile. There's some gospel here, too: "Praise the Good Lord" is a dreamy a capella song by the women, and it's followed by "God Is On Your Side," offered in English and with rhythm. With one of Mahlathini's best vocals and a catchy hook, "Won't You Please Sing Along" is one of the group's most popular songs. From 1990.

LINK➤ *Various Artists — Jive Soweto*   Earthworks (Stern's Africa) 26
The fourth volume in the consistently fine series called The Indestructible Beat of Soweto, *this 1992 collection is heavy on light-touch work from the Soul Brothers (South Africa's biggest sellers).*

Women of the World   Shanachie 64047

After three decades, a 1993 album without a male groaner. As one would expect from experienced backup singers, the harmonies are precise, but there are times, as on the gospel "Don't Be Late for Heaven" when a passionate lead singer would add focus. Then again, the unison and harmony are marvelous on their version of the Paul Simon/Ladysmith Black Mambazo song "Homeless," and it's better still on a version of Dylan's "I Shall Be Released." South African songs like "Malaika" and "Mbube" are competently handled. Is this their best work? Maybe not. But it's great to hear the women free and on their own.

LINK➤ *Sapphire — The Uppity Blues Women*   Alligator 4780
Three mature women sing boogie-woogie blues, and have a whole lot of fun doing it.

South African Makeba started working professionally at age 18 with various bands and a variety of touring troupes. After she appeared in an anti-apartheid film and attended its premiere at the 1959 Venice Film Festival, Makeba saw the chance to move to the U.S., a longtime dream. Her passport revoked, Makeba befriended Harry Belafonte, who helped her build a U.S. career by arranging NYC club dates and an appearance on Steve Allen's *The Tonight Show*. Hit records followed, accompanied by political activism. She testified against apartheid at the UN in 1963 (causing South Africa to ban her records). Later, she divorced South African musician Hugh Masekela and married Black Panther Stokely Carmichael. They moved to Guinea, in West Africa; she continued to tour Africa and Europe, frequently appearing at festivals. She was Guinea's UN delegate in the 1980s and won the Dag Hammarskjold Peace Prize in 1986. Makeba also worked with Paul Simon on the *Graceland* project and tour.

Africa   Novus 3155

Every few minutes, a familiar song materializes, a song heard long ago. "Lakutshn Ilanga" recalls a café, a slow guitar, and piano, and a pretty melody with a nostalgic air. "Mbube" was the basis for "Wimoweh." The upbeat "Dubula," with its stop-and-start dance, its harmonizing male background singers, and the percussive snap of the mouth on "The Click Song" sound so familiar. No wonder! This was probably the first world music I heard, played by well-intentioned NYC schoolteachers in the early 1960s. They chose well: Makeba's talent is huge; her voice and interpretive skills are without equal. This is essential world music, the best of four early 1960s albums for RCA.

LINK➤ *Harry Belafonte — Calypso*   RCA 53801
Belafonte grew up in Harlem, became an actor, and studied the music of the Caribbean. He introduced a generation of listeners to West Indian music ("Day O," "Jamaica Farewell"). Belafonte used his power to make a difference—introducing music from elsewhere in the African diaspora, too and giving his time to social justice. He's part of world music history.

Sangoma   Warner Brothers 25673

A sangoma, like Makeba's mother, is possessed by ancestral spirits and endowed with special powers. In Makeba's 1988 comeback album, she spreads her share of ancient magic by singing songs she learned as a child, and other traditional songs from home. Makeba laid the vocal tracks and most of the backing vocal tracks before any instruments were added. The result is an album of South African street choruses, with just the right percussion accents from Hugh Masekela. "Ingwemabala (Spotted Leopard)" is a remarkable cycle of chants and harmonies with lyrics that resonate with Makeba's own life: "I left my home not intending to go away forever." Recorded at The Hit Factory in NYC.

LINK➤ *Various Artists —*
Holding Up Half the Sky: Voices of African Women   Shanachie 64073
Nicely varied collection of spectacular voices from Senegal (Kiné Lam), Zaire (M'Bilia Bel), Nigeria (Lijadu Sisters), Ethiopia (Netsanet Mellesse), Mauritania (Malouma Mint Miadeh). and Dorothy Makusa (a Zairean who made a career in South Africa). Makeba, too. Very high quality.

Maná is an enormously popular rock band from Guadalajara, the second largest city in **Mexico**. By the early 1980s, the group was playing locally as Sombrero Verde (Green Hat) with lead singer Fernando Olvera (now simply called "Fehr"), guitarist Sergio Vallín, bass player Juan Calleros, and drummer/vocalist Alex González. By 1987, the band had changed its name and was recording for a major label. Maná toured for two years, working hard to encourage Mexican and Latin radio stations to play its music (most played only love songs, not Mexican rock). The strategy worked: by 1993, the band was drawing 10,000 people to its concerts. Maná records became popular in the U.S. and Europe. By 1994, the group was winning awards, and its concerts were selling out. This newfound clout is being used to make an impact: Selva Negra (Black Forest) is Maná's environmental foundation, dedicated to improving the world by working with local organizations.

Donde Jugarán Los Niños? WEA Latina 95790

If the group members didn't sing in Spanish, mainstream rock stations in the U.S. would have picked up on the fact that these guys are major international rock stars. The title song asks "Where Will the Children Play?" It's one of several social and environmentally conscious songs in the repertoire. Alex Gonzales is a solid rock drummer, skillfully driving "De Pies a Cabeza," and Fehr's lead vocal recalls Sting, Robert Plant, and a touch of Bob Marley. (There's some reggae here.) "Oye Mi Amor" has Latin influences and maybe a touch of Santana's group vocals, but the lead and rhythm guitars keep things rocking. It's good rock songwriting. Recorded in 1992.

LINK➤ *Santana – Viva Santana* **Columbia 44344**
Before Maná, the last great band to make a real impact in the U.S. This is wonderful music, but it's a mighty long time between sensations. (Still, don't miss this 2-CD set; it's even better now than it was years ago.) Includes a family tree showing 34 different versions of the band.

Cuando Los Angeles Lloran
WEA Latina 99707

The album gets off to a rocking start with "Como Un Perro Enloquecido" and "Selva Negra (Black Forest)." The latter, in rock-reggae fusion, lashes out at those who deprive indigenous people and fauna of their natural lands. In "Ana," Fher sings about a 15-year-old girl, pregnant, boyfriend gone, hiding her secret. A church bell chimes, flutes play, and a Mexican groove tells the story of Chico Mendes, an environmental martyr from Brazil. (Mendes's story is told in the film *The Burning Season*.) It's the title song (translated as "When the Angels Cry"). A party atmosphere sets up "El Borracho (The Drunkard)." Released in 1995, this is a great rock album in any language.

LINK➤ *Rubén Blades – Buscando America* **Elektra 60352**
Probably his best album, sung all in Spanish (with English translations in the liner notes; something Maná should do). Includes some of his best social conscience songs, like "Despariciones" and "El Padre Antonio y El Monaguillo Andres."

You can buy a mbira at any African shop; it's also called a thumb piano. The mbira is part of **Zimbabwe**'s culture. It's often heard at bira ceremonies, with a trance-like sound to contact ancestors. The mbira, played acoustically, electronically, or simulated on guitars or other instruments, became the basis of Mapfumo's work in the 1970s as he moved from cover bands to his own music and messages in the Shona language. At that time, he was often heard at all-night liberation meetings as his country was moving toward independence. "Chimurenga," which means "struggle," named his style, and his early political songs brought renown and notoriety as a political activist. With the country's independence in 1980, and a new band called Blacks Unlimited, Mapfumo's music remained politically aware, if not as overtly or consistently message-laden.

The Chimurenga Singles
Shanachie 43066

These are songs of struggle, recorded in a war-torn Zimbabwe in the second half of the 1970s. By today's standards, the sound is remarkably gentle: chants whose rhythm instruments are either the mbira (African thumb piano), or guitars or horns that sound like the mbira. The messages are anything but gentle. Mapfumo begs for "happiness in Zimbabwe," which he defines as "somewhere to sleep..., some clothes..., and some food."

In "Tozveireva Kupiko (Who Shall We Share Our Frustrations With?)," he sings, "Our country is becoming a desert/There is no rain here/Our children go unclothed." Most songs are recorded with Blacks Unlimited; two were made with the Acid Band.

LINK➤ *Woody Guthrie — Dust Bowl Ballads*   Rounder 1040
The music might sound different, but the gentility and messages are remarkably similar: "I Ain't Got No Home," "Blowing Down the Road (I Ain't Gonna Be Treated This Way)." With a cultural difference—the American psyche is more individually independent.

Best of Thomas Mapfumo: Chimurenga Forever   EMI 35582
The lion, a common animal in Zimbabwe, is a symbol for two representative songs. One is "Mhondoro (Ancestral Lion)," which conjures the animal's spirit to fill the heart of Zimbabwe. "Shumba (The Lion)," which became very famous during the war for independence, cautions citizens to be wary of their environment and to refrain from discussing political issues in public. Other songs in this 1978-93 greatest hits compilation encourage Africans to unite, and community leaders to be ready to fight and talk about poverty, family relations, excess drinking, and other difficulties of daily life.

LINK➤ *Bhundu Boys — True Jit*   *Mango 9812*
Zimbabwe's Bhundu Boys became popular by mixing unequal parts of chimurenga, finger-picked electric guitar and dance music from surrounding countries as "jit." Pamberi! (Mango 9858) from 1989 and Muchitedza (Out of the Dark) from 1997 are also good choices. But start with 1988's True Jit.

Mari Boine, formerly known as Mari Boine Persen, is a singer and percussionist from **Norway**. To be more accurate, she is a Sami. The Sami are the indigenous people of Scandinavia's northlands (they were formerly known as "Lapps," a derogatory term). She was born and raised in the small village of Gamehisnjárga, which is on the Anajohka River. Her parents earned their living by farming and salmon fishing. Mari Boine grew up within Sami culture, where the land is revered and music is central to religion. As she entered the larger Norwegian world through school and friends, she struggled to balance her conflicting values and feelings. This tension inspired her early songwriting and eventually placed her in the position of a spokesperson for both Sami culture and the importance of indigenous peoples. To emphasize her connection with other indigenous cultures, she performs with South American and African instruments, notably an African drum.

Gula Gula
RealWorld (Caroline) 2312

The title translates as "Hear the Voices of the Foremothers," and immediately sets the tone. Boine's African drum beats out an earthy rhythm to accompany a chantlike vocal that says, "They ask why you let the earth become polluted. Pointed. Exhausted. They remind you where you come from....If we take her life, we die with her." Her voice's range and vitality energize "It Sat Duolmma Mu (Free at Last)," in which she sings out against the dull institution of formal education and the liberty of the real world. It's performed with folk–jazz accompaniment from Ale Møller and other top musicians. Released under the name Mari Boine Persen in 1989.

LINK➤ *Jan Garbarek — Twelve Moons*
ECM 1500

Garbarek, who became well known when he worked with Keith Jarrett, is one of Scandinavia's distinguished jazz players. His abstract style suits Mari Boine's voice. Agnes Buen Garnås also sings.

Radiant Warmth
Antilles 533-520

A considerably more elaborate 1996 production, this is a star turn presented in an ultramodern cardboard CD jacket. "Goaskinviellaja (Eagle Brother)" flies high with electric guitars and synthesizers, yet maintains the integrity of her simpler songs. "Åle Sat" (No More)" is nearly spoken, and practically without accompaniment. "Radiant Warmth" delivers on the "relentless groove" promised on the CD's cover art; it's sung with a repetitive, often double-tracked vocal to thick drums, bass, and the twists of some wind instruments in the deep background. An ambient treatment provides the background for Boine's finest vocal, "Skádja (Reverberation)." Ambience also plays a role in "Mu Áhkku (Grandma)."

LINK➤ *Dawn Upshaw — White Moon: Songs to Morpheus*
Nonesuch 79364

The 1990s are an era in which extraordinary female voices are celebrated. Upshaw, an operatic soprano, performs songs associated with nighttime, sleep, the moon, early dawn, and Morpheus, a spirit who soothes suffering. Dappled and relaxed.

Bob Marley and the Wailers

Born in Nine Miles, **Jamaica**, in 1945 to a 51-year-old white British Army officer and a 19-year old black woman, Marley grew up in the rough Trenchtown section of West Kingston. With boyhood friends Bunny Livingstone (later renamed Bunny Wailer) and Peter Mackintosh (later, Peter Tosh), he formed the Wailin' Wailers, whose 1964 hit, "Simmer Down," topped the Jamaican charts and began a productive decade that culminated in a 1972 contract with Island Records. Tosh and Livingstone soon left for solo careers, but Marley became famous as a musician and spokesman for freedom. Two famous concerts were politically inspired: 1978's "One Love," which attempted to unite opposing Jamaican party leaders, and a 1980 Zimbabwe independence celebration. For his work in Africa, Marley received a UN Peace Medal. His post-Wailers band included a female backup group, the I-Threes (Rita Marley, Marcia Griffiths, and Judy Mowatt). In 1981, Marley died of cancer at age 36.

Catch a Fire   Tuff Gong 846-201

By today's standards, these 1973 recordings are quite simple. Marley sings lead, with Mackintosh and Livingston singing backup. Mackintosh plays piano, organ, and guitar. The reggae beat is established by the Barrett brothers on bass and drums, and Livingston on bongos or congas. Five guys in a recording studio, this time with a budget to do the job right. Marley's "Stir It Up," with its resonating bass line, and Mackintosh's "Stop That Train" are highlights. The mix of straight pop ("Baby We've Got a Date") and street conscience ("Concrete Jungle," "No More Trouble") shows a band finding its identity. Gold disc pressing (Mobile Fidelity 654) offers better bass and cleaner voices.

LINK➤ *Bob Marley and the Wailers —*
One Love   *Heartbeat (Rounder) 111/112*
Interesting early work without the strident reggae beat. Some distinctive reggae ("One Love"), the first rude boy song ("Hooligan"), but many pop songs like "Teenager in Love."

Burnin'   Tuff Gong 846-200

Credited only to the Wailers, this album is immediately more funky, more focused, and more politically aware than its predecessor. Released in 1973, it begins with "Get Up, Stand Up" (the lyrics continue, "don't give up the fight"). Eric Clapton had a hit on Marley's composition, "I Shot the Sheriff"; the Wailers' original benefits from a credible context and a superior arrangement. Reggae rhythm and social commentary anchor almost every song; "Burnin' and Lootin'" provides the album's center and title. Tight vocals and rhythms brighten new versions of older material, notably "Put It On" and "Small Axe." The last album with Mackintosh and Livingston.

LINK➤ *Abyssinians — Satta Massagna*   *Heartbeat (Rounder) 120*
Blended harmonies and gentle passion brought the title song from Jamaica's pop scene to Rastafarian churches. Tight vocal work, direct messages, invigorating and pure reggae. One of the best reggae albums of the 1970s.

Natty Dread

Tuff Gong 846-204

The Barretts are still Marley's rhythm section, but the sound of Touter's piano and organ is more expansive. Marley is more of a solo singer with a backup band. The I Threes now sing backup vocals. The album leads off with three fine songs: "Lively Up Yourself," "No Woman No Cry," and "Them Belly Full (But We Hungry)." The dramatic organ stings, sad roadside harmonica, and acid I-Threes vocals set up a yearning "Rebel Music (3 O'Clock Roadblock)," one of several protest songs. The group is also becoming more musically adventurous; jazz fusion blends into the reggae mix on "So Jah Seh." From 1975.

LINK➤ *Steel Pulse — Sound System: The Island Anthology*
Island Jamaica 524–320

With Marley's encouragement, Steel Pulse became a popular band in the late 1970s and continued through the 1980s. Somewhat uneven. Lots of dub in later years.

Live!

Tuff Gong 422-806

One of the all-time great live albums. The venue was London's Lyceum Ballroom. The date was July 18, 1975. The crowd is totally into the show, and the band is totally into the crowd. The group opens with "Trenchtown Rock," then does a funky version of "Burnin' and Lootin'." Turn it up loud to imagine the audience dancing to "Them Belly Full (But We Hungry)," and singing along to "Lively Up Yourself." An easy organ introduction gets the crowd quietly singing long before Marley passionately sings "No Woman No Cry." "I Shot the Sheriff" heats things up, and the relentless "Get Up Stand Up" ends the concert at a fever pitch. A Marley collection without this live album is woefully incomplete.

LINK➤ *Twinkle Brothers — Free Africa*   *Frontline (Caroline) 1684*
Norman Grant's group has always emphasized the vocal quality of reggae music; there are few better. Every reggae collection should include some Twinkle Brothers; sadly, most of their material is unavailable in the U.S.

Rastaman Vibration

Tuff Gong 846205

By 1976, Marley was a more secure social commentator, and a more effective solo singer. The seriousness of "War" anchors the album. The lyrics come from a speech by Haile Selassie: "Until the philosophy which holds one race superior and another inferior is finally and permanently discredited and abandoned...." Lighter essays complain about the "Rat Race," and working on a "Night Shift." Rita Marley wrote some of the better songs, including "Johnny Was," about a mother coping with the death of a son killed by a stray bullet, and "Crazy Baldhead," about native pride. More hard-boiled than the older Wailers hits.

LINK➤ *Culture — Two Sevens Clash*   *Shanachie 44001*
1978 album from another popular reggae band of the time. Their harmonies are super-tight, their sense of rhythm superb, and their social conscience, strong. A greatest hits import called Strictly Culture *(Music Club) is also worth seeking out.*

Exodus

Mobile Fidelity 628

Several later albums bring together Marley's outspoken militancy, a funkier reggae sound, and melodic songwriting that recalls earlier work. Three others, 1978's *Kaya* (846-209), 1979's *Survival* (846-202), and 1980's *Uprising* (846-211), are also recommended. This 1977 album contains more riches (and more singalong tunes) than the others: "So Much Things to Say," "Waiting in Vain," "Jamming," and a delightful medley of "One Love" and Curtis Mayfield's "People Get Ready." Mid-1970s band with the Barretts, Tyrone Downie on keyboards and percussion, and Alvin "Seeco" Patterson, also on percussion, is joined by the talented Julian (Junior) Marvin on lead guitar.

LINK➤ *Ziggy Marley and the Melody Makers — The Best of (1988-1993)*
Virgin 44098

Formed by the children of Bob and Rita Marley, this group had hits, but not much respect. Moving from 1988's "Tumblin' Down" to 1991's dance-hall "Kozmik" and "Rainbow Country," the story improves.

Babylon by Bus

Tuff Gong 846-197

Marley's live performances were wildly energetic. The infectious energy comes across on record, and the European audiences are very much a part of the show. Recorded on tour in Paris, Copenhagen, London, and Amsterdam in 1978, the performing troupe is larger than before. Marley and the I-Threes share the front line; the backup band (technically called The Wailers, but bearing no real resemblance to the earlier trio) consists of long-time reggae players like Carlton and Aston "Familyman" Barrett (drums and bass), Alvin "Seeco" Patterson (Percussion), and others. The choice of material reflects greater social consciousness: "Positive Vibration," "Exodus," "Concrete Jungle," and "Rebel Music."

LINK➤ *Judy Mowatt — Black Woman*
Shanachie 43011

Don't classify Mowatt, or any of the I-Threes, as just backup singers. Each woman enjoyed a solo career independent of Marley. This is a fantastic reggae album, smart, sophisticated and very musical. Very highly recommended!

Legend (The Best of Bob Marley and the Wailers)

Tuff Gong 846-210

An unconditionally joyful portrait of a man and a band who changed the planet. This single CD focuses attention on a stellar catalog of songs recorded mostly in a five-year period (1973-78). Every song is special: "Stir It Up," with those funny little organ sound effects; the boundless joy of the I-Threes vocals on "Three Little Birds"; the positive vibrations of "Get Up Stand Up"; the goofy, slightly off-key falsettos on "I Shot the Sheriff"; the desperate love songs like "Waiting in Vain"; the embracing friendship of "Jamming." Maybe best of all is "Buffalo Soldier," with its encouraging historical accuracy and that perfect reggae beat.

LINK➤ *Various Artists —*
Tougher Than Tough: The Story of Jamaican Music   **Mango 539-935**
This 4-CD set tells the story of ska, rock steady, reggae, dub, dance hall, ragga...and just about every important reggae artist through 1993. With this added context, Marley's accomplishments are even more impressive.

Rita Marley is probably best-known as Bob Marley's wife, but she had her own career before meeting Marley, one that she continued after his death. Born Rita Anderson, she became a backup singer (one of three in the Soulettes) for Studio One, a popular Jamaican label. She then went out on her own and through a series of hit singles, became one of **Jamaica**'s hitmakers. At Studio One, she backed up the Wailers and many other acts. In the early 1970s, she joined forces with two other top pop singers, Judy Mowatt and Marcia Griffiths, to form the I Threes. The group performed on its own for awhile, then joined Bob after Peter Tosh and Bunny Livingstone left the Wailers. She continued to work until the mid-1980s, when issues relating to her husband's estate occupied much of her time. Reggae star Ziggy Marley is their child.

Who Feels It Knows it
Shanachie 43003

The wondrous creative spirit of the Wailers lives on in Rita Marley's music. This is very much a group effort with contributions from more than two dozen musicians, including Tyrone Downie, the Barretts, Junior Marvin, and others who were once Wailers. Marley, who co-produced and composed these songs, is expert in selecting material that suits her experienced voice. While there's no question that this is reggae, she adds a bluesy vocal treatment for "That's the Way," a folk-rock style for "Good Morning Jah," a 1950s girl group sound for "Play Play," some gospel, and so on. A very elaborate 1989 production with endlessly inventive instrument sounds, even some sound effects.

LINK➤ *Various Artists — Holding Up Half the Sky:*
Women in Reggae: Roots Daughters   ***Shanachie 45027***
Worth the price just to hear the I Threes sing "Many Are Called," this collection emphasizes the 1970s (when reggae was as much a women's sport); good work from Nadine Sutherland, Hortense Ellis, Dhaima, Barbara Paige, and others who should have become famous.

We Must Carry On   Shanachie 43082
Even better! Brill Building meets Trenchtown on the beautifully arranged reggae pop tune, "I Know a Place." It borrows the escapist lyrics and pace of "Up on the Roof," and combines elements of the reggae anthem, "One Love." Bob and Rita Marley co-wrote the song. "Dem a Fight (Freedom)" is most like a Wailers song. Written by Rita Marley and Winston Holness (a top reggae producer also known as Niney the Observer), it chants "the whole world is fighting...no more fighting!" Son Steven Marley raps on "Who Colt the Game," one of several lesser-known Bob Marley songs here. Skillfully coproduced by Rita Marley and Niney the Observer.

LINK➤ *Bob Marley & the Wailers — Rastaman Vibration*
Tuff Gong 846-205
Actually, Bob Marley with the I-Threes. Good songs: "Roots, Rock, Reggae," "Night Shift," "Crazy Bald Head." On this record, the I Threes are an important part of the act.

Brian Jones of the Rolling Stones made these musicians famous in 1968 by producing an album of psychedelic music called *Brian Jones Presents the Pipes of Pan at Jajouka* (Point Music 446-612; special limited edition). Their unadorned sound is even more interesting, as is the story before and after Jones. Jajouka is a mountain village in northern **Morocco**. A local myth tells of Attar, who learned to play a magical flute from Boujeloud, who was half-man, half-goat. (Pan, the Greek god of woods and pastures, is also half-man, half-goat, and plays the flute.) The villagers learned to play by stealing Boujeloud's music. They've been exempted from farm work and deal instead with magical forces through their music. In the 1800s, this meant royal treatment and presence at the Sultan's court. Even as late as the 1940s, these artists were allowed to collect a tithe from neighboring villages. They are virtuoso players from many generations.

The Master Musicians of Jajouka
Genes 3000

The Primal Energy: The Master Musicians of the Rif. Jajouka, Morocco.

Producers Joel and Mark Rubiner recorded this album in 1992, a year after Brian Jones's exploitative release (no money returned to the village). The musicians gathered in a one-room schoolhouse and played concise abridgements of their long pieces. There are four "raitas," performed by a pair of double-reed horn players and a drummer. Circular breathing (simultaneously blowing in and breathing out) creates a bagpipe-like effect on the horns, an expression of spiritual and psychic power. Three versions of "Boujeloud" are played on flutes, then rhaita, then on gimbris (lutes) and drums. The women sing "Teasing Boujeloud" as a street chant with hand-clap percussion.

LINK➤ *Various Artists — Songs and Rhythms of Morocco*

Lyrichord 7336

A more varied collection with wedding songs, harvest songs, and even a song celebrating hashish.

Apocalypse Across the Sky
Axiom 510-857

There are six principal musicians. Bachir Attar plays the gimbri and the ghaita (or raita), a long flute similar to the Turkish ney or the Armenian dudek. He is also featured on the lira (or lyre). Others play similar instruments and some percussion (clay pots covered with skins, for example). The effect sounds exotic to Western ears: similar, perhaps, to Indian music but with an Arab rhythm. "A Habibi Ouajee T'Allel Allaiya" follows a traditional Arab drum pattern, nasal lead vocal, and repeating male chorus with various string embellishments. "Memories of My Father" features mostly the gimbri and ghaita; their intertwined sounds are then joined by heavy drumming. From 1991.

LINK➤ *Kudsi Erguner — Works of Kemani Tatyos Efendi*

Traditional Crossroads 4277

Very classical in form. It's interesting to hear some similar instrument sounds in a very different setting and with very different historical development. Still, there are the ney, the ud (a lute), and the tanbur (skin drum).

Margareth Menezes

Somewhere in the midst of artificial labels like **Brazilian** Afro-pop and samba-reggae lies the intense soul of Menezes's music. She's a singer who got her start in Salvador, the biggest city in Bahia, Brazil, in 1983 and became popular locally. In the late 1980s, she toured with Gilberto Gil, who introduced her to Brazilian audiences outside Bahia. Her first album, *Elegibo*, became popular in Germany, Holland, and Spain. This prompted David Byrne to ask her to tour the world as his opening act; they did 74 concerts together in 1989 and 1990. Problems related to management and an unfortunate lack of record promotion following the sucessful tour did not allow her career to blossom. Instead, she lost ground. In 1995, she released a comeback album called *Luz Dorado*. Menezes's talent and stage presence are phenomenal.

Elegibo
Mango 539-855

This album made Menezes a star. Two of the tracks were produced by David Byrne, with whom she toured as opening act during a 1989 world tour. Producer and engineer Nestor Madrid deserves more credit for her sound—the fearless voice rising above a sizzling rhythm section. Most of the songs are upbeat dances. "Abra a Boca e Feche os Olhos (Open Your Mouth)," sung in Portuguese, French, and Yoruban, is a lambada. "Tudo à Toa (All for Nothing)" is a funky electric samba. Lyrics are not included, but songs are generally critical of social conditions in Brazil.

LINK➤ *Various Artists — Brazilliance!: The Music of Rhythm*
Rykodisc 20153

Upbeat collection by João Bosco, Paulinho da Viola, Martinho da Vila, Chico Buaraque, and others, mostly from the 1980s, shows how innovative Menezes was, in her time.

Kindala
Mango 539-917

Ramiro Mussoto's ominous programmed drum machine reflects the heavier, angrier tone of this album's music and sets up "Fé Cega, Faca Amolada (Blind Faith, Sharp Knife)," Milton Nascimento's call to oppose the Brazilian military dictatorship. "Jet Ski" criticizes São Paolo's environmental destruction. "Me Abraça e me Beija (Hug Me and Kiss Me), performed with Jimmy Cliff, and "Vendaval Temporal (Wind Storm)" further acknowledge nature's importance in everyday events. Several dances connect Brazilian culture with Africa: the samba-reggae "Negro Nagô (Black Man)" and the soulful áfoxe "Menina Dandára (A Girl Named Dandára)." Best of all, of course, is Menezes's big voice and easy handling of any musical style.

LINK➤ *Olodom — Revolution in Motion*   *World Circuit (Import)*
Olodom's group percussion inspired the rhythms on Paul Simon's The Rhythm of the Saints *(Warner Brothers 26098). The group's from Bahia, but there's a strong African influence.*

One of the world's most popular singers, Miguel was born in Puerto Rico but grew up in **Mexico**. By age 12, he was already a star. At age 14, in 1982, Miguel toured internationally, singing romantic songs from his first four albums. The same year, he made his movie debut in *Nunca Más* (Never Again) and won a gold record for his interpretations of the soundtrack's music. By 1985, he'd won numerous awards, including a Grammy for his duet with Sheena Easton. A year later, *Soy Como Quiero Ser* (I'm the Way I Want to Be) sold enough copies to win gold records in eight countries and platinum records in five more. The next years brought more awards (from countries as far from Mexico as Korea) and sold-out concerts in major arenas throughout Latin America, the U.S., and Europe. In 1996, Miguel received the ultimate show business milestone: his own star on Hollywood's Walk of Fame.

El Concierto
WEA Latina 11212

Luis Miguel is one of Latin America's biggest pop stars. And this is a huge media event. Giant screaming crowds. Exacting production techniques. A 2-CD set tied into a home video release on videocassette and laserdisc. A highly rated international TV special. But most of all, a seasoned performer. Some songs will be familiar: "No Sé Tú" was heard in the movie *Speechless*. Performances tend to be larger than life, but the set does include an appealing series of Mexican songs with mariachi accompaniment, love songs, danceable pop tunes, and the best of Miguel's repertoire. "El Día Que Me Quieras (The Day You Love Me)," sung against delicate concertina accompaniment, is one of his best.

LINK➤ *Pedro Fernández — Deseos y Delirios*   Mercury 534-120
The title translates, roughly, into "Wishes and Ravings." Greatest hits from the first half of the 1990s, when Fernández became one of Mexico's most popular singers. Unapologetically sentimental love songs, a passionate and amorous voice accompanied by syrupy strings, very traditional (nearly stereotypical) horns, and strummed acoustic guitar.

Aries
WEA Latina 92933

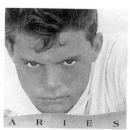

Miguel's ninth album as a performer, but his first as producer. He took the job very seriously and created his best recording. Just about every song is engaging, and the restrained use of a complex, large-scale mix demonstrates fine taste and extraordinary care for every nuance. Long time creative collaborator and guitar player Kiko Cibrian gets co-producer credit. The 1993 album opens with one of Cibrian's catchiest tunes, "Suave (Dream)," a great dance song with a memorable hook (used in Disney's *The Hunchback of Notre Dame*). Tower of Power's horns drive a surging arrangement of "Que Nivel de Mujer." "Tu Y Yo (You and Me)" is a memorable love song.

LINK➤ *Emmanuel — Amor Total*   Mercury 534-063
Emmanuel is another of Mexico's biggest popular music stars. He has been recording since the 1970s. Traditional acoustic music inspires simple, elegant, and very contemporary treatments. "Tarumba" is a fine example of his skill in blending these worlds.

Mauritania is a huge country, mostly desert, in northern Africa. Its history is filled with tales of Bedouin nomads, Berbers fleeing from nearby Morocco, and liberated Arab slaves. France occupied Mauritania for about 50 years until the country declared independence in 1960. Its national anthem was written by Dimi Mint Abba's father, Sidati Well Abba, when she was 2 years old. Her mother taught her to play traditional women's instruments and encouraged her to sing (her mother's name was Abba, and "Mint" means "daughter of," so "Dimi Mint Abba" is Dimi, daughter of Abba). At 16, she sang on Mauritanian radio and soon won one song contest, and then another, larger competition in Tunisia. This led to touring Europe and Northern Africa, fame as the most popular female singer in the Maghreb world, and the leadership of a musical community in her home city (and Mauritania's capital), Nouakchott. Khalifa Ould Eide, her husband, is a well-respected Mauritanian guitar player.

Moorish Music from Mauritania
World Circuit 19

Look for this album under Khalifa Ould Eide and Dimi Mint Abba. Both are among Mauritania's most esteemed musicians. Both come from musical families. Ould Eide plays the tidinit (a rustic lute). Music is created within a rigid structure; then, they improvise. Mint Abba's vocals are often passionate, sometimes ecstatic, but also quiet and pensive. On "Yar Allahoo," accompaniment is provided by tidnit, drum, and tamborine (plus hand claps). When Ould Eide sings, his voice is more studied and less likely to rise up in prayer. In addition to songs of praise and Arab poetry, the two sing about love of country and independence. Their "Oh Lord, Bring Apartheid Crashing Down" contains some superb harmonies.

LINK➤ *Steve Shehan & Baly Othmani — Assarouf*
Worldly (Triloka) 534-757

The Tuareg are Muslim nomads in the Sahara. This music is based on their songs. It's a typically modern (1997) world fusion mix with interesting North African instrumentation and vocals.

Musique & Chants de Mauritanie   Auvidis Ethnic 6768

The title translates into "Music and Songs of Mauritania." Liner notes begin to detail the various modes on which Mauritanian music is based (it's a complex system). "El Belloutou" is a second mode (Vaghou) song Mint Abba wrote for her youngest daughter, the desert's little princess. "Wezene" was composed in the first mode (Karr); it's an instrumental that sounds a bit like a desert jam session. Mint Abba performs in this 1992 album with four others: two percussionists (one on tambourine), Ahmed Ould Abba on tidinit and guitar, and Abba Ould Badous on tidnit. The rough instrumentation is quite beautiful, and the subtle changes in rhythm can be entrancing.

LINK➤ *Various Artists — Desert Blues*   **Network (Stern's) 58.774**
Excellent 2-CD collection of popular and traditional music from northern Africa. In addition to the usual suspects (Ali Farka Toure, Oumou Sangare, Hassan Hakmoun, Youssou N'Dour, etc.), Dimi Mint Abba, Kante Manfila, Mahmoud Ahmed, and others who aren't as "famous" in the U.S. appear. Recommended.

One of the most popular singers in **Brazil**, Monte is among the newer performers in modern popular music. Born in 1967 and just a year old when the Tropicálismo movement began, Monte started taking her voice seriously as a teenager. After high school, she studied in Italy for a year and opted for Brazilian music instead of opera. By age 19, Monte was building a pop music career. Her first album, *Marisa Monte* (World Pacific 91761), was recorded live in 1988; it's an eclectic mix designed to demonstrate her versatility. Monte's second album, 1991's *Mais* (96104), was produced by Arto Lindsay and became a tremendous hit. On that album, she also worked with two members of Titãs, a 1980s rock band notable for chameleon-like changes with each album. All of this set the stage for international renown in the mid-1990s. Fans are encouraged to visit www.marisamonte.com.

Rose and Charcoal
Metro Blue 30080

A wonderful record. On "Maria de Verdade (Mary for Real)," Monte easily shifts from a prayer-like reverie to a romping life-as-carnival melody. The giant hit song "Segue O Seco (The Draught Goes On)" is more guttural, as the raw percussion and crowd noises swell into something akin to a rain dance; it's an unusual work that implies a connection between weather and societal draught. Both were written by Carlinhos Brown, who co-produced. Her writing partner, Nando Reis (from Titãs), contributed "A Meu Redor (All Around Me)," a moody treat for her splendid voice (with a nicely textured arrangement). Reis, Brown, and Monte wrote "Na Estrada (On the Road)," another delight. From 1994.

LINK➤ *Daniela Mercury — Feijão com Arroz*   Sony Latin 82188
Another very popular Brazilian vocalist with a lovely voice, Mercury's orientation is more like pop rock. The carnival song "Rapunzel" is very exciting (it was co-written and co-arranged by Carlinhos Brown). Mercury's unaccompanied vocal solo on "Nobre Vagabundo" is impressive.

A Great Noise   Metro Blue 53353

Carlinhos Brown wrote and co-produced several songs on this 1996 release including "Magamalabares," whose combination of strings and thick percussion provides Monte's special voice with a particularly effective background. Twelve other songs were recorded live during the *Rose and Charcoal* tour in 1994 and 1995. Monte does an especially fine job with the Caetano Veloso–Gilberto Gil song "Panis et Circenses," one of several older Brazilian songs here. The best material is newer; the pop song "Ainda Lembro" shows off Monte's range. Liner notes are decorated with erotic drawings by Carlos Zéfiro, an underground Brazilian artist popular in the 1950s and early 1960s.

LINK➤ *Carlinhos Brown — Alfagamabetizado*   Metro Blue 38269
The 1997 U.S. breakthrough for a percussionist and innovator who's become a leading force in Brazilian music. "Parndeiro-Diero" is samplings and street funk; "Quixabeira" is a pretty duet piece whose acoustic guitar is shut out by thundering percussion. Very eclectic. The future!

Jamaican singer Judy Mowatt was born in 1952 and while in her teens, worked steadily as a member of the Gaylettes (also called the Gaytones), a backup group. When the other two Gaylettes left for the U.S. in 1970, Mowatt started a solo career, but she did not record only under her name. A complicated tangle of contract issues (not uncommon in Jamaica) found her recording under various names for various labels. With singer Dennis Brown and other upcoming Jamaican performers, she joined the Twelve Tribes of Israel, while continuing a solo career. By the mid-1970s, Mowatt was performing regularly with Marcia Griffiths and Rita Marley, a trio that evolved into the I Threes, and became Bob Marley's backup group. Through it all, Mowatt raised a family, became an articulate spokeswoman for Jamaican women, and flourished as a solo singer. After the I Threes, she continued her solo career.

Black Woman   Shanachie 43011

Mowatt wrote most of the songs on and produced this extraordinary 1980 album. It's one of the all-time reggae classics, and with good reason. She starts with "Strength to Go Through," weaving her solo voice through reggae horns, then breaking into the chorus. Her version of Bob Marley's "Concrete Jungle" is dense and dangerous. The song works because she effectively mixes a dark chorus with a slow rhythm, with an ominous organ and electric guitar peering in from around corners. "Joseph," more uplifting and inspirational, is her nearly spiritual tribute to Marley. The mix of instrument sounds is sophisticated throughout, far beyond any familiar formula. Essential.

LINK➤ *Various Artists — By the Rivers of Babylon:*
Timeless Rhythms of Rastafari   *Shanachie 45031*
Surprisingly effective 1997 collection of songs related to Rastafarianism and its beliefs. Mowatt sings "King of Kings." Other superb work includes The Melodians' "The Rivers of Babylon," Ras Michael's "New Name," and Augustus Pablo's "Chant to King Selassie I."

Only a Woman   Shanachie 43007

Mowatt composed almost everything and produced this confident 1988 album. The embracing "You're My People" is a typically upbeat reggae anthem ("we must organize, centralize...we must be unified, civilized...."); good guitar riffs, too. There's a feminist edge through much of this music. Although there have been many songs like "I'm Not Mechanical" and "Only a Woman" (demanding better treatment) in the U.S., Mowatt is

a respected spokeswoman for Jamaicans. "Think" encourages you to "exercise your mind" and to think for yourself. She sings Curtis Mayfield's "You Don't Care" with just the right blend of reggae and R&B; the background voices register the perfect emotion.

LINK➤ *Joe Higgs — Blackman Know Yourself*   *Shanachie 43077*
Higgs influenced just about every reggae singer (and worked with many of them, including Mowatt). He's been singing reggae and R&B since the 1950s. A classic figure, and a 1991 album with endless integrity.

Metqâl Qenâwi is the lead singer of Les Musiciens du Nil, as they're known in **Egypt**. He's called "rais," which means "leader" or "president," because he often represents Egypt on cultural visits to other countries. He's a virtuoso player on the rabâbah (a stringed instrument). Other members sing the traditional songs of northern Egypt and play the Egyptian double clarinet (called the arghûl), tablah, and mizmar. The sounds are quite exotic, and the lyrics are regarded as clever. Much of the credit for the long-term success of the Musicians of the Nile goes to musical director and producer Alain Weber, who has been associated with the group since 1975. That same year, the Musicians of the Nile was introduced to a world audience at the Chateauvallon Festival, where they were seen with Keith Jarrett, Sun Ra, and other notable jazz musicians.

Luxor to Isna   RealWorld (Caroline) 2307

A remarkble introduction to the native instruments of Egypt, circa 1989. "Al Bahr al Gharam Wasah" is a series of solos played on rababah (traditional fiddle) with sharp percussion breaks. "Zahrafat al Sa'id" is all percussion—a demonstration of classical hand-drumming techniques on a tablah (fish skin stretched over a clay pot). Circular breathing (a continuous breathing technique) enables amazingly long notes played on the zumarin (oboes) on "Ya Tir Ala Shadjarah." The most engaging music is made by the arghul, or double-reed clarinet, on an expressive drone, "Kol Elle Qlaboh Ankawa." Several interludes of Egyptian street sounds establish a sense of place.

LINK➤ *Hossam Ramzy — Source of Fire*   ARC Music 1305
Ramzy played on Robert Plant and Jimmy Page's 1994 No Quarter—Unledded album and the subsequent tour. He's one of Egypt's top percussionists, and this 1995 album demonstrates his jazz improvisations on belly dance rhythms.

Charcoal Gypsies   RealWorld (Caroline) 2366

An emphasis on vocals makes this 1996 CD an ideal complement to From Luxor to Isna. Yussef' ali Bakâsh, a new young singer with a huge voice and a gift for sensitive lyricism, energizes the group's sound on "Bitnadini Tani Lih (Why Are You Calling Me Again?)" and "Al-Ward Al-Foll (The Perfume of the Rose)." Group leader Metqâl Qenâwi Metqâl's vocals resonate with character, tradition, and long experience. Shamandi Tewfiq Metqâl sings "Eb'at Djawaben," a love song. As before, the rababah, arghûl, and tabla are key instruments, but they're most often heard as background instruments for male solo and group singing.

LINK➤ *Various Artists — Egypt: Echoes of the Nile*
                                          Multicultural Media 3005
Interesting variety of musical types found along the Nile. This ethnomusicological survey finds Nubian folk songs, modern Arab music, as well as Coptic and Islamic religious music.

Youssou N'Dour

Possessing a voice with remarkable range, N'Dour is a modern griot, a unique social class known for storytelling. Born in Dakar, **Senegal**, in 1959, he first became well known as lead singer in the Star Band de Dakar and later in his own band, Etoile de Dakar, formed in 1977. He combined the sound of Cuban horns with the traditional mbung mbung griot drum rhythm played on guitar, and added various forms of griot singing and chant; he called the sound "mbalax," the griot term for mbung mbung drumming. He spent time in Paris, and bowing to the demand for a more international sound, corrected his course. N'Dour is now one of world music's biggest stars. His music and life are secure, centered in Dakar, where he records in his own modern studio and enjoys family life with three children. His work with Paul Simon and Peter Gabriel helped to make him an international star.

Immigrés
Melodie 66709

Very much a classic, and somewhat hard to find. Smooth, a tad gritty, and full of energy. The blend of instrument sounds, rhythms, and message songs sets N'Dour apart as a modern storyteller and visionary music maker. His voice combines power with thoughtful persuasion. Le Super Etoile de Dakar is an unusual band; its horn arrangements come from Cuba, and both the guitars and drums carry out the mbalax rhythms rooted in griot tradition. Jimmy Mbaye's guitar solos ring out, most often to punctuate the meaning in N'Dour's lyrics. N'Dour wrote the title song, "Immigrés," imploring Senegal's immigrants to Paris to bring their social status and smarts back home.

LINK➤ *Etoile de Dakar — Volume 2: Thiapathioly*   Stern's Africa 3006
1980 studio recordings by N'Dour's group. The title song was a huge hit. Volume 1: Absa Gueye (3004) was recorded live at a club in 1979. More studio recordings on Volume 3: Lay Suma Lay (3012). N'Dour is one lead singer; the other is El Hadji Faye. Just adequate sound.

Nelson Mandela
Polydor 831-294

Listen carefully to "Donkaasi Gi"—the repeating drum pattern emerges. Akin to reggae with different beats accented, it's catchy. The cascading rhythm is called mbalax (the word means "rhythmic accompaniment"). The words are in Wolof, the language of N'Dour's people. While printed (and translated) lyrics would have been helpful, the passion in N'Dour's voice needs no translation on "Nelson Mandela." A reworking of the Spinners' hit "Rubberband Man" is easier to understand; gritty background vocals (in English), interesting percussion, and N'Dour's Wolof vocals aren't as slick as the American sound, but that's just the point. Recorded in 1985.

LINK➤ *Yandé Codou Sène — Night Sky in Sine Saloum*
Shanachie 64085

A mid-1990s tour with N'Dour brought this legendary griotte (praise singer) to listeners outside Senegal. This is traditional Senegalese music sung to the accompaniment of xalam (guitar), kora, riti (violin), and several dominant percussion instruments. Sine Saloum is her home village.

Set
Virgin 91426

His best work. "Set (Clean)" became a youth anthem. N'Dour's band, the Super Etoile de Dakar, is a talented outfit of a dozen musicians. The elegant dance "Sabar" showcases guitar player Jimi Mbaye and Assane Thiam, who plays the tama (Senegalese talking drum). Mbaye's guitar perfectly captures the dripping poison in "Toxiques," N'Dour's attack on rich countries that pay poor ones to store toxic waste. "Sinebar" cooks with big horns and drums. "Medina" mellows with soft keyboards and calming percussion. A wonderful record, but it might be hard to find. (Don't bother with his first Virgin album, *The Lion*, which strives for commercial success and sacrifices its soul along the way.)

LINK➤ *Pierre Akendengué — Passé Composé* Melodie (Stern's) 493402
A real find. Gabon's Akendengué is one of West Africa's most creative musicians. This 1970s–80s compilation drifts from acoustic folk to traditional dance.

Eyes Open
Columbia 48714

Expertly recorded in Paris in 1990, N'Dour's mbalax rhythm drives a smart collection of songs about fascination with TV (CNN, MTV, BBC, etc.), parenting in the modern world, money spent on weapons while people continue to starve, and other contemporary issues. "New Africa" instructs Africans to work together, to ignore borders, and to take responsibility for their countries and their lives. "Marie-Madeleine Saint-Louisienne" evokes the spirit of a fashionable, elegant woman who holds her head high in Senegalese society despite "polygamy's complications and tyrannical husbands." The pace is generally relaxed with fine vocals and careful choruses, and a spectacular complex of tiny sounds in a skillful mix.

LINK➤ *Sékouba Bambino Diabaté — Le Destin*
Out of Africa (World Circuit) 202
From nearby Guinea, the second album by a very popular singer (this album sold hundreds of thousands of copies). Former lead singer for Bembeya Jazz; performed with traditional instruments and a female chorus.

The Guide (Wommat)
Chaos 53828

N'Dour and the Super Etoile have come a very long way. This sophisticated music is still anchored by mbalax rhythm, but the instrumentation and mix are so much more elaborate and so tastefully produced that these tracks only vaguely resemble work done from a few years earlier. Branford Marsalis contributes a sad and lovely saxophone solo to N'Dour's yearning vocal on "Without a Smile," lamenting once-lush land that's now dry and leafless. "Tourista" salutes Senegalese hospitality and its promise for the tourist trade. On "How You Are," N'Dour sings about responsibilities attached to national independence. The album ends with Bob Dylan's "Chimes of Freedom," sung in Wolof with powerful mbalax drumming.

LINK➤ *Cheikh Lô — Ne La Thiass* **World Circuit 46**
N'Dour not only produced this 1996 album, but also provided half the band and sings a handsome duet with the singer-songwriter. Arrangements are light and jazzy; Lô's soulful vocals are easy to enjoy. A more relaxed take on N'Dour's mbalax dance rhythm.

Nakai's Native American flute has been popular with his own people and with world music and new age audiences. His heritage is **Navajo-Ute**. Nakai was born in Flagstaff, Arizona, in 1946 and as a teenager, became interested in the history and culture of his tribe and other North American tribes. He came to the flute after studying classical trumpet at North Arizona University, making it his principal instrument in 1973. Serious studies of the Plains and Woodlands Indians followed, providing a base for Nakai's improvisations. By 1983, he was recording regularly, sometimes adding synthesizer or other instruments to magnify the impact of his music. He has also worked with jazz ensembles, and his work has inspired "Night Chant," a ballet performed by the Martha Graham Dance Company throughout the U.S., Canada, South America, and Europe. Nakai also plays harp, guitar, and several instruments of his own invention.

Earth Spirit
Canyon 612

Fifteen evocative songs performed with nobility and grace by an American artist. Mostly, Nakai creates his music on a handcrafted siyótanka (Lakota for this particular Native American flute). It covers roughly the clarinet's range, but the material is red cedar hardwood, providing added resonance and a sound closer to nature. Inspiration comes from many sources: "Shaman's Call" emulates the call of a soaring eagle; "Song of the Evening Star" is a traditional Kiowa song; "Nemi" ponders the stone grooves in Monument Valley; and "Gateway" reflects on Nakai's presence in St. Louis at 9:20 a.m. on May 3, 1986. Several birdlike songs are performed on a sacred eagle's bone whistle. From 1987.

LINK➤ *Kevin Locke — Open Circle*
Earthbeat! 42538

Very New Age combination of acoustic instruments and natural sounds (it opens with room-filling ocean waves). In addition to flute from the northern Plains, berimbau (Brazilian single-stringed harp), didgeridoo, and several African drums. Good engineering.

Canyon Trilogy
Canyon 610

Although some Nakai albums add jazz or classical instruments, his best work is generally done alone. This gentle watercolor was again recorded on Native American flute, but modern electronics also played a role. Nakai composed a series of three musings on places where the Anasazi and Sinagua people lived. To simulate a canyon's ambience, Nakai ran his flute recording through a Roland SDE 3000 Digital Delay unit. To enhance the mythic story, he also multitracked the flute. The effect is particularly striking on "Canyon People" and "World of Rainbows," but the entire trilogy is coherent and inspiring. Released in 1989.

LINK➤ *John Huling — Desert Places*
Novox Music 1005

A recording of Native American instrumental and environmental sounds, some recorded among the Anasazi ruins in the Southwest.

Unlike many performers who have become internationally famous, Nascimento has remained very close to home in **Brazil**. Born in Rio de Janiero in 1942, he was raised in Minas Gerais, the large Brazilian state north of Rio, and this has always been his home. Nascimento brought together mineiro folk music (from Minas Gerais), jazz, bossa nova, and American sounds, and became famous as a songwriter and singer in the mid-1960s. He started recording in 1967, and became known to the American jazz community for collaborations with Pat Metheny, Herbie Hancock, and particularly Wayne Shorter, with whom he created the Native Dancer album. Nascimento can be heard with other Brazilian performers on

Paul Simon's *Rhythm of the Saints* album. Often political, critical, and outspoken on environmental issues, Nascimento's original work is the most satisfying. His distinctive tenor voice and under-the-skin falsetto make him unique and special

Sentinela   Verve 813-357

Some of Nascimento's magnetic power and connection with the supernatural world comes from his interest in Brazilian folk culture. Part of "Sentinela (Sentinel)" begins with a prayer for the dead: Nana Caymmi's celestial voice sweeps in, a perfect contrast with Nascimento's deeper attempt to meet life head-on. The richness of Mercedes Sosa's experienced voice transforms "Sueño con Serpientes (Dream with Serpents)" into a transcendent work of art. The percussion is provided by a low-toned native flute. "Canção da América (Song for America)" is sung as an anthem with the help of the vocal group Boca Libre. Recorded in 1980, this album is one of Nascimento's best.

**LINK➤ *Nana Caymmi — Nunca Mais*   *Planet 6008*
Intriguing album from one of Brazil's most talented voices.

Missas Dos Quilombos   Verve 513-034

The title of this impressive work from 1980 translates as "Mass of the Runaway Slave Colonies." Based on a text prepared by activist Dom Pedro Casaldáliga, it is structured as an Easter Mass, a story of death and resurrection. Here, the hero is Zumbi, the leader of a runaway slave colony in Brazil's northeast. The sequence of events that began this creative endeavor occurred in the Recife, the Brazil square where Zumbi was beheaded. Far more than a folk Mass, this is a large-scale musical celebration with full chorus, and both rock and traditional instruments. The album is a full-blooded expression of the sacred and honorable.

**LINK➤ *Wynton Marsalis — Blood on the Fields*   *Columbia 57694*
Not a Mass, but the story of U.S. slavery from its beginnings in Africa through social imprisonment after emancipation. Told through jazz, blues, R&B, gospel, and other U.S. forms. With Cassandra Wilson.

Anima
Verve 813296

While seeking out 1973's *Geraes* (released by EMI Brazil) and 1976's *Milton* (released in the U.S. by A&M and now out-of-print), start with this 1982 release. "Evocacão das Montanhas (Evocation of the Mountains)" is an ethereal cross between Delius and new age music. "Tiea de Renda (Lace Web)" is more typical, an easy tempo punctuated by guitar and keyboard with fluegelhorn breaks. Arrangements are artful, but not always optimistic. "Olha (Look)" slashes critics who make life difficult for Brazilian artists. At this stage, Nascimento was at his best on poetic songs like "Filho (Son)" with balmy accompaniment and his easy maneuvering from a tenor to a falsetto singing voice.

LINK➤ *Various Artists — Brazil Classics 1*   *Luaka Bop 25805*
Snappy modern collection of Brazilian music places Nascimento in context with stunning performances by Chico Buaraque, Jorge Ben, Caetano Veloso, and Gilberto Gil.

Yauaretê
Columbia 44277

Paul Simon joins Nascimento for a very sweet solo on "O Vendedor De Sonhos (Dream Merchant)," with a wisp of a melody and the sort of mood that Nascimento so expertly sets (this time with the help of Herbie Hancock on keyboards). The title cut, which translates into "Jaguar," has more instrumental bite and lyrics linking man to beast ("needing to war, to struggle, to slay, to be able to survive"). Nascimento is cautiously optimistic about Brazil's future in "Carta À República (Letter to the Republic)," and returns to mythic imagery for "Mountain," performed with a Hancock piano solo, Don Grusin on keyboards, and Eric Gale on electric guitar.

LINK➤ *Tony Mola — Bragadá*   *Blue Jackel 5006*
"Pega Pega" and "Vem Benzinho" are among the hits on this popular 1996 Brazilian album. Mola and his band, called Bragadá, effectively mix more traditional Brazilian rhythms with hot mixes of hip-hop and dance music.

Angelus
Warner Brothers 45499

Nascimento's influence on jazz composers and performers has been significant. Ron Carter, Jack DeJohnette, Herbie Hancock, and Pat Metheny provide a soft, tropical fusion bed for Nascimento's vocal on "Vera Cruz." Wayner Shorter's tenor sax easily fits into Nascimento's music, adding spice and a well-integrated jazz feeling; he's the guest on "De Um Modo Geral...(Generally Speaking)" as it shuttles between jazz-rock fusion and a balmier Brazilian style. James Taylor wrote the music for "Only a Dream in Rio," a slow folk-rock duet. Nana Vasconcelos, Peter Gabriel, and Jon Anderson (from Yes) are among other guests. Generally pleasing, there are times when Nascimento gets overcooked, as on the Beatles' "Hello Goodbye."

LINK➤ *Wayne Shorter — Native Dancer*   *Columbia 46159*
1974 jazz album with Nascimento on vocals. Updates the older Getz/Gilberto formula with greater abstraction, sharper intonations, more of a fusion mix. Most people either love it or hate it.

Ebenezer Obey

One of **Nigeria**'s biggest stars and the country's best-selling juju artist, Obey has recorded more than 50 albums. Twenty of these albums have gone gold, and several have gone platinum, a remarkable achievement in any country. Obey was born in a small town in western Nigeria in 1942 and started his own band before he was a teenager. He moved to the big city of Lagos in 1963 and started updating the juju dance music that been played since the 1930s. Obey added drums from the music of the Yoruba people, and the high-life guitar that was heard in Ghana. He brought in electric guitars, bass guitars, and more talking drums. Some of his music has been recorded with very large ensembles. Most of his work is available only in Nigeria, but several Obey albums were released in the U.S. in the 1980s.

Juju Jubilee   Shanachie 43031

Simon Adeleke's talking drums establish the beat. Guitars play staccato. Obey sings, and the chorus answers. Everything grooves along slowly. Sometimes, Obey's guitar sounds Hawaiian or like Dick Dale's surf music. The breezy "Awa Ewe Iwoyi" differs in style, rhythm, and approach from the intricate guitar riffs and mica-like fraility of percussion heard on "Ko Easy Lati Je Omo Okunrin." Dance to the music, but listen carefully to the clever use of the recording studio's mixing board and the ease with which the guitar players adapt various Western styles for their own use. It's Juju as art form. From 1988.

LINK➤ *Ebenezer Obey — Je Ka Jo*   *Virgin – UK (Import)*
His first album intended for international release, from 1984. Not generally available in the U.S., but well worth the higher price for an import. Put this CD on the shopping list if you visit England (or know somebody who is planning a trip there).

Get Yer Jujus Out   Rykodisc 20111

Keep your eyes open for *Solution* (LP only), or *Je Ka Jo*. Short of that, this 1989 Juju workout is a good choice. "Ose Olorum Oba" keeps its intensity constant but with a low flame: the drums keep the energy flowing, the vocalists are slow and dreamy, and the electric guitar hits just right. Sadly, the sound is just distant enough to zap some of what should have been blistering guitar riffs on "Sis Ba Millionaire Lo." Good drumming on just about every song, particularly through "Koseni Tomo Ojo Ola." Mostly, this is a drum record.

LINK➤ *Sir Shina Peters — Shinamania*   *Flame Tree (Stern's) 501*
The next generation of Juju, with a more modern sound and even more emphasis on percussion. Like Obey, Peters is from Nigeria.

At first, Okosuns thought he'd be an actor. He spent a year with the Eastern **Nigeria** Theatre, but by 1964, at age 17, Okosuns joined the Postmen, singing Western rock songs and becoming famous. The band lasted until 1967 (a civil war contributed to the breakup). Okosuns experimented with reggae. He toured West Africa and Japan for two years with the Melody Maestros, then formed Paperback Unlimited, a progressive rock group, in 1971. While continuing to blend Western rock with Nigerian high-life and other dance music, he re-named his music Ozidizm (for an African river god), and his band Ozzidi. The band was very popular, but by the early 1980s, Okosuns moved on to Afro-Carnival, a fusion style combining funk, Western rock, and traditional Nigerian music. Despite extensive touring, Okosuns never became a big worldwide star. Today, he concentrates only on Africa, where he has always been successful.

Liberation Shanachie 43019

Okosuns is a glib, passionate singer who often performs in English. His production style tends toward the slick, and his writing toward memorable hooks. At his best, Okosuns is a perfectionist producer of the highest order. On "Highlife," horns establish the melody line, which is then repeated by an organ. Okosuns recaps the melody and leads into the chorus, which is restated by the female vocalists. It's a textbook hit radio arrangement, and Okosuns almost always gets it right. But not every song is so carefully tailored. "Amen" and "Liberation" are rougher, more like the music of other African bands. From 1984.

LINK▶ *Various Artists — Black Star Liner: Reggae from Africa*
Heartbeat (Rounder) 16

Contains Okosuns's hit song "Fire in Soweto," along with work by some performers who are not well known in the U.S.: Cloud 7, Bongos Ikwue, Victor Uwaifo, and others.

African Soldiers Profile 1414

One of the best African reggae records, circa 1991. The title cut, "African Soldiers," salutes freedom fighters against a powerful reggae beat. Okosuns's production instincts are again impeccable. The song gains impact through structure. There is a perfect horn section in the middle of the song. "King of Kings" is a simple reggae song about Jesus. It comes to life because of Okosuns's ability to write memorable hooks. "Babylon" begins with a female chorus (similar to the I-Threes), then Okosuns pleads, "Africa should be one nation" and "my country should be one people." These are familiar reggae unity themes delivered by a master. With songs like these, why isn't Okosuns world famous?

LINK▶ *Various Artists —*
Fly African Eagle: The Best Of African Reggae Shanachie 45033
As a rule, Shanachie's world music collections are excellent. This one, with Alpha Blondy, Okosuns, and others, is no exception.

Babatunde Olatunji

Percussion virtuoso Olatunji was born in **Nigeria**, but he has mainly worked in the U.S. In the 1950s, he attended Morehouse College, an all-black university in Atlanta, then New York University's graduate School. At Morehouse, Olatunji played for fun, but by the late 1950s, growing interest in world music encouraged him to pursue a professional career. He recorded one of the first world beat albums in 1959 for Columbia Records. Based in Harlem, he founded a school for African culture (dance, crafts, arts, and drumming) and became something of an institution himself, often representing Africa at cultural gatherings. Through the 1960s, Olatunji appeared on highbrow TV shows like the *Bell Telephone Hour*, and as spice for *The Tonight Show* and *The Mike Douglas Show*. He has also written music for Broadway and scored films (including some work on Spike Lee's *She's Gotta Have It*). In the late 1980s, Olatunji worked with the Grateful Dead's Mickey Hart on several world music projects.

Drums of Passion   Columbia 8210

An essential African drumming record, first released in 1959. It's easy to understand why this album sold so well and why it affected U.S. jazz musicians so deeply. Four drummers and nine choral singers (mostly female) are thrilling on "Shango (Chant to the God of Thunder)." "Oya (Primitive Fire)" follows the life cycle of a fire from kindling, to blaze, to burnout, with group drumming and choral chanting. "Akiwow (Chant to the Trainman)" adopts a freight train's rhythm and salutes a famous conductor. "Kiyakika (Why Do You Run Away?)" ponders the importance of friendship in a world that moves too fast.

LINK➤ *Various Artists —*
Gathering of Champions: The Winner's Circle   *SOAR 171*
The North American drumming tradition lives through 1992-94 Pow Wow winners. Includes Assiniboine, Jr., Whitefish Bay, Whitefish Jr.

Drums of Passion: The Beat   Rykodisc 10107

One of two 1986 sessions produced by Mickey Hart of the Grateful Dead, with Olatunji and Brazilian percussionist Airto Moreira. Neither captures the depth of the bass or the raw energy of Olatunji's 1959 release. There's more emphasis on vocals. Carlos Santana plays lead guitar in spots, and there is a greater rhythmic complexity, as well as other miscellaneous sounds mixed in. "The Beat of My Drum" includes a terrific sequence with multiple drums, and a revised "Akiwowo (Chant to the Trainman)" begins with clear a capella lyrics, then dives in with railroad rhythms. The other CD, *Drums of Passion: The Invocation* (10102), bears a strong similarity to *The Lion King* soundtrack.

LINK➤ *Various Artists — The Big Bang*   *Ellipsis Arts 3402/3403/3404*
A 3-CD percussion celebration with many surprises. Best: water drums from the Baka forest, Carlos Patato Valdés on congas, and the Orchestra of Chinese Central Music College with a full-scale symphonic recording with gongs and cymbals. Also rock, jazz drumming. The best drum collection available.

Ongala was born into a musical family in the eastern Belgian Congo in 1947 (now the Democratic Republic of Congo). As a teenager, he played the drums and sang for Bantu Success, a local band. He dropped out, learned guitar, and worked with a succession of other local bands. At age 30, Ongala moved to the big **Tanzanian** city of Dar Es Salaam to join Orchestra Makassy (his uncle's band). When Makassay moved to Kenya, Ongala remained in Dar Es Salaam, joined and subsequently led Orchestra Matimila (now called Super Matimila). The sound is big band with horns and guitars, and the music is "ubongo," a Swahili word for "music of the brain." Ongala takes on causes with his lyrics, both political and social, and his works are often lengthy explorations of these themes. Considerable touring with WOMAD shows has created some conflict; WOMAD books Ongala as traditionally Zairean soukous, but Ongala is more complex and much more outspoken.

Songs for the Poor Man   RealWorld (Caroline) 2305

Ogala's soukous is often slower and far more serious than its Congolese counterpart. The same components are present: a ringing electric guitar, a relentless beat, and a male solo singer. Not to say that this music doesn't cook—the electric guitars and drums really mix it up in the middle of "Nasikitika." The song, however, is about such African complaints as hypocrisy, suffering, and lack of respect. Depth and style are strong suits, as in "Sauit Ya Mnyonge (The Voice of the Underdog)," and on the bluesy love song, "Mariam Wango (My Own Mariam)." Ongala's intellectual curiosity keeps this music fresh. "Muziki Asili Yake Wapi" is an exploration of music's role in Tanzania. From 1990.

LINK➤ *Kanda Bongo Man — Kwaasa Kwaasa* Hannibal (Rykodisc) 1343
This 1988 album captures Kanda Bongo Man at the height of his popularity in Paris's soukous scene. It's dance music that flows easily, but lacks the ultimate staying power of Ongala's more complex approach to a similar form.

Mambo   RealWorld (Caroline) 92129

This album is even better! In Swahili, "mambo" means "concerns" or "observations." Ongala is one of Tanzania's more eloquent spokespeople, and he uses that role effectively. One of his big hits (not included here) was "Mambo Kwa Socks (Things with Socks)" promoting condoms to prevent AIDS. Ongala answers his critics on this album with "What Can I Say." The lyrics: "People fear my face, but my soul is clean." Tanzania's new capital city is celebrated with hope in "Dodoma," and although he's quick to criticize, Ongala also compliments. "Mrema" is a song praising the government agency of the same name that catches thieves and prevents animal poaching. Some lyrics are sung in English. Passionate for all the right reasons (and danceable, too).

LINK➤ *Hukwe Zawose — Chibite*   RealWorld (Caroline) 2358
Magical music from one of Tanzania's mythical figures. To the subtle ringing of the ilimba (thumb piano), Zawose sings music for the spirit. His voice is engaging, and the rhythms are mesmerizing. Truly delightful.

One of **Cuba**'s all-time favorite bands, Orquesta Aragon was formed in 1939 by Orestes Aragón, a carpenter who played contrabass in the southern city of Cienfuegos. The band found work in social clubs and union parties and, for promotional purposes, its members played free for a nearby radio station. Rafael Lay, the 14-year-old son of a tobacco worker, took lessons from the band's leader, and in 1941 joined the band as a violinist. Lay took over when Aragon retired in 1949. By 1955 Orquesta Aragon moved to Havana and became famous for playing the chachacha. The 1960s and 1970s brought international tours. Lay died in a car crash in 1982, and his son took over. In fact, the band is very much a family affair, with sons and nephews of original members playing today. Look for 1988's *50 Años de Oro* (50 Golden Years) on Cuba's Egrem label. (It's not available in the U.S.)

That Cuban Cha-Cha-Cha RCA 2446

Recorded in Havana in 1955 and 1956, this album reveals considerable sophistication beyond the chachacha. With its Spanish-style violin arrangement, "Silenco" is nearly a danzón, a formal Cuban dance performed mainly by violins and flute, with a smooth, relaxed male vocal chorus (members of the band). "Sabrosona" is a more stereotypical chacha dance: rhythmic singing set to flowing percussion, brief melody segments performed on flute, and male voices punctuated by a cowbell. "No Me Molesto" is one of many songs here that follow a similar format, but this music is always distinctive. Egües's flute arrangements are a big reason why; Rafael Lay's skill in orchestrating violins is another.

LINK➤ *Various Artists — Cuban Gold 3: The 60s: ¡El Mambo Me Priva!*
Qbadisc 9024

Interesting survey includes Estrellas de Chocolate (whose electric guitars and horns forecast salsa), Orquesta Ideal with a danzón, and other fine performances by top bands.

The Heart of Havana RCA 3204

"La Gloria Eres Tú" is arranged with the lightest touch. It opens with Richard Egües's flute over a bed of violins and a piano's rhythm. Then, the ballad (or bolero) takes shape with Pepe Olmo's warm, romantic voice. The mid-tempo "No Te Vuelvas Loco" is again led with Egües's flute, but this time, violin and piano are dominated by percussion and bandmembers' rhythmic singing. The rhythm pattern becomes familiar as a chachacha, broken by drum rolls as progressive choruses roll in. "La Cantina" also combines Egües's flute with the timbales, congos, and guero (a gourd with notches, stroked with a stick) associated with chachacha. Recorded 1956-57 and still a classic.

LINK➤ *Afro-Cuban All-Stars* *World Circuit 47*

One of several extraordinary 1997 releases that brought together classic Cuban musicians from various eras, notably singer Ibrahím Ferrer and 78-year-old pianist Rubén González. (Introducing...Rubén González [World Circuit 49] is also superb.)

When Oryema was a child in Kampala, the capital city of **Uganda**, the country was a relatively quiet British protectorate. (Oryema was born in 1953; Uganda became a republic within the Commonwealth in 1962.) His father was a government minister, and the family was comfortable. Oryema would sit by his father's side and listen to him play the nanga (seven-string harp). Later, as a teenager, he absorbed the Western music he heard from schoolmates. In 1977, during Idi Amin's Reign of Terror, Oryema's father was assassinated. Oryema escaped by traveling to nearby Kenya in the trunk of a car. Already a working musician in Africa, he eventually moved to Paris, where he currently lives and works. Although his music is modern, the foundation of his work is the folklore he learned as a child. He continues to sing in Swahili and Acoli, his native language.

Beat the Border
RealWorld (Caroline) 2333

Oryema's approach is ambient: lush vocals combine with synthesizers to create a room-filling atmosphere. His vocals, often in English, are poetic and sung with a moody ease. This dreamy music drifts into a rhythmic pattern with African percussion. That's the structure of "The River," but it's typical of many of the songs on this 1993 album. An acoustic guitar and light rainy-day effects keep the accompaniment appropriately simple on "Lapwony (Teacher)." It's about an unhappy man struck down by lightning during a torrential rain; his washed-out farewell letter is printed in the liner notes. "Umoja" has a typical pop tune structure: verse, chorus, guitar break, and so on. The melody is pretty, too.

LINK▶ *Various Artists — Ngoma*   **Music of the World 142**
Research into Uganda's varied musical heritage results in a pleasant, interesting, well-annotated hour of music. The Ngoma Project uses the latest technology to capture Uganda's fine and performing arts.

Night to Night   RealWorld (Caroline) 2357
This 1996 pop album was a big international hit. "Sardinia Memories (After Hours)" is a café memoir, sung to a melancholy accordion. (The Sardinia is an after-hours bar in Kampala, Uganda's capital city.) Oryema's choirboy voice comes alive in "Medieval Dream." The cut features a synthesized drum overtaking a haunting chime, and Oreyema's multitracked voice floating above techno-strings. "Miracle Man" is a song with a style reminiscent of Paul McCartney; unfortunately, it's performed with an intensity that gets lost amid fancy production and a busybody chorus. "Gari Moshi (Steam Train)" feels like a railroad blues—it's got the beat, the R&B chorus, and the guitar riffs.

LINK▶ *Geoffrey Oryema — Exile*   *RealWorld (Caroline) 2313*
All three of Oryema's albums are worth owning. This 1990 release includes songs about a neighborhood terrorist, the pain of leaving a motherland, and a call for peace in Uganda. Fine work.

A central figure in NYC's **salsa** scene, Johnny Pacheco was the co-founder of one of the most successful Latin record labels, Fania (with partner Gerald Masucci, an attorney). Pacheco was born in Santiago de los Caballeros, Dominican Republic, and moved to NYC as a teenager. In short order, he became a serious musician who could play the flute, saxophone, and percussion. He was hired by Charlie Palmieri, who would soon become famous for charanga music (Latin music played with flutes and violins). By 1959, Pacheco had his own band, and by 1961, he was one of the most influential Latin musicians. His strong suit was aggressive dance music, which he called "Pachanga." He rode that wave until 1964, when he formed Fania. The label became the central focus for salsa, a hot Latin dance music that dominated the scene for a decade.

Los Compadres   Fania 400

Typical of Pacheco's playful perspective, the band offers small pieces of candy to the old folks on the dance floor; they gobble up the candy and get the energy to dance to "Dolce Con Dolce (Sweet and Sweeter)." "Baldemira" was written for a woman who danced in front of the stage. "Soy El Mejor (I Am the Best)" salutes the Spanish Harlem music scene and mentions the names of many club owners, dancers, and friends. It's all salsa (sauce), the umbrella term Pacheco created to include not only his musicians from varied backgrounds, but also the range of NYC-influenced Cuban music recorded by Fania. The vocalist is Pete (El Conde) Rodriguez. From 1967.

LINK➤ *Orchestra Harlow — Tribute to Arsenio Rodriguez*   *Fania 404*
Rodriguez was a hero to lovers of Afro-Cuban music. The album begins with an original homage written by Harlow and vocalist Ismael Miranda, but the albums' heart is four songs composed by Rodriguez: "Tumba & Bongo," "No Me Llores," "Sueltala," and "El Terror."

La Perfecta Combinacion   Fania 380

Pacheco's philosophy is simple and effective: have fun, hire the best sonores (singers), and play music that makes people want to dance. That formula works to perfection on this album (released in 1968). Pacheco also had the right partner in Pete Rodriguez. Rodriguez is a romantic crooner on "Blanca," a bolero with horn accents that melt the heart. "Baila Vincente" is a 1950s tune previously played by Sonora Mantancena. Vincente, as the story goes, is the best dancer around. The chorus encourages him to dance up a storm. "Sonero" heats up with a great lead vocal, but also with a fine guitar spot and superb work on the congas.

LINK➤ *Celia Cruz & Johnny Pacheco — Eternos*   *Vaya 80*
The second of two albums recorded by two of salsa's most popular performers, from 1978. Try also Celia and Johnny *(Vaya 31) from several years earlier. Very exciting music!*

Pacheco the Artist
Fania 503

It's 1977. Trumpeters Hector Zarzuela and Luis "Perico" Ortiz are more clearly recorded. The vocalist is Hector Casanova. There are lots of hit songs on this album (as there are on most Pacheco albums of this era). "Esa Prieta (That Dark-Skinned Woman)," is one of many salsa songs whose Caribbean origins remain vague. (The composer is listed as "D.R." This stands for "derecho/reservado," or "rights reserved, author unknown.") "La Chiva" (also D.R.) is about an extremely well-educated

goat; Casanova's big voice plays it straight, but the chorus and some of the instrumentation are tongue-in-cheek. "El Inventor," also a favorite, is about a braggart who claims to have invented ice, snow, cigars, even black beans!

LINK➤ Johnny Pacheco — Champ   *Musica Latina 581*
Good collection with songs performed with Casanova, Pete "El Conde" Rodriguez, Wilfrido Vargas, and Luis "Melon" Silva. Nice introduction to varied styles of salsa's 1970s singers.

Los Amigos
Fania 540

More great music from Pacheco with Hector Casanova. The fun begins with "Los Pollos No Tienen Dientes (Chicken Have No Teeth)." Amid salsa rhythm, horns, and chorus, Casanova tells the story of a husband whose woman explains the odd little love bites on her body by claiming she was bitten by a chicken. Tata Guerra wrote that song, as well as "Si La Tierra Tiembla (If the Earth Shakes)," which is about a man terrified of earthquakes. Pacheco wrote the rather involved story of a man whose wallet is stolen, which means that his green card is gone and he'll probably be deported: "Me Llevan La Cartera (Someone Stole My Wallet)."

LINK➤ Cachao — The Master Sessions   *Crescent Moon (Epic)*
Actor Andy Garcia helped make this project happen (he also sings a bit): a great Cuban composer and bandleader finally gets his due. Two volumes recorded with top musicians in 1992.

The Champ
Musica Latina International 581

This album is a collection of Pacheco's work from the late 1970s, an especially productive period. "Si La Tierra Tiembla" and "Me Llevaron La Cartera" are here; so is "Esa Prieta." The dance hit "Guaguanco Pa'l Que Sabe" has a self-referential title: it's a song for those in the know about the magic of the guaguaco rhythm. "Primoroso Cantar" celebrates the great feeling of singing and enjoying salsa. It's a good-time tune sung by Pete Rodriguez with an excellent piano solo by Bapo Lucca, plenty of open space for Johnny Rodriguez on conga and Luis Mangual on bongos, and most of all, for trumpeters Zarazuela and Ortiz. Released in 1980. Highly recommended.

LINK➤ Various Artists — Cumbia Cumbia   *World Circuit (Rounder) 16*
In Colombia, salsa is called cumbia. Rudolfo y Su Tipica's "La Colegia" was a big international hit, but all of these this is high-grade, danceable, and very entertaining. Also try Cumbia Cumbia 2 (World Circuit 33).

Pahinui Brothers

Gabby Pahinui (1921–80) is generally recognized as the father of modern slack key guitar. (See Keola Beamer's biography in this book for the history of **Hawaiian** slack key guitar.) At a time when interest in the style waned, Pahinui kept it alive and developed new techniques. He also transformed an instrument previously used for accompaniment into a solo instrument for creative interpretation of traditional Hawaiian music. It's worth searching Hawaiian record stores (and related Web sites) for records made by Pahinui in the 1950s, 1960s, and 1970s (mostly released on the Panini and Waikiki labels). The 1970s band (in various configurations) included Atta Isaacs, Sonny Chillingworth, and Pahinui's sons Philip, James ("Bla"), Cyril, and Martin (who also worked as the Pahinui Brothers, and in other groups, including the Sunday Manoa).

Pahinui Brothers
Private Music 82098

Cyril Pahinui plays 6- and 12-string slack key guitar, brother James ("Bla") is on rhythm guitar, and Martin Pahinui is the bassist. They're joined by world music adventurers Ry Cooder and David Lindley on various guitars and ukeleles; some tracks also feature session drummer Jim Keltner and keyboard player Van Dyke Parks. When things come together, as they do on "Isa Lei," it's easy to delight in the combination of guitar sounds as they sting, glide, glisten, and breeze alongside vocals that seem to combine Hawaiian pop with folk-rock. "Mele of My Tute E" is pure pop with Hawaiian stylings. Fabulous guitar playing throughout.

LINK➤ *Sol Hoopii — Master of the Hawaiian Guitar, Vol. 1* Rounder 1024
A Hawaiian music craze began in the mid-1920s, and because Hoopii was the best steel guitar player around, he became well known. He appeared in movies, played nightclubs, and made lots of records. Vol. 1 contains jazzy interpretations of "I Ain't Got Nobody" and other songs from the late 1920s. Vol. 2 (Rounder 1025) continues the story through 1951.

Cyril Pahinui — 6 & 12 String Slack Key
Dancing Cat (Windham Hill) 38010

This 1994 solo album by Cyril Pahinui is one of the best in Dancing Cat's Hawaiian Slack Key Guitar Masters Series. Pahinui's approach to slack key emphasizes the music's rhythms, and depends less upon decorative nuances and more upon solid, straightforward guitar playing. "Young Street Blues" represents him well: it's an original melody laden with imaginative flights of improvisation, all within a sturdy rhythmic structure. Many of the tracks are instrumentals, but Pahinui does sing some songs. "Ipo Lei Manu" is a love song previously recorded by his father; the song is dominated by guitar, with some brief vocal breaks. Pahinui's voice is generally a pleasant high tenor that sometimes stretches into a falsetto.

LINK➤ *Sonny Chillingworth — Sonny Solo*   *Dancing Cat 38005*
Chillingworth has been recording since the 1950s, but this is the first time he's been recorded solo. Confident and refined guitar playing. When he sings (not often), his voice is deeply romantic.

Palmieri is another of the many spectacular **Latin** artists who have somehow eluded mainstream audiences. Nominated for endless Grammy awards, his CDs are hard to find (sometimes, they're filed in jazz, and sometimes, they're in Latin pop), but the search is worth the time and trouble. Palmieri was born in NYC in 1936, and after a false start as a vocalist, he became a pianist (like his older brother Charlie, who led a series of successful bands). His style combined bebop and the unconventional rhythms of free jazz. Palmieri worked with several NYC Latin orchestras, eventually creating an unusual, acclaimed two-trombone front line sound he called "trombanga." In the 1970s, Palmieri worked with the Tico All-Stars and the Fania All-Stars, and on his own original work, often combining jazz, pop, and African music. He has remained one of the Latin community's most enduring and interesting artists.

Palo Pá Rumba   Fania 56

After his brother Charlie suffered a heart attack, Eddie Palmieri moved to Puerto Rico and recorded this 1983 album, his first with an all–Puerto Rican band. Palmieri celebrates the beautiful island on a sweeping jazz-salsa tune called "1983"; it's breezy with occasional bursts of energetic horns and percussion. The title track is probably the best known, spiced by three trumpets and three trombones. "Bajo con Tumbao" is a popular salsa song that has been covered by many artists, and Palmieri delivers a spirited version backed by a male chorus. "Venezuela" is another salute to the riches of the country's people and land. Mostly, this is dance music. Charlie Palmieri contributes percussion.

LINK➤ *Charlie Palmieri — Adelante Gigante*   *Alegre (Import)*
Eddie's talented brother was one of Latin music's innovators through the 1960s. If this album proves hard to find, try for Impulsos *(on MPL), or almost anything else released under his name in the 1960s or 1970s.*

Palmas   Elektra 61649

Self-confident and energetic, this 1994 album set the standard for contemporary Latin jazz. Palmieri is joined by nine modern jazz players, notably Donald Harrison (saxophone), Brian Lynch (trumpet), and Conrad Herwig (trombone). A solid foundation of Latin percussion from Richie Flores (congas), Anthony Carrillo (bongos), and Jose Claussell (timbales) sets the rhythmic flow, but Palmieri's skillful manipulation of jazz and Latin sensibilities creates something entirely original. Dense and thrilling, "Palmas" is a smart dance piece that also works as intellectual jazz. "Bouncer" remembers when NYC salsa bands competed in stickball tournaments; the song is dedicated to one of the best of NYC's street athletes. "Slowvisor" is a sleek, long-lined melody with some neat improvisations.

LINK➤ *Gonzalo Rubalcaba — The Blessing*   *Blue Note 795478*
Rubalcaba is an extraordinarily talented pianist from Cuba. His work with Cuban music is terrific, but overall, this grouping of U.S. jazz favorites is his best album to date. From 1991.

Bulgarian weddings are large-scale celebrations for hundreds and, sometimes, thousands of people that last 24 hours or more (often, much more). Bulgarian wedding music, called stambolovo, combines Thracian music, gypsy themes, folk, jazz, Turkish music, and lots of other styles. Papasov is Bulgaria's most famous wedding musician. Couples schedule wedding dates based on his availability, and hundreds of uninvited guests show up just to hear him play. Papasov plays loud (as loud as rock music in concert), and he's extremely unconventional in his use of time and in his improvisations—embracing and improving upon stambolovo tradition. Born in 1952, a Turkish gypsy, Papasov started with a jazz-folk group and survived political imprisonment in the early 1980s. By the mid-1980s, the government was sponsoring folk concerts. In December 1989, the oppressive Zhivhov regime fell, and a commercial economy was introduced. This exposed Papasov to a larger audience.

Orpheus Ascending Hannibal (Rykodisc) 1346

Papasov starts with a long solo. He often begins this way, with a meandering line (and phenomenal tone) that might have intrigued jazz's Eric Dolphy or Yusef Lateef. But the bass's distant thunder suggests an approaching downpour. Papasov begins a more complicated passage. Then comes the big accordion, the drums, the sax, and the extraordinary tempo. "Bulchenska Ratchenitsa" gets the wedding on its feet. Very fast tempos and huge dance numbers abound, but Papasov's quiet jazz clarinet improvisations, on such tracks as "Byala Stala," and the complex tremelo voice of Maria Karafizieva, suggest this is far more than simple peasant dance music. From 1989.

LINK➤ *Various Artists — Unblocked* *Ellipsis Arts 3570*
Spectacular 3-CD set features music from Eastern Europe. Lots of fast-paced wedding music to appeal to Papasov fans, plus wonderful folk music, polyphonic singing, many treasures. Don't hesitate on this one!

Balkanology Hannibal (Rykodisc) 1363

The pace is generally faster; the songs are more like the hora (often danced at Jewish weddings); and the influences from Turkey, Greece, and neighboring regions are more pronounced on this album. Papasov's alarmingly fast clarinet gets more of a showcase; drummer Stefan Angelov, a local celebrity, also proves himself. On "Mladeshki Dance," for example, it's impossible to dance as fast as these men play—or even think that fast! The three-way improvisation on "Hrisianova Kopanitsa" (Papasov, Youri Younakov on sax, Neshko Neshev on accordion) is stellar. The slow "Kasapsko Horo" demonstrates Papasov's facility with Greek folk music, made even more impressive by the restrained power of his rhythm section.

LINK➤ *Ashkabad — City of Love* *Caroline RealWorld 2329*
While not from the same culture, this wildly unrestrained music from Turkmenistan (north of Iran, east of the Caspian Sea) has some of the same appeal. Music is played on saxophone, clarinet, soprano sax, accordion, plus tar, dutar, dep, sarp, and nagara. Outrageous!

Flamenco guitar master Peña was born in Córdoba, **Spain**. A child prodigy, he first performed for an audience at age 12, and soon after became a popular performer in London. (He has since appeared at London's top jazz and classical venues, and seats are typically hard to come by.) By 1970, Peña was touring with a full ensemble of dancers, guitar players, and singers. He founded the "Centro Flamenco Paco Peña" in his hometown in 1981, a forum dedicated to the art form and to music played on guitar. The center's workshops and concerts have featured Paco de Lucia, guitarist John Williams, and most of flamenco's legends. Two years later, Peña won the Ramon Montoya prize for his work. Through the 1980s, he won poll after poll as the best flamenco guitarist in the world. Still, Peña's work is not as well known in the U.S. as it is in Europe.

The Art of Paco Peña
Nimbus 7011

Peña recorded three albums for Nimbus filled with classic flamenco guitar, plus an original Mass whose liturgy is celebrated through flamenco (*Misa Flamenca* [Nimbus 5288]). A solo album (*Azahara* [5116]) with Tito Losada on second guitar provides four elegant songs: an alegría, "La Rosa"; a malagueña, "Salobre"; a fandango, "Riomar"; and a tango, "Claroscuro." Peña's homage to Ramón Montoya, who brought together classical and flamenco guitar in the first half of this century, includes several songs of tantalizing complexity. The same album celebrates master modernist Niño Ricardo (*Flamenco Guitar Music of Ramón Montoya and Niño Ricardo* [5093]). The recordings were made during the period 1987-90. The compilation was released in 1993.

LINK➤ *Various Artists — The Story of Flamenco*
Hemispheres (Metro Blue) 55680
From Hispavox and EMI-Odeon Spain, a collection highlighting many flamenco styles. Includes work by many of the greats, such as Carmen Linares and La Niña de La Puebla.

Flamenco
Philips 826-904

A textbook demonstration of flamenco guitar, recorded in 1971 with the microphone so close that the guitar sounds like it's in the listener's lap. Peña explains that the rasgueado is the framework; the rhythm, the chords that provide the compás, or structure of the work. The falseta is the melodic part of the music, and it's here that the flamenco guitar player brings out his personality. With this recording, it's easy to dissect the music (though that's hardly the point of listening). The songs are very different from one another, and even within a single song, there is a great variety of moods and tempos.

LINK➤ *Paco de Lucia — Dos Guitarras Flamencos en America Latina*
Philips 842-952
Another exquisite example of the flamenco art, in a similar setting. Recorded in 1967, but sounds newer.

The **French** singer extraordinaire was born in 1915 to a mother who abandoned her and a father who left her in the care of a brothel madame. At 15, Piaf earned money by singing in the streets. Five years later, she got a job in a nightclub; this led to a Polydor contract and a connection to the club owner's murder. Through the 1930s, Piaf worked her way up through better clubs and music halls, while recording hits. This continued through the 1940s, but repeatedly falling in love hard, and in full public view, took its toll. Success in NYC and a new record label (Pathé) advanced her career, but a lover's death moved her to drugs and alcohol. During the 1950s, Piaf worked in films and played to adoring audiences throughout Europe and the U.S. She collapsed during a NYC performance in 1959. Songs and new loves kept coming, but by 1963, she was exhausted. When she died in October of that year, it was said she had tears in her eyes.

30e Anniversaire   Capitol 27097

This 2-CD set celebrates two anniveraries: 30 years of Piaf onstage and 30 more since her 1963 death. Not all of her recordings are included here. The set picks up Piaf's story in 1946, when she left Polydor and signed with Pathe. With the exception of some early hits, like "Mon légionnaire," most of the songs Piaf made famous are in this extraordinary box. Some songs will be immediately familiar, if not in Piaf's original, then in covers by Louis Armstrong and other American or European singers. These include "La Vie en Rose," "Milord" (which Liza Minnelli sang with gusto), and "La Goulalante du Pauvre Jean (The Poor People of Paris)." Piaf's late 1940s work photographs a Parisian era: "Bal Dans Ma Rue," the mournful "Hyme a L' Amour (If You Love Me, Really Love Me)," the small French circus band treatment on "Bravo pour le Clown," "L'Accordéoniste," "Les Amants d'un Jour." No Paris portrait is more touching than the well-known "Sous Le Ciel de Paris." Piaf's signature vocal style, that triumphant voice, is perfection on "Non, Je Ne Regrette Rien" and "Le Flonflons du Bal." Her nostalgic "Le Vieux Piano (The Old Piano)" is French cabaret at its best. Duets with Charles Dumont ("Les Amants") and Theo Sarapo ("A Quoi Ça Sert L'Amour") are superb. The arrangements are all distinctively post-war French, an era well-represented in film but more magically brought to life here.

LINK➤ *Edith Piaf – L'integrale*   *Verve 834-506*

A complete collection of Piaf's recordings for Polydor (1936-1945). A single-CD sampler called Master Series *(Verve 832-189) is also available. And by the way, the above 2-CD set samples a 9-CD box called* Piaf: Her Complete Recordings 1946-1963 *(Angel 90384).*

The tango, now associated with sophisticated ballroom dancing, grew up in the brothels and immigrant streets of Buenos Aires, **Argentina**. Blending influences from Italy, Cuba, Africa, and all corners of South America, the tango became tough and competitive (male dancers vied for the few females in Buenos Aires by showing off tango skills). Lyrics were often obscene. When Rudolph Valentino danced the tango in the 1926 movie, *The Four Horsemen of the Apocalypse*, a sanitized tango became an international sensation. Piazzolla was born in Argentina in 1921 but was raised in NYC. He started playing professionally at age 16, and moved to Argentina to play the bandoneón in dance orchestras (the bandoneón is the accordion heard in tango). After studying with classical music teacher Nadia Boulanger in Paris, Piazzolla reshaped tango as a legitimate modern art form, a step beyond dance music. His work was revered by many musicians. Piazzolla died a legend in 1992.

La Historia Del Tango, Vol. 1   Polydor 511-638

Piazzolla recorded two albums in 1967 that recalled his work from the late 1940s and early 1950s. The arrangements are intentionally old-fashioned, but the recording quality is fine. *Volume 1* pays homage to the old guard, "La Guardia Vieja," and *Volume 2* (Polydor 511-639) looks back at "La Epoca Romantica," the romantic era. "Sentimento Gaucho" is typical. Piazzolla's bandoneón plays a clean lead, often against a thick string background. Masses of violins then repeat or answer his phrases. Often, a chime marks the beat. Emotion is kept in check. The tango is always presented as sanitized, socially acceptable dance music. Still, it's interesting as history.

LINK➤ *Carlos Gardel – Las 60 Mejores Canciones de Carlos Gardel*
Planet Records (F.T.C.) 6006/6007
A 2-CD set with 60 vocal performances by the most famous tango singer in history. 1927-1935 recordings sound pretty good. Gardel gave 13-year-old Piazzolla his first job (on a film), but Piazzolla turned down his Latin American tour. On that tour, Gardel's plane went down over Colombia.

Zero Hour   American Clave (temporarily out-of-print)

Until new distribution is arranged, haunt used CD stores for this 1986 CD either alone or as part of the 3-CD set, *The Late Masterpieces*. *Zero Hour* is a true virtuoso turn: it's romantic, soulful, and cinematic. The masterpiece is "Milonga Del Angel." Pablo Zeigler's piano and Hector Console's bass describe a lonely street. Piazzolla's despondent melody, sometimes propped up by nostalgia, passes by the sad café and keeps moving. Fernando Suarez Paz's violin calls out, but the tragedy is all-consuming. Piazzolla's control over every microtone is total. Guitarist Horacio Malvicino, Sr., completes the extraordinary "Quinteto Nuevo."

LINK➤ *Michael Tilson-Thomas & New World Symphony –*
Alma Brasiliera: Music of Villa Lobos   *RCA 68538*
Four of the Bachianas Brasileiras: inspiring classical suites addressing Brazil's natural wonder and the special character of its people. Highly recommended.

The Central Park Concert
Chesky 107

The best sampler album: a 1987 concert recorded for radio released on CD in 1994. *Zero Hour*'s New Tango Quartet plays here; four of *Zero Hour*'s six songs are here, too. "Adios Nonino," one of Piazzolla's most popular songs, begins with Ziegler's romantic piano interpretation; after a few minutes, Piazzolla captures the audience on bandoneón, working closely with violinist Paz, who makes the work his own for another extended solo. The interaction between the players is seamless. In "Muerte del Angel (Death of the Angel)," a tango mixes the improvisational eloquence of jazz with the dramatic intensity of classical music.

LINK➤ *Laurindo Almeida & Charlie Byrd — Tango* Concord Picante 4290
Easy listening by two deeply experienced guitar players. In addition to "La Rosita," "Tango Alegre," "La Cumparsita," and other tango delights, there's "Blue Tango" written by Leroy Anderson and Broadway's stereotypical tango, "Hernando's Hideaway."

Concierto Para Bandoneón; Tres Tangos
Nonesuch 79174

Piazzolla's nuevo tango is a comfortable kin to jazz and classical music. Two of his best works commissioned for classical orchestra are included here. Piazzolla performs on bandoneón with NYC's Orchestra of St. Luke's, conducted by Lalo Schifrin. The first work was commissioned by an Argentine bank. In its second movement, Piazzolla's subtle tones and his blending with the strings develop into the lightest possible pastel vision of nostalgic tango. The third movement moves from loose and street smart, to romantic, to passionate and fiery. The second piece distills the noble and expressive quality of these Argentinian blues. Recorded in 1987 at Princeton University.

LINK➤ *Dino Saluzzi — Cité de la Musique*
ECM 1616
A more modern, impressionistic treatment of tango-like music, performed by one of the world's best bandoneón players with son José on acoustic guitar and key contributor Marc Johnson on bass. Music to fill a late-night room with shadows.

La Camorra: La Soledad de la Provocación Apasionada
American Clave (temporarily out-of-print)

This CD is comparable to Zero Hour, and no less hard to find. It's also part of the 3-CD box, *The Late Masterpieces*. The title translates into "The Rumble: The Solitude of Passionate Provocation." The story begins with "Soledad (Solitude)"; a slow tango finds the neighborhood quiet. Then there are three cammoras, or gang fights. The music swells, there's sadness, and then another fight, more severe than before. So it goes until the "Fugata (Fugue)," played first by bandoneón, then by bandoneón and violin, then with the progressive addition of bass, electric guitar, and piano. The final two pieces, about dreams and regressing, complete the structure. Recorded in 1988.

LINK➤ *Various Artists — The Story of Tango*
Hemisphere (Metro Blue) 55646
From EMI-Odeon in Argentina, a comprehensive survey. Good introduction to composer and conductor Mariano Mores, Sexteto Mayor (who might be familiar from the Tango Argentino musical revue), and master bandoneon player Anibal Troilo.

For three years, from 1972 until 1975, Planxty was the best acoustic band in **Ireland**. The group got started when folksinger Christy Moore hired Donal Lunny and Andy Irvine as a backup band; then added Liam O'Flynn and started gigging together. The word "planxty" is a toast, rather like "cheers!," and a title for some traditional Irish songs. The first single, "Cliff of Dooneen," was a hit, and a Polydor recording contract followed. Purist appeal was important, and the presence of O'Flynn, a respected pipe player, added credibility. But before the second album, Lunny left, replaced by Johnny Moynihan, and touring became a way of life. Moore was not well suited to roadwork, and wanted more time at home. Moore was replaced by an American, Paul Brady, but he never recorded with the group. There were just three Planxty albums. Moore continued as a successful solo singer and songwriter. Very influential.

Planxty
Shanachie 79009

Radiant Celtic music. The first Planxty album, and probably the best, released in 1973. A fine recording, too, the better to hear these clear, strong, sensitive voices and the light touch of the accompaniment. The intimate homage to Ireland and its heroes, "Only Our Rivers," told first in a touching vocal and then by the Uilleann pipes, is pure poetry. "The Jolly Beggar," with the chorus "we'll go no more a roving, a roving in the night...," is the story of a beggar and a farmer's daughter. It became one of the group's most popular songs. "Planxty Irwin," played on the pipes, is a harp tune by O'Carolan.

LINK➤ *Patrick Street — Irish Times*   *Green Linnet 1105*
Formed in the mid-1980s with a fiddler, guitar player, and singer from the Bothy Band, DeDannan, and Planxty (plus one more guitar player), Patrick Street added Uilleann pipes, and a fiddle to fill out the sound for this 1990 album. It's their best.

The Well Below the Valley
Shanachie 79010

The second album, also from 1973. "Cúnla" is a bit of vocal quick-stepping against the drone of soft background instruments. The lonely Irish love "As I Roved Out" is beautifully sung with pretty accompaniment. "Pat Reilly" tells of a young soldier who gets drunk and blames his miseries on his father. There are two jigs, two reels, two hornpipes, and a double jig. The recording doesn't quite render the depths of the bodhrán's drumming and misses some of the nuances of the Irish bagpipes, but energy and skillful music-making more than compensate. The third Planxty album, *Cold Blow and the Rainy Night* (Shanachie 79011), is similar, and also recommended.

LINK➤ *Various Artists — Playing with Fire: The Celtic Fiddle Collection*
Green Linnet 1101

Superior Green Linnet sampler featuring some incredible fiddling. There's some Eileen Ivers, Liz Carroll (with Dáithí Sproule on guitar), Kevin Burke, Sea Keane, Altan, John Cunningham.

One of the most enduring **Latin** musicians and bandleaders, Puente's musical career began aboard a ship during World War II, an education later formalized at NYC's Julliard School. In the late 1940s, Puente played percussion for several Latin Bands, formed the Piccadilly Boys, and subsequently changed the group's name to the Tito Puente Orchestra. He was the first artist signed to Tico, an important Latin label, and ignited the mambo craze. Later in the 1950s, he moved to RCA, reworking traditional Cuban songs into brassy dance hits. He also nurtured younger musicians, notably Willie Bobo, Ray Barretto, Mongo Santamaria, and Johnny Pacheco. Through the 1960s and 1970s, Puente's focus was big band, salsa, boogaloo, and Latin jazz, infused with Cuban and African influences. Through the 1980s, and 1990s, he worked with a variety of jazz stars, won a Grammy in 1983, and appeared in the 1992 motion picture, *The Mambo Kings*.

50 Years of Swing   RMM 82050

After more than 100 albums, Puente's career is reviewed in a 3-CD box. Because Puente was such a pivotal figure in the Latin music scene, the box is also a history of the scene itself. Featured: Tito Rodríguez, La Lupe, Machito, Mongo Santamaria, Willie Bobo, Hilton Ruíz, Santos Colón, Celia Cruz, Ray Barretto, Johnny Pacheco, Cheo Feliciano, Oscar D'Leon, Héctor Lavoe, India, and many other top artists. 1940s and early 1950s material is mainly mambo and other dances. "Para Los Rumberos," from 1956, is one of the best. Although Puente returns to those forms time and again, always with great success, there's much more here. His virtuosity on timbales (a pair of drums played with sticks, not hands) gets a workout on "Tito on Timbales" with Mongo Santamaria from 1955. There's an even better 1957 version with Santamaria and Willie Bobo, as well. As with any box, there are inevitable pop curiosities: a 1973 Spanish-language version of "Crystal Blue Persuasion," and Abbe Lane singing a blown-out Hollywood version production number on "Babalú." There's even some jazz, too: "Lullaby of Birdland" features pianist George Shearing, and "On Broadway" is done up with a massive Latin big band arrangement. Stevie Wonder's "Don't You Worry About a Thing" has never sounded better than the version Puente recorded with Lionel Hampton. An expansive live version of "Oye Como Va," a cha-cha composed by Puente but made famous by Santana, ends the album with a celebration. The 2-CD *Fania Legends of Salsa, Volume 3* (Fania 704) focuses on dance music from 60 albums.

LINK➤ *Tito Rodriguez — Mambo Mona*   *Tumbao (F.T.C.) 14*
At the Palladium dance hall on NYC's Broadway, Tito Puente, Machito, and Tito Rodriguez were the mambo kings—and every collection should include at least one CD from each bandleader. This set was recorded by his Los Lobos del Mambo in 1949-51. Rodriguez was the lead singer and played percussion.

The Best of Dance Mania
RCA Latin 21009

Recorded in 1957 and 1960, this is the music that most people continue to associate with Tito Puente. Make no mistake, this is terrific work played with great passion, but it's only part of his story. "El Cayuco" is played with eight horns (four trumpets, four saxophones); it's a cha-cha with a sexy vocal by Santos Colón, thrilling percussion work by Puente (timbales) and Ray Barretto (congas), and a piercing arrangement. Puente plays vibraphone to begin "Una Mujer," a ballad showcasing the riches and depths of Colón's voice; once again, the arrangement makes a good song extraordinary. Many other hits are included, and the recording quality is impressive as well.

LINK➤ *Various Artists — Mambo Mania!: The Kings & Queens of Mambo*
Rhino 71881

Essential introduction to Celia Cruz con La Sonora Matancera, Pérez Prado, Mongo Santamaria, Desi Arnaz & His Latinos, La India de Oriente, Tito Rodriguez, Machito, Xavier Cugat, and others who made the transition from Cuban to U.S. Latin music.

Homenaje A Beny
Tico 1425

Among fans of Cuban music of the 1950s, Beny Moré is held in very high esteem. A popular bandleader, he was also a legendary singer. In 1978, Puente released this homage to Moré, and followed it a year later with *Homenaje a Beny, Vol. II* (Tico 1436). Puente produced the album and conducts the orchestra; lead vocalists change with each song. Vocalists featured on both volumes include Celia Cruz, Ismael Quintana, Santos Colon, Hector Lavoe, and Chea Feliciano. The music is vintage, notable not only because Puente got his start here, but also because it's so lovingly performed. In typical Tico fashion, there are no liner notes.

LINK➤ *Beny Moré — Baila Mi Son*   *Caney (F.T.C.) 506*
Essential 1953-58 hits collection by a musician many consider to be Cuba's greatest singer. Listen to the warmth and memories of sorrow in that voice, the way he wraps himself around and under lyrics. And as a bandleader, few could compare with his son–montuno.

Special Delivery
Concord Picante 4732

This is one of several excellent contemporary Latin jazz albums recorded for Concord Picante in the 1990s. Compositions are mostly jazz standards like "Stablemates," "On Green Dolphin Street," "Be-Bop," "Venus De Milo," and "Flying Home" by composers like Benny Golson, Horace Silver, and Dizzy Gillespie. Maynard Ferguson is a featured trumpeter. All of this becomes Latin as three traditions are blended into large-group jazz: Latin percussion (including Puente's timbales), a front line of eight horns (four trumpets, four trombones) playing often in the Cuban style, and arrangements that have more to do with Cuban big band music than the music typically defined as jazz. But in 1996, the distinction is blurry.

LINK➤ *Machito and his Afro-Cubans — Carambola*   *Tumbao (F.T.C.) 24*
Machito's work profoundly influenced Dizzy Gillespie (and Stan Kenton). Mario Bauza is one of three trumpeters. Zoot Sims guests on two tracks. Recorded at NYC's Birdland jazz club in June and November, 1951. Certainly as essential as Puente's earlier work. Adequate recording quality.

Jazz musicians have been deeply influenced by Cuban bands, but **Cuba** has another tradition whose impact has run as deep: the troubador's song, typically performed with acoustic guitar. Many of these songs, or canciónes, were both patriotic and romantic; one famous example is "Guantanamera," which combines the love of a woman and love of country. Rodriguez was one of several students at Havana's ICAIC film school who modernized the form, which later became known as "nueva canción" (new song) or "nueva trova" (new troubador's song). This movement came together in the late 1960s, in some ways inspired by U.S. protest singers. In a country already revolutionized, protest music didn't quite work. Rodriguez instead concentrated on lyrics as poetry, and eventually earned a reputation as Cuba's leading poet. Along with musical influences from the Beatles and Dylan to Stravinsky and Mozart, Rodriguez also credits literary influences including Edgar Allan Poe and Lord Byron.

Cuba Classics 1: Los Grandes Exitos
Luaka Bop 26480

Luaka Bop is to be congratulated for providing access to one of Latin America's most important songwriters and performers. These songs come from 1978–86. On "Causes y Azares (Causes and Fate)," Rodriguez opens and closes with rousing Cuban horns, but the song's heart is sung simply, on acoustic guitar with gentle percussion accompaniment. Rodriguez's muted electric guitar adds a touch of spice and steps up the tempo slightly. It's a call-and-response with metallic percussion. Rodriguez is an artisan at work, one who knows how to bring in the older Cuban forms and satisfy his own creative soul. A talented poet on the order of Caetano Veloso, Rodriguez sings in "Canto Arena," (translated from Spanish): "Today I continued to head toward my destiny, nailing up signs, deciphering crossroads...." He does this with a jazzy piano meandering through his impassioned vocal. A single trumpet speeds along the beach as Rodriguez sings of "the rock that becomes the multitude in clear water." He saves a quicker Latino rhythm for "Canción Urgente Para Nicaragua (Urgent Song for Nicaragua)," offering consolation from a Cuban who has "bled along with you." Rodriguez sings of unicorns and serpents, but his most important song, "No Hacen Falta Alas" promises "You don't need wings to build a dream. Hands are enough. Heart is enough. Legs are enough. And determination." This is wonderfully creative, lyrically magnificent, and intelligently crafted music that everyone should own. (When it comes back in print, buy *Dias Y Flores*, too!)

LINK➤ *Caetano Veloso — Cores Nomes*   Verve 838-464

Lacking a single high-quality collection of Veloso's music, this is one of his best albums. As Rodriguez did in Cuba, Veloso transformed Brazilian music with imaginative melodies and poetry disguised as song lyrics. All of Veloso's work is worth exploring.

Palm wine is homegrown brew in the poor country of **Sierra Leone**, and "palm wine music" has been the drink's dreamy, relaxed musical counterpart for as long as anyone can remember. Born in 1926, Sooliman Rogie was a tailor who sang palm wine music. He became well known with several hit songs in the 1960s, notably "My Lovely Elizabeth." Rogie remained in Sierra Leone until 1973, then moved to Philadelphia, and then to San Francisco, where he recorded an educational program for schools and won a Congressional award. He also absorbed the work of B.B. King, John Lee Hooker, and other blues artists. In 1989, Rogie moved to England to appear on a BBC radio program. There, he continued to sing his palm wine music in schools and sometimes in clubs. At age 67, a few months before he died, Rogie made his first recording for a major label.

Dead Men Don't Smoke Marijuana
RealWorld (Caroline) 2344

Wonderfully gentle music evokes a warm, dry day with palm trees lazy in the breeze, a feeling of blues and a feeling of where acoustic blues might have originated. The production suits the mood and effectively simulates a few friends singing and drinking outdoors. Rogie sings lead: a peaceful, slightly reedy baritone voice accompanied mostly by his own acoustic guitar. He sings in English on "A Time in My Life," sounding very much like Jimmy Rodgers or Mississippi Fred McDowell. Other songs are performed in his native tongue. "Nor Weigh Me Lek Dat (Woman to Woman)" sways with another of many memorable melodies; his voice gets near a growl as background vocalists come in for a chorus. The variety of his melodies and his guitar patterns keep this music fresh, every song is quite different from the one before. "Dieman Noba Smoke Tafee" (the title song) contains a lovely acoustic guitar solo that reaches out to Hawaii and Madagascar. The overall presentation is deepened with the subtle addition of double bass by Danny Thompson and the occasional improvisation electric guitar. Then, the vocal slides in so easily, like a dream.

LINK➤ *Mississippi John Hurt — Avalon Blues*   *Rounder 1081*
Elegant acoustic guitar, a refined rhythmic sense, and a relaxed style make Hurt one of the easiest blues players to enjoy. These recordings were made in 1963, when the U.S. was enjoying a rediscovery of early blues players.

When Paul Bert Rahasimanana was 7 years old, a friend gave him an accordion. He listened to the radio and imitated what he heard; by high school, he was playing in a band. After school, he moved from a poor neighborhood in **Madagascar's** capital city, Antananarivo, to a comparatively freer society on the northeast coast (he moved to be with his father). And everywhere he went, Rossy absorbed music. Rossy started with the vakisova, a choral music with hand-clapping in place of instruments, and his fame grew from there. He taught himself to play kabosy (a small guitar), valiha (a 21-string zither), sodina (a kind of flute), and to imitate Europop, zouk, reggae, music from the coastal highlands, roots music, and salegy (popular in the Northeast). He reworked all of these styles into a sound for his own group, called Rossy Band. It's one of Madagascar's most successful.

Island of Ghosts
RealWorld (Caroline) 2318

A celebratory combination of hand claps, organ, and chanting vocals begins this expanded version of a television soundtrack. The song is "Madagasikara," a plea to preserve the island for generations to come. So begins a 1991 trip into a land that isn't especially well known, an island sufficiently far from the African coast to have its own animals, its own traditions, and its own music. Rossy's gentle high tenor nicely complements the subtle instrumentation and easy harmonies. "Maki" is an accompanied solo on the valiha, a bamboo zither native to the island. "Hazofotsky" is played on the kabosy, a local variation on the guitar.

LINK➤ D'Gary – Malagasy Guitar
Shanachie 65009

D'Gary imitates various instruments from Madagascar while playing some extraordinary guitar. He's also from the island.

One Eye on the Future, One Eye on the Past
Shanachie 64046

A 1993 disc produced by Rossy with Henry Kaiser of *A World Out of Time*. It includes the band's best song, "Zana Drazana," a true kaleidoscope of Madagascar's musical styles and instruments. On "Ny Any Aminay," Rossy plays a valiha and a Madagascar acoustic guitar. Add the band's mellow vocals and it's quiet magic. "Anamalo" is a rural folk song (about a spinach-like vegetable) brought up to date. The accordion on "Taiko" suggests Eastern European folk dancing, but it comes from Madagascar's eastern coast. The military sound of "Ramasay" comes from the amponga (big drum) and langoraony (snare drum). It was written when the French colonized the island. Pure uncommercial music in pristine form.

LINK➤ Various Artists – Resting Place of the Mists
Shanachie 64752

Excellent collection of music played on the valiha and marovany. Artists include Sylvestre Randafison (an old master), plus well-known world music stars like Sammy (of Tarika Sammy fame), and Pana (who appears on some D'Gary songs).

The Sabri Brothers have been somewhat overshadowed by the phenomenal success of another qawwali singer, Nusrat Fateh Ali Kahn. Their qawwali (devotional music from India and Pakistan) is more traditional, but no less theatrical. Ghulam Farid Sabri was born in East Punjab, now part of **Pakistan**, in 1930. His brother, Maqbool Ahmed Sabri, was born in 1945. The family's musical background extends for generations, back to a a musician in the court of Akbar in the late 1500s. The ensemble, or qawwal party, consists of ten musicians; it more or less began in 1956 and continues today, though the size and shape and members of the organization have varied over time. This is religious music, but it's also show business. Ghulum Farid Sabri, as a sideline, used to be a voiceover actor, his deep voice ideal for villains. When he died in 1994, tens of thousands of mourners attended his funeral.

Ya Habib   RealWorld (Caroline) 2311

Sufi devotional music has found a large audience, and this 1990 recording is one reason why. The tabla and other drums develop an interesting rhythm, while the harmonium spreads a comforting drone as a background for the four brothers' voices. Their group vocals are often melodic. Although passionate, their glorification is comforting and, after a spell, familiar. Four long songs induce a connection among musician, listener, and the Beloved. "Ya Sahib-Ul-Jamal" praises the luminescent beauty of God; the sun, stars, and moon are dim in comparison. "Kali Kamaliya Wale" evokes a vision of the Beloved. In qawwali music, this is the best starting place. Highest recommendation.

LINK▶ *Ravi Shankar — Chants of India*   *Angel 55948*

The basis for much of this work is traditional Sanskrit mantras and couplets, essentially prayers for emotional, physical, mental, and spiritual well-being. Presented in a variety of instrumental settings. Very satisfying.

The Greatest Hits   Shanachie 64090

An odd title for an album of sacred music. These are five popular songs by the qawwali party recorded by EMI-Pakistan before the group was discovered by world music listeners. The harmonium's plaintive opening on "Tajar-E-Harman" is a cleansing sound that purifies; prayerful vocals grow from the midst, wind in and around, and become one with the soul. Then, the chants and percussion begin. "Sultan-E-Haram" is dominated by a group chant, albeit one with melody and improvisations spun from the basic theme that become higher-pitched and ecstatic. The tabla and hand claps provide continuous rhythm, as various vocalists step out from the group for a brief solo. Then, a group melodic chant.

LINK▶ *Nusrat Fateh Ali Khan — Devotional and Love Songs*
RealWorld (Caroline) 2300

1985 album of traditional music, and astonishing vocal work, with enough variety to keep newcomers fascinated.

Bally Sagoo was born in Delhi, **India**, in 1964, but his father moved the family to Birmingham, England, before his first birthday. His father was a musician who owned a record store that imported Indian music. As a teenager, he paid more attention to hip-hop, ragga, soul, and dance music. He mixed tapes for friends, then began selling his mixes and working as a DJ. Slowly, he became interested in his parents' music. After college, he worked as a stereo salesman. Bally's father made a connection with Oriental Star, a leading Indian record label, and Bally began working on remixes (he kept the day job at the stereo shop). By 1990, he was remixing Oriental Star's catalog of Bhangra (Indian pop) tracks, and becoming well known on the international dance scene. After several hits, he took a full-time job at Oriental Star. His work has been widely bootlegged worldwide.

Bollywood Flashback
Columbia 477697

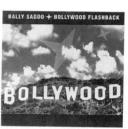

BALLY SAGOO + BOLLYWOOD FLASHBACK

The music on this 1994 album comes from a wide range of influences. It's dedicated to R.D. Burman, who composed Indian film soundtracks in the 1970s and 1980s. Sagoo uses this film music as the underlying layer in a more complicated mix. On "Chura Liya," the first Indian record to reach Number 1 on the English charts, Burman's work is heard beneath a dance beat, and male and female singers Reema Das Gupta and Debashish Das Gupta. Muhammed Yunus's lead vocal emphasizes Indian roots in a crowded dance mix involving mostly digital percussion, synthesizers, and sampling. Sagoo skillfully blends international rhythms with Indian rhythms to appeal to a broad audience.

LINK➤ *Najma – Forbidden Kiss*   *Shanachie 64063*

A 1996 release of music from composer S.D. Burman's many Indian film soundtracks, presented in intriguing modern interpretations by Najma, an Indian singer raised in England. S.D. Burman worked mainly from the 1950s through the 1970s. R.D. Burman was his son.

Rising from the East   Tristar 36850

By the time Sagoo recorded his eighth album in 1996, remixes combining Indian and Western influences had made him an international star. This album changes direction: all original songs (cowritten with S.M. Sadiq) and a predominantly Indian sound. Singer Shabnam Majid offers a very delicate approach to "Tum Bin Jiya," mixed with mostly Indian instrumentation, a drum machine, and the restrained use of sampling. Udit Narayan sings "Ban Mein Aati Thi," which is more elaborately manufactured with effects, strings, and a prominent dance beat. An early Sagoo success was a Nusrat Fateh Ali Khan remix. Of the three qawwali works here, the best is "Nach Malanga," sung by Badan Ali Khan.

LINK➤ *Talvin Singh – Anokha: Sounds of the Asian Underground*
    Polygram 524–341
A stunning blend of traditional Asian music and electronic rhythms, this electronica collection was very popular in 1997. Strictly dancing.

As Samite was growing up in **Uganda**, his family experienced atrocities associated with Idi Amin's regime; his brother was taken away by the police and killed. Samite fled to a refugee camp in Kenya in 1985, and to the U.S. in 1987. (He's now headquartered near Ithaca, NY.) Encouraged by a teacher, he learned to play the Western flute, and eventually added other African acoustic instruments. Samite first worked with a cover band called the Mixed Talents; he worked in Kenya with the Bacchus Jazz Band, the African Heritage Band, and as a solo artist. In the U.S., Samite established himself by opening for Ladysmith Black Mambazo. Fortune smiled when the producers of *Good Morning America* used a song he'd written for the African Heritage Band; Samite built a studio with the royalties. He often performs for children in the U.S., teaching them about Africa.

Abaana Bakesa-
Dance My Children, Dance
Shanachie 65003

Joyful acoustic music. Samite's voice is friendly and inviting. He plays kalimba (finger piano), litungu (a large string instrument), African marimba, African and Western flutes, and various African percussion instruments. His instinct for blending their sounds is organic; the music just seems to flow like a brook or a stream, while his gentle voice tells his stories. "Anzala" is one of the most intriguing soundscapes; a young man wants the easy answer to questions about life's meaning. "Kakokolo" is a folk tale about a forest creature who entices a child with his magical music. Released in 1988. *Pearl of Africa Reborn* (Shanachie 65008), from 1992, adds more elaborate instrumentation.

LINK➤ *Various Artists – African Tranquility* Shanachie 64762
A collection of spiritual, reflective, and generally acoustic music from Africa. Several artists from Madascar: Mahaleo, Taika Sammy, Rossy; from Tanzania, Geoffrey Oryema; from Nubia, Hamza El Din; plus Ladysmith Black Mambazo.

Silina Musango
Xenophile (Green Linnet) 4047

It's 1996, and Samite has lost none of his magic. He continues to play many instruments, but coproducer Tony Cedras's guitar adds structure, and a percussionist or drummer is often used as well. The traditional "Ekibobo" is a children's song. For young children, Ekibobo is the monster of their dreams; older, wiser children tease and challenge the monster to come out and play. "Kalimba" considers the musician's relationship to a sometimes-magical instrument (the percussion track is fascinating). "Nalubale (Lake Victoria)" retells the legends of an enormous, powerful lake. In "Bandekawo," an innocent war orphan wants to know what happened to his family. A sad flute provides the only answer.

LINK➤ *The Pan-African Orchestra – Opus 1* RealWorld (Caroline) 2350
By combining the formality of Western classical music with flutes, gylie (xylophones), kora (harp-lutes), gonje (African violins), and African percussion, director Nana Danso Abiam has truly created something new, and enormously appealing. Very highly recommended. From 1994.

Wassalou is a southern region in the North African country of **Mali**. The people are Bamana and Fula, and their music follows ancient traditions related to the hunt. In the 1960s, a Wassalou pop music sound emerged, music sung mostly by young women. Sangare is the most successful of the many female Wassalou singers; her first album (Moussolou) sold in excess of 200,000 copies (plus many more pirated cassettes, a common distribution system in Africa and elsewhere). Sangare's mother and grandmother sang, and Oumou started singing at about age 5. As a teenager, she toured the French Caribbean and Europe with a folklore troupe. Her work uses native instruments. Her songs directly address issues related to women's changing roles and the way women are perceived in Africa. Sangare often sings out against long-engrained ideas she hates, including tribal traditions like polygamy and arranged marriage.

Moussolou
World Circuit 21

A hypnotic groove from 1989. It's generated by the kamelngoni (ordinarily associated with youthful energy, it's a small harp used by youthful hunters), bongos, guitar, violin, and bass. Sangare sings with two very precise, somewhat nasal and acidic backup singers. Vaguely Arab sound. Icy intensity. "Moussolou" means "Women." Sangare encourages women to take pride in themselves and in all they do. "Dajama Kaissoumou (Let's Talk)" provides friends and strangers with an intimate view of Wassalou beliefs and Sangare's personal life. Translated lyrics, complete with footnotes explaining unfamiliar words and customs, fill the liner notes. 1991's Ko Sira (World Circuit 36) also encourages women to stand up for themselves.

LINK> *Various Artists — The Wassoulou Sound: Women of Mali*
Stern's Africa 1035
Opportunity to hear the Wassoulou sound's creator, Coumba Sibide; Kagbe Sidibe, who has been a star since the 1960s; and Sangare's contemporary, Sali Sabide.

Oumou Sangare 'Worotan'

Worotan
World Circuit 45

Sangare's formula remains essentially unchanged. The title refers to a bride's dowry and the value of a woman. Four songs are accented with tenor sax, trombone, and trumpet. One is reminded of the relationship between horns and acoustic instruments in American blues. Her lyrics echo societal concerns. "N'Guatu (Burning Grass)" encourages young men to work the fields, not flee to the city for easier work. Even when Sangare lovingly sings "Baba (Father)," the lyrics refer to bruised bones. "Tièbaw (Big Men)" looks to God for help with the impossible strains of polygamy. Pee Wee Ellis, who played for James Brown, played sax and arranged the horns. Released in 1996.

LINK> *Najat Aâtabou — Country Girls & City Women*
Rounder 5077
Aâtabou grew up in the Atlas Mountains of Morocco, and although she's Arab, her themes are similar to Sangare's: women taking control of their own lives. Extensive liner notes explain Moroccan culture, and even include recipes and tourist sites. From 1995.

Hungary's folk dance music became the basis for a popular form called tánchéz. In the 1970s, tánchéz musicians scoured the countryside for old music. Much of the music was collected from Transylvania, where the Ceaucescu regime severely limited people's access to tradition. In Hungary, the tánchéz movement grew, in part as a kind of protest, both against mistreatment of Transylvanian kin, and also as a reaction to Hungary's government-approved form of folk music.  Muzsikás became a popular tánchéz group in clubs and festivals. For several years, Márta Sebestyén sang lead for Muzsikás. She had been singing since childhood; her mother studied with Kodaly, taught music, and collected rural folk music. Sebestyén came up through Hungary's rock music scene. In 1983, she sang lead in a rock opera. During the late 1980s, Sebestyén joined Muzsikás for a series of albums that sold well enough for her to launch a solo career.

The Prisoner's Song   Hannibal (Rykodisc) 1341

A world music classic from 1986. Most songs are about imprisonment: dangerous musings about contemporary politics, with lyrics about dungeons, chains, empty cages, and never seeing home again. The collected folklore is centuries old, but sounds new. It's lovingly performed by vocalist Márta Sebestyén (also recorder), Sándor Csoóri (bagpipe, hurdy-gurdy, violin, vocals), Mihaly Sipos (violin, zither, vocals), Péter Eri (buzuki, Turkish horn, cello, viola, vocals), and Dániel Hamar (bass, hurdy-gurdy, vocals). Chilling interaction between Sebestyén's voice and the deep-voiced strings on "Hidegen Fújnak a Szelek," one of many remarkable tracks. "Szerelem, Szerelem (Love, Love)" was the romantic theme in the film *The English Patient*. Listed under Muzsikás.

LINK➤ *The Tribunia Family Band — Music of the Tatra Mountains*
Nimbus 5437
From the highlands in Poland (the Podhale region), folk music performed by male and female singers with distinctive string accompaniment. Recommended.

Muzsikas   Hannibal (Rykodisc) 1330

Sebestyén was already a popular tánchéz singer when she recorded this 1987 album with Muzsikás. The surging, pulsating rhythm behind "Egy Pár Tánc Mezöségröl (Mezoseg Dance)" is extraordinary; it sounds as if power is being turned on and off every few seconds. "Vetettem Violát (I Planted a Violet)" is a simple, charming song with distinctive accompaniment from a hurdy-gurdy, recorder, buzuki, and zither. The carefree "Szeress Egyet, S Legyen Szép (Love Just One)" begins with a violin solo; Sebestyén happily sings along. "Fújnaka Fellegek (Dark Winds Come)" begins as an eerie unaccompanied solo (her voice is magnificent); it's then sung against moody woodwinds.

LINK➤ *Márta Sebestyén — The Best of Márta Sebestyén* Hannibal 1412
This 1997 collection includes songs from albums issued under her name and the group's name. An excellent introduction, but be warned: most people end up buying the whole series of albums.

Blues for Transylvania

Hannibal (Rykodisc) 1350

Transylvania was once a part of Hungary, and Transylvania's Hungarian minority has long been a thorn in the side of the Roumanian government. Despite Roumania's oppressive regimes, Hungarian folk culture lived on. Music is one reason why; something, perhaps, in the spirit of a csárdás (the prototypical Hungarian dance). When the dance is over, it's nearly dawn, and "Bodonkúti Hajnali (Dawn Song from Bodonkút)" is heard, nearly a capella, from Sebestyén. The soulful sound of the hurdy-gurdy on "Old Song from Somogy," and the contra and sad violins on "The Time Is Autumn" (a conscription blues) begin to fill in the details of a culture. Extraordinary.

LINK➤ *Vujisics*

Hannibal (Rykodisc) 1310

Sebestyén often performs with Vujicsics (pronounced vuy-chitch), and sings here as part of the ensemble. Traditional music from Hungary's south.

Apocrypha

Hannibal (Rykodisc) 1368

All of these haunting songs are based on traditional melodies. Károly Cserepes, who plays winds and synthesizers, arranged the songs and produced some of them. They were originally released on three other albums in 1984, 1985, and 1989. On "Tavasz, Tavasz (Spring, Spring)," Sebestyén's peaceful vocal moves with Cserepes's long flute and tilinka (a Rumanian flute), and Ferenc Kiss's recorder. Lázslo Hortobágyi's chimes set the mood for "Ne Menz Szivem (Don't Go Sweetheart)," set against unorthodox percussion. Sebestyén's theme from *The English Patient*, "Szerelem, Szerelem (Love, Love)," is included with elaborate synthesizer accompaniment (it sounds better unaccompanied on the Muzsikás CD, *The Prisoner's Song* [Hannibal 1341]).

LINK➤ *Muzikás & Márta Sebestyén — Morning Star*

Hannibal (Rykodisc) 1401

This spectacular 1997 recording brings out resonant stereo-effect percussion and succulent fiddle tone on "Kerekes Héjsza És Sebes." One of their best!

Kismet

Hannibal (Rykodisc) 1392

Sebestyén expands her world view; she sings songs from Ireland, Greece, Bosnia, the Balkans, Bulgaria, and elsewhere. She has also moved toward more modern instruments. She learned "The Shores of Loch Brann," which she sings beautifully, from Dolores Keane; for years, Sebestyén has performed it in concert together with "Hazafelé," a folk song from southwestern Hungary. She performs "Leaving Derry Quay" with the Greek "Eleni." She learned "Hindi Lullabye" from a book found in a used bookstore. Arranger Nikola Parov deserves much of the credit; he skillfully absorbed music from a dozen cultures and transformed it into a hybrid magically suited to Sebestyén's special voice.

LINK➤ *Dolores Keane and John Faulkner — Brokenhearted I'll Wander*

Green Linnet 3004

She's the singer from western Ireland, and he's the Scottish musician with the ability to play a variety of instruments. Of this duo's several CDs, this one's probably the best. Released in 1979.

The queen of **Tejano** music, Selena was born in 1971 in Lake Jackson, Texas. She started performing at age 9 in an act called Selena y Los Dinos ("Los Dinos" is slang for "the guys") and began recording three years later. By 1987, Selena was an experienced professional, winner of the Female Vocalist of the Year and Performer of the Year at the Tejano Music Awards. This led to an EMI contract, and, in 1990, her first album was released. Her first gold record followed a year later, then came a Grammy, and by 1994, Selena was a true star. She launched a clothing line (Selena, Etc.), planned a line of perfumes, sang in the film Don Juan DeMarco, and by 1995, *Hispanic Business* magazine reported assests of $5 million. The much-loved Selena was murdered on March 31, 1995, in a Corpus Christi, Texas motel room by former fan club president Yolanda Saldivar.

Mis Mejores Canciones   EMI Latin 27190

Released in 1993, this is a good collection of Selena's earlier hits. Here's the original version of "Como La Flor (Like a Flower)," with its overheated drum machine. Also included is Selena's despairing vocal on "Custombres (Habits)," with a wide-open organ sound that would be restrained a bit on later versions. Selena excels at love songs and dances. There are plenty of good dances here: "La Carcacha," "Mentiras (Lies)," and an especially slick version of "Baila Esta Cumbia." The fast version of "No Quiero Saber" is very different from the melancholy masterpiece on *Siempe Selena*. Many of these songs were rerecorded with new arrangements for later albums, but this is still essential Selena.

LINK➤ *Selena: Original Motion Picture Soundtrack*   *EMI Latin 55352*
A more complete picture than any album. Best is a disco medley with "I Will Survive," and another with "On the Radio." The dance version of West Side Story's *"A Boy Like That" is a knockout. Some (but not lots) of her own Tejano songs. Selena sings almost every song. Rent the movie, too!*

Live   EMI Latin 42770

Recorded in 1993 in Corpus Christi, Texas. Selena opens with the mid-tempo "Como La Flor (Like a Flower)," and the crowd sings along on the choruses. Next there is a quick transition to "Baila Esta Cumbia," one of Selena's best dance songs. There are lots of fireworks from the drum machines. On "Ven Conmigo," guest David Lee Garza's accordion solo invites the crowd to sing every word. Selena gets just the right attitude (angry and hurt) on "No Debes Jugar (Don't Play)." The song is played against a rock organ. "Tu Robaste Mi Corazon (You Stole My Heart)" is a great love duet, but the energetic "La Llamada" closes the show with a bang. Good accompaniment from Los Dinos.

LINK➤ *La Fiebre — Nuestras Mejores Canciones: 17 Super Exitos*
                                             EMI Latin 27602
Greatest hits compilation from a popular Tejano band. Johnny Perez is a gifted pop songwriter who makes excellent use of traditional styles. Very enjoyable.

Amor Prohibido
EMI Latin 28803

"Amor Prohibido (Forbidden Love)" is one of Selena's best love songs. Love is forbidden because she is a poor girl and lives in a different world from her beloved. Still, she's convinced that true love is what matters. "No Me Queda Mas (I've Got Nothing Left)" is sung with an even more desperate, sentimental voice, and an arrangement that wishes for the best. In "El Chico del Apartamento 512 (The Guy in Apartment 512)," Selena is a woman in love whose heart breaks when she comes to his door and a white woman answers. One great song follows another; production is perfect; Selena's voice sounds fabulous. A very popular album from 1994.

LINK➤ *Tish Hinojosa — Frontejas*   *Rounder 3132*
Born to Mexican parents, Texan singer Hinojosa usually sings (beautifully) in English. Here, she returns to Mexican border music recalled from childhood. Superb recording, even better instrumentalists (Flaco Jimeniz, Peter Rowan, etc.) Hinojosa's bi-lingual children's album, Cado Niño (Every Child) (Rounder 8032) is also special.

Siempre Selena
EMI Latin 53585

Here are the songs that Selena's fans loved. Not exactly a greatest hits album, it's more of a fan's remembrance. There are two songs in English: "Only Love" and "A Million to One"; both are top-notch pop songs. Once again, Selena is best with Tejano arrangements. "Cien Años (A Hundred Years)" and "Tú Robaste Mi Corazón (You Stole My Heart)" are graceful love songs. Sentimental Mexican guitar, violin, and horns accompany her world-weary "No Quiero Saber (I Don't Want to Know)." It features one of Selena's finest vocals. "Siempre Hace Frio" is similar. The up-tempo dance "Ya No" shuts a heartless lover out of her life.

LINK➤ *Carlos Vives — Clasicos de la Provincia*   *Philips 518-884*
Like Selena, Vives has been a Latin show business phenomenon. A former actor, the Colombia native has combined traditional vallenato (which is heavy on accordion) with rock to create something new—and very popular. This is a 1993 tribute to vallenato masters like Alejo Duran.

Dreaming of You
EMI Latin 34123

Had Selena lived, this 1995 album would have made her a major rock star. She repeats "Amor Prohibido" and somehow manages an even better performance (she sounds like she's singing for Olympic gold). "Techno Cubia," which also appeared on Amor Prohibido, is a hot combination of rap, techno, and late 1950s urban street-song. "Bidi Bidi Bom Bom," another popular Selena song, describes the sound her heart makes when "he" walks by. Cowriter David Byrne does a great job with percussion on "Baila Conmigo (Dance with Me)," which he wrote with and sings with Selena. It all comes together with elegance on "Dreaming of You."

LINK➤ *La Mafia — Nuestras Mejores Canciones: 17 Super Exitos*
EMI Latin 42868
Greatest hits from mid-1980s through 1993 by a Norteño band that's sold millions of records. The music is sort of a cross between the Texas Tornados and a more traditional Mexican band.

Shaggy was born in **Jamaica** in 1968, but left for Brooklyn, NY, at 18 to be with his mother. His given name was Orville Richard Burrell, but friends called him Shaggy (from the Scooby Doo cartoon character). He started chatting lyrics over his high school's public address system, then at clubs; by age 20, Shaggy was cutting records for a NYC label. Soon after, he worked with NYC reggae radio disc jockey Sting to produce the hits "Mampie" (about overweight women) and "Big Up," with the singer Rayvon (also from Brooklyn). Still, it was tough to earn a living, and life in his Brooklyn neighborhood could be harsh. So he joined the Marines. When the Gulf War broke out, he was sent to the front line. After returning to North Carolina's Camp LeJeune, he drove 18 hours each weekend to work in NYC. That's when he recorded "Oh Carolina," an international hit that led to stardom.

Boombastic
Virgin 40158

A major-league crossover album. The title song made the Top 10 on just about every chart, including the top pop singles. The term "boombastic," dreamed up to rhyme with "romantic" and "fantastic," makes a joke of Shaggy's sudden status as any kind of sex symbol. His dance-hall pop style is easily enjoyed on this song and on most of the other tracks. "The Train Is Coming," made with old-time singer Ken Booth, was featured on *The Money Train's* soundtrack. The most fun is a reworking of the old Mungo Jerry jug-band tune, "In the Summertime," performed with Shaggy's boyhood buddy, Rayvon. "Why You Treat Me So Bad" is done with former Brand Nubian, Grand Pubah.

LINK➤ *Various Artists — Joy Ride*   **Madhouse (VP) 3103**

Producer David Kelly, who has worked with Shaggy, serves up a great collection by Wayne Wonder, Beenie Man, Spragga Benz, Lady Saw, Tanya Stephens, and others. One of the better 1990s sets, and well worth owning.

Pure Pleasure
Virgin 44487

This 1997 album should appeal to both contemporary reggae fans and those who are stuck in the 1970s. On some songs, like "My Dream," Shaggy successfully dances between 1970s folk rock, spoken word against hard percussion, and a breezy reggae rhythm. "Perfect Song," done with Maxi Priest, contrasts a harder 1990s sound with a voice that naturally drifts toward the melody line. "Tender Love" is sweet with a lilting choral backup. It features a combination of some old-time country resonance and street raps. "Piece of My Heart" is pure soul from singer Marsha, with rap-reggae on top from Shaggy. The way he sublimates the influences makes this music considerably more interesting than standard fare.

LINK➤ *Super Cat — Don Dade*   **Columbia 54435**

Super Cat's dance-hall heyday was in the late 1980s and very early 1990s. When this album was released in 1991, he became known as a hip-hop artist for songs like "Ghetto Red Hot" and the title track.

Son of noted Indian violinist V. Laksminarayana, Shankar was raised in southern **India** in the 1950s and 1960s. A prodigy, he began voice lessons at age 2 and violin lessons (with his father) at age 5. In 1969, he moved to the U.S., hoping to perform Indian classical music for Western audiences, and to work with Western musicians. He became well known as a classical artist. And in 1976, he formed a fusion band (jazz-rock fusion plus Indian music). The band was Shakti, a successful group he co-led in the 1970s with guitar player John McLaughlin. Later, he worked with McLaughlin in his One Truth Band. Shankar has also recorded and toured with various rock artists, notably Frank Zappa, who produced Shankar's album, *Touch Me There* (Zappa 1602), a rock album with an emphasis on blues. An annual two-month tour of India is part of Shakar's regular schedule.

Raga Aberi   Music of the World 131

A 1995 Grammy nominee, this remarkable album contains one long (48 1/2-minute) original raga. Shankar performs on a 10-string double violin, an unusual instrument with a pair of fret boards hanging beneath its sound box. Its range includes that of the violin, viola, and cello. Long-time collaborator Zakir Hussain plays the tabla, and Vikku Vinayakram performs on clay pot. The liner notes explain the structure and forms of South Indian classical music. The patterns are distinctively Indian, but the sound of Shankar's violin provides Western listeners with a comforting path. Mostly, this is Shankar with subtle accompaniment. Improvisations are stimulating and elaborate, often with fantastic speed and unexpected sonic textures.

LINK➤ *Kayhan Kalhor (and others) — Ghazal: Lost Songs of the Silk Road*
                                                                        Shanachie (TK)
Persian virtuoso on the kamancheh (spike fiddle) and setar meets Indian musicians Shujaat Hussain Khan (sitar) and Swapan Chaudhuri (tabla). Kahlor's Eastern Apertures (Keresmah) is also recommended.

Shakti with John McLaughlin   Columbia 46868

Just over two decades ago, British guitar player John McLaughlin became fascinated with Indian music and formed a group called Shakti. Shankar, then known as L. Shankar, played violin. Shakti was one of the first world music fusion groups. The formula works. There's a section about halfway through the 18-minute "Joy," for example, when Shankar's fast violin work and his perfectly trimmed high notes get right to the heart of mid-1970s jazz, followed by some equally amazing work by McLaughlin, who essentially mimics Shankar. Add percussion from Zakir Hussain on tabla and two other musicians on mridangam (drum), and the mix is spectacular! Also try *The Best of Shakti* (Moment 1011).

LINK➤ *John McLaughlin — My Goal's Beyond*   Rykodisc 10051
Very original 1970 acoustic guitar work based on a broad range of international styles. Masterful musicianship with underplayed accompaniment by top jazz studio musicians.

Shankar was born in 1920 to a well-educated (but not wealthy) Brahmin family in Varansai, a large metropolitan area in West Bengal, **India**. He became entranced by storytelling (even those told in comic books). As a young teenager, Shankar toured and danced with brother Uday's Company of Hindu Dance and Music. Master musician Ustad Allaudin Khan joined the troupe in 1935 and became Shankar's mentor; Alluadin's son, Ali Akbar Khan, became Shankar's friend. Then came years of rigorous schooling on the sitar. In the 1940s, Shankar wrote film scores and ballets and performed throughout India. He was music director for All India Radio from 1949 until 1956. In the mid-1950s, Shankar toured Western Europe and the U.S. In 1966, George Harrison traveled to India to study sitar with him. Two years later, Shankar performed at Woodstock. Shankar worked with Harrison on the first large-scale international music relief effort, Concert for Bangladesh in the early 1970s. Shankar still tours and continues to innovate and influence other musicians.

Live at Monterey-1967 Ravi Shankar Music Circle 101

When Shankar makes his unlikely appearance at 1967's Monterey Pop Festival, the crowd is genuinely anxious to hear him play. After a brief explanation of the music's structure comes the flash, the shimmering sitar sound that fit so perfectly into psychedelia. "Raga Todi" is a devotional late-morning raga; Shankar sounds like he's playing two or three instruments simultaneously. It's easy to understand the appeal. Shankar sounds like an astonishing electric guitar player on a miraculous voyage of discovery, all the more remarkable because he's performing a song written for the 16th century court of Moghul Emperor Akbar. This album contains two long ragas and a tabla solo by Alla Rakha.

LINK➤ *Pandit Kamalesh Maitra and Trilok Gurtu —*
Tabla Tarang—Melody on Drums **Smithsonian Folkways 40436**
The tabla is a highly resonant, tunable drum. A tabla tarang is a semicircle of 10 to 16 tuned tablas. Maitra is the master of tabla tarang, and this is his recital (on an audiophile recording). Gurtu plays a bass tabla. A 54-page book explains tabla, tabla tarang, and provides Maitra's life story.

In Celebration Angel 55577

George Harrison produced this 75th birthday tribute. He also produced a respectable percentage of the music contained on these 4 CDs. This is a lovely set, ornately packaged as a 58-page, full-color hardcover book. Each CD is silkscreened with Indian art. The book tells Shankar's story and offers insight into each piece of music. The first CD appropriately begins with five offerings on sitar. The first, "Charu Keshi," was recorded in 1957. Shankar combined raga scales from southern India and reworked them for his own northern style. "Bhatiyar" is a morning raga, peaceful and glimmering, recorded at 4 a.m. at the end of a long concert in 1991. "Marwa" is an evening raga, a song that drills down to the desolate depths to explore the soul of sadness. The second CD is filled with ensemble work. "Jait" is based on an evening raga. It's notable both for extraordinary rhythms led by the tabla and for the many melodic variations, a concept more easily understood by listening to "Sandhya Raga." The latter was performed inside the Kremlin in 1988. "Gahanashyam" is probably most accessible; it's an uptempo opening to a ballet with clear melody lines repeated by sitar, sarod (another stringed instrument), keyboard, and flute. The third CD contains seven collaborations with Western classical artists. Yehudi Menuhin's violin and Shankar's sitar are restrained and magnificent on their 1968 duet. Shankar's masterful concerto for orchestra, recorded by André Previn and the London Symphony Orchestra, is a seamless interweaving of two generally unrelated musical styles. There are two pretty pieces with Jean-Pierre Rampal. The "Indo-Japan Finale," played with koto, Japanese flute, and Indian instruments, is captivating. The fourth CD covers vocal and experimental music. On "Hey Nath," from the Philip Glass collaboration, *Passages* (Private Music 2074), Shankar sings against a lush meditation of subtle Western and Indian instruments and an understated chorus. George Harrison plays an exquisite autoharp in a small 1986 ensemble piece, "Friar Park," but Harrison's 1974 "I Am Missing You," with drummer Ringo Starr, keyboard player Billy Preston, bassist Klaus Voorman, and Shankar's sister-in-law Lakshmi on lead vocals is a more typical Harrison concoction.

Chants of India   Angel 55948

Created in response to the success of other chant records in the early 1990s, Shankar composed and arranged these 16 chants. The basis for much of this work is traditional Sanskrit mantras and couplets, essentially prayers for emotional, physical, mental, and spiritual well-being. Shankar also created some new material. Some chants are accompanied by heavier string sounds, some with an Indian chorus, and some with a Western chorus. "Prabhujee," a Shankar original, features flute, male and female lead vocals (sometimes individual, sometimes in duet), a male chorus, and Indian instruments. "Sahanaa Vavatu" is more mystical and slower; it is a wish for peace. Produced by George Harrison, the album was released in 1997.

LINK➤ *Sheila Chandra — Quiet*   *RealWorld (Caroline) 1782*
Of the many Chandra recordings based upon Indian chants, this one is closest to the traditional roots.

The early evolution of Silly Wizard began in 1971, when Gordon Jones, Bob Thomas, and Johnny Cunningham played together in the clubs of Edinburgh, **Scotland**. A year or so later, Andy M. Stewart's band, Puddock's Well, broke up, and he joined Silly Wizard. With the addition of Cunningham's brother Phil on accordion, Silly Wizard became a popular festival attraction. In time, Thomas left, and Johnny moved to the U.S., replaced by Dougie MacLean, who has since been successful as a solo artist. Silly Wizard stayed together for nine albums and 17 years of live performances. The final gig was in a club in Voorheesville, NY, in 1988. Stewart has continued a solo career, but also works in TV production. Johnny records solo and with other artists. Phil often performs live with Aly Bain (formerly of Boys of the Lough). For more, visit the website: http://www.rootsworld.com/harbourtown/silly_wizard.html.

Wild & Beautiful
Shanachie 79028

Old Scottish songs provide either material or inspiration for this 1981 album. "Hame, Hame, Hame (Home, Home, Home)" follows a defeated soldier home from 1746's Battle of Culloden. "Tha Mi Sgith (I Am Tired)," a Gaelic lullaby, follows. Four sprightly jigs lift the spirit, particularly "The Orphan," featuring Stewart's tenor banjo. Phil Cunningham's low whistle and guest Dougie MacLean's fiddle are dreamy on "The Pearl." The gracious (almost waltz–like) strathspey is a form used in "That Mi Sgith." In many Scottish and Irish ballads, a man leaves and a woman waits. "If I Was a Blackbird" twists the usual ending: he returns just as she leaves for a voyage. The group's best.

LINK▶ *The House Band — Rockall*   *Green Linnet 1174*
Like Silly Wizard in its day, this 1990s group is full of rocking energy, which brings an audience beyond the Celtic community. Very much in the 1990s world music tradition, the House Band also brings in some Bulgarian and African influences. Mostly Celtic.

Live Wizardry
Green Linnet 3036

The mood is different here, more aggressive and direct. Every song is thrilling; this is a fabulous album! On "The New Bob," Johnny Cunningham's fiddle gets everyone up and dancing. Andy Stewart's slow verses have a way of ending fast, leading into quick dance steps on "The Parish of Dunkeld." Stewart begins "A Ramblin' Rover" unaccompanied; humor and good fellowship arrive as the lads join him for the choruses (lyrics notable for rhyming "arthritis" with "colitis"). The traditional songs are all super, but Stewart's originals, particularly "The Queen of Argyll," are even better. A very fortunate audience saw this show live in Cambridge, Massachusetts, in 1988. Buy this album today.

LINK▶ *Aly Bain and Phil Cunningham — The Pearl*   *Green Linnet 3107*
Lively fiddle (Bain) and accordion (Cunningham) album from 1994: jigs, reels, and other tunes, some original, some collected. Cunningham also plays keyboards and other instruments.

Solas is a 1990s **Irish-American** phenomenon. The group's story begins with Seamus Egan, who was born in Philadelphia in 1969, then moved to Ireland at age 4, where he later became an all-Ireland champion on several instruments, including the banjo, mandolin, and flute. He returned to Philadelphia and performed with his sisters and with the Green Fields of America. While on tour, Egan's car broke down, and a kind family helped. As it happened, the family's son was involved with a small film, *The Brothers McMullen*. Egan's music became a major part of the soundtrack. Singer Karan Casey grew up in Waterford County, Ireland, and sang jazz in NYC's Irish clubs in the early 1990s. Fiddler Winifred Horan worked with Cherish the Ladies. Guitar player John Doyle is from Ireland, as are the parents of accordion player John Williams. As these musicians crossed professional paths, Solas took shape in 1995.

Solas   Shanachie 78002

This demonstration-quality recording could actually be played to audition high-end loudspeakers. The album features Irish songs collected over the centuries. The arrangements are snappy and have a contemporary flair. The depth of Seamus Egan's bodhrán against Karan Casey's pure, clear voice can be heard on "Níl 'Na Lá." Here, the fiddle and the guitar trade off and the choruses are spirited— the song is a fine rendition of an old drinking song. The resonances of guitar and violin on "Crested Hens" create a lovely air, though Egan's low whistle on "Lament for Frankie," another air, is even more chilling. Among the reels, "The Flowing Bowl" is a favorite, and among the jigs, "The White Petticoat." An extraordinary album in every way.

LINK➤ *Seamus Egan — A Week in January*   *Shanachie 65052*
Several tracks on this 1990 album find Egan trading banjo licks with Dirk Powell, but his handsome tin whistle work on some reels and his flute playing are also highlights. 1996's When Juniper Sleeps *(Shanachie 79972) combines Solas's sensibility with a mild contemporary flavor.*

Sunny Spells and Scattered Showers   Shanachie 78010

"The Wind That Shakes the Barley" makes quite a racket in a way that Riverdance fans will find familiar. At the same time, the song gives Karan Casey her showcase: an earnest commemoration of an Irish union uprising. Several reels follow (once again, the superior engineering of Solas records brings out the nuances). "The Maid on the Shore" is a story song with an edge: she's persuaded by a captain and his sailors to come on board, she sings them to sleep, and then she robs them all blind! Solas is superb with instrumental work, but Casey's winning voice raises the songs to a still higher level.

LINK➤ *Karan Casey — Songlines*   *Shanachie 78007*
Precisely the album that Casey fans hoped to see: a cache of traditional Irish songs with surprising stories, plus carefully selected contemporary folk material. Casey sings Ewan MacColl's frustrated "Ballad of Accounting" and Jean Ritchie's "One, I Love." Produced by Egan. Various performances by Solas members, too.

Songhai has never been a permanent group. Instead, it's a collaboration of musicians from different backgrounds who have recorded a pair of popular albums. The story begins in London in October 1987. The Spanish flamenco group Ketama had just played five dates and heard Mali's leading kora player, Toumani Diabate, at a party. A musicologist named Lucy Duran, who was half-Spanish and spoke Mandinka, got everyone together. Rehearsals soon began. Ketama and Diabate performed together at a club, and the audience went crazy. Bassist Danny Thompson was added for the first recording. (Thompson's credits include work with Elvis Costello, Kate Bush, Pentangle, and many others.) The album was successful, so the musicians returned to the studio in 1994. For the second album, a combination of **Spanish and African** vocalists were added, along with Keletigui Diabate on balafon (similar to a xylophone), and Basekou Kouyate on ngoni (a five-string lute with a resonating box covered in cowhide).

Songhai

Hannibal (Rykodisc) 1323

The first Songhai album was recorded in 1988. "A Toumani" was written by José Soto. Diabate's kora opens by playing a flamenco lead. Then the group sings together, and the kora returns with flamenco guitar backup. "Mani Mani Kuru" reverses the strategy. It begins with a flamenco guitar, then Diaw Kouyate and Djanka Diabate from Mory Kante's group come in on vocals, along with Toumani and members of Ketama. The song is catchy, but it will turn your head around. The African vocals sometimes sound like flamenco vocals, and the flamenco guitars sometimes sound like they're playing kora melodies. Consistently excellent.

LINK➤ *Radio Tarifa — Rumba Argelina* **World Circuit (Nonesuch) 79472**
1992 recording (released in the U.S. in 1997) blending Arab rhythms with Spanish accordion and guitars, and other interesting instrumentation from around the Mediterranean. Generally more Moroccan than West African.

Songhai 2

Hannibal (Rykodisc) 1383

The second Songhai album leaps out with "Sute Monebo (Shouting Won't Raise the Dead)," an ambitious rhumba with a big sound and a taste of Mali wisdom: losing your temper doesn't help at all. On the Wolof song "Niani," flamenco guitars follow Diabate's traditional kora lead. "Monte de Los Suspiros (Mountain of Sighs)" is a tanguillo, a flamenco form with North African rhythm, comfortably blending the musicians' roots. "Mali Sajio" tells the story of a hippopotamus that became a village's mascot, only to be shot by white hunters. It's sung by the great Mali singer Kasse Mady, accompanied by kora melodies played on kora and on flamenco guitar.

LINK➤ *Jali Musa Jawara — Soubindoor* **World Circuit 8**
The interplay between Jali Musa Jawara's kora and Kalifa Kamara's balaphon (xylophone) is one of the great pleasures in West African music. Jawara is Mory Kante's brother.

Historically, the mandolin has been associated with love songs in Naples and with bluegrass music in the U.S. In 1975, when he was just 6 years old, Upalappu Srinivas began playing his father's electric mandolin. In the south **Indian** state of Andhra Pradesh, Srinivas's father, who played clarinet in his own orchestra, taught his son some songs. The boy became interested in Carnatic music (south Indian classical music), but the mandolin was not typically used to play these ragas. No formal mandolin instruction was available (Carnatic music is typically played on violin or the sitar-like veena), so a teacher instructed Srinivas by singing; the young musician then repeated what he heard on mandolin. By 1982, critics recognized a musical genius. Since then, Srinivas has routinely traveled the world, astonishing audiences in Mexico, Germany, Spain, and elsewhere. Srinivas plays a five-string mandolin because the standard eight-string version cannot be used for Indian music.

Rama Sreerama
RealWorld (Caroline) 2345

An exceptionally fast-paced combination of electric mandolin and two remarkable percussion instruments, mridangam and ghatam, builds to an incendiary climax on "Gajavadhana." The musical style is called raga Hamsavinodhini, meaning "the sound of swans." The instrumental song invokes Lord Ganesha, who has the power to destroy obstacles. The title track is not one, but a stream, of ragas. Beginning nearly motionless, it gradually becomes a slow, filagreed duet for mandolin (sounding here remarkably like an Indian string instrument) and violin. The pace and difficulty increase as the song progresses. This is music of awesome improvisational beauty, masterfully performed by Srinivas. One can only imagine the technical challenge. From 1994.

LINK➤ *Dr. L. Subramanian — Raga Hemavati*   *Nimbus 5227*
The violin has become a popular instrument in the karnatak music of southern India. Subramanian has played with jazz artists in the U.S., but this music is his home.

Dream   RealWorld (Caroline) 2352
After the first album was recorded (later that same night, in fact), Srinivas and violinst Bhasakaran returned to the studio to experiment with sampling and other techniques. Additional musicians were later brought into the studio to experiment with Michael Brook, the first album's producer and this one's co-creator. Srinivas's improvisations on "Dance," derived from Indian meditations, are mixed with a drum machine's dense texture, keyboard bass, and synthesized sounds, plus percussion from Nana Vasconcelos and violin from classical star Nigel Kennedy. "Think," played with violin, cello, and Brook's electronics, combines meditation and ambient music. "Dream" is mostly about textures. It includes mystical vocalizing by Jane Siberry and the deepest bass on record.

LINK➤ *Michael Brook — Hybrid*   *EG (Caroline) 41*
Brook has become well known as a collaborator, but this 1985 debut album showed how clearly he understood the fusion of world music with sonic landscaping.

One of **England's** great folk rock bands, Steeleye Span took its name from a character in a song, a wagonmaker from Lincolnshire. The band got off to a rocky start with some early personnel changes but eventually settled into the familiar lineup of Ashley Hutchings on bass, Tim Hart on vocals and dulcimer, Maddy Prior on vocals, Terry Woods on vocals and guitar, and Wood's wife Gay on vocals. Bringing folk-rock to high art, Steeleye Span became a very popular band. The Woods left after two albums and were replaced by guitar player and vocalist Martin Carthy and by fiddler and vocalist Peter Knight. In time, Carthy returned to his solo career, Hutchings left for the Albion Country Band (more traditional British music), and Steeleye Span became more of a rock band, with a big label deal, and ultimately, fewer fans. After more personnel changes, Steeleye Span disbanded in 1987, and reunited in the 1990s.

Spanning the Years   Chrysalis 32236

Vintage 1970s material on a definitive 2-CD retrospective released in 1995. From 1970's *Hark! The Village Wait* (Shanachie 79052—and a splendid album in its own right; a "wait" was a medieval village band) come Gay Woods and Maddy Prior in an a capella duet on "My Johnny Was a Shoemaker." The virile hammer of a drum sound plays against Prior's pained, but hopeful, voice on "The Blacksmith," put together from various collected songs and texts. Another collected song, "John Barleycorn," is sung by Tim Hart. It's from the fourth album, 1972's *Below the Salt* (79039). "Alison Gross" is one of several songs from 1973's *Parcel of Rogues* (79045), which eases electric guitars and other rock sounds into otherwise traditional (albeit contemporary) folk music. The extra edge suits the lyrics well. But they're even heavier into 1970s guitar pyrotechnics on "Robbery with Violins," which is rather like work from Jethro Tull. Prior's voice, particularly when it's harmonizing with Tim Hart and other male voices, can be extremely effective, as on the anthem "Rogues in a Nation"; however, it's odd to hear the same voices singing "To Know Him Is to Love Him" just three tracks later. The band reached its commercial peak with "Black Jack Davey" from 1975's *All Around My Hat* (79059). CD2 contains lesser-known songs. Many are excellent, but there are a few odd choices, such as "Rag Doll."

LINK▶ *Maddy Prior — Memento: The Best of Maddy Prior*   Park 28
Magnificent voice, but she's not locked into any one sort of song. "Baggy Pants" is a stagey shuffle that's lots of fun, and "Commit the Crime" is a deadly serious song about forgiveness. A spectacular collection.

Andy M. Stewart

Stewart came to be well known as the lead singer of Silly Wizard, arguably the best Scottish band to combine traditional and contemporary music. Stewart was born in **Scotland** in 1952, and grew up with music: his father collected traditional songs, and his mother was a poet and songwriter. After playing in pick-up bands and sessions, Stewart joined a band called Puddock's Well in 1973, working with Dougie MacLean and others, then moved on to Silly Wizard in 1974. That group's popularity grew, and Stewart gained fame as a songwriter. Early in the 1980s, he moved on to a successful solo career, often collaborating with bouzouki and guitar player Manus Lunny. He has also worked on projects with Phil Cunningham, who played the accordion for Silly Wizard. The best way to approach Stewart is to begin with the Silly Wizard material, then move on to the solo work.

By the Hush   Green Linnet 3030

Recorded while Stewart was part of Silly Wizard, this album won *Melody Maker* magazine's Folk Album of the Year Award in 1983. It's lovely Scottish folk music, half originals and half traditionals reworked by Stewart and Phil Cunningham, who plays whistles, accordion, keyboards, and acoustic guitar. Martin Hadden completes the trio on acoustic guitar and electric bass. Accompaniment is always second to Stewart's commanding vocals. Some songs, like "The Parish of Dunkeld/ The Curlew" and "The Ramblin' Rover," are associated with Silly Wizard. "They Wounded Old Ireland" shows Stewart at his best, passionately telling a version of history and praying for peace.

LINK➤ *Silly Wizard — The Best of Silly Wizard*   *Shanachie 79048*
The original Silly Wizard versions of some sungs heard on By the Hush, *plus a lot of other fine material. Great band, great collection.*

Dublin Lady   Green Linnet 1083

Jointly credited to Stewart and Manus Lunny. Their finest collaboration. It's 1987. Stewart sings; Lunny plays guitars, bouzouki, and bodhrán, and sings. The title song is a folk classic. The spirited reel "Take Her in Your Arms" has the sort of lyric Stewart delivers so well: "If you're gonna love a woman then be sure you do it right!" The century-old "Tak' It, Man, Tak' It" tells of a miller who can't help but cheat his customers. The texture and weave of Lunny's artisty could be missed for Stewart's compelling vocals; pay attention or you'll miss half the show! With Aly Bain (fiddle), Phil Cunningham (accordion, keyboards), Sean Og Potts (Uilleann pipes, whistle).

LINK➤ *Archie Fisher — Sunsets I've Galloped Into...*   *Red House 82*
Fisher became well known singing with his brothers and sisters in Scotland. This 1995 album features him singing favorite songs from his repertoire from the past 20 years. Fisher is a quiet, articulate, and experienced musician.

Alan Stivell

Born Alain Cochevelou in 1944, Stivell and his Breton harp are a focal point for regional identity in **Brittany**, a corner of France with strong ties to the Celtic world. In fact, this story begins with Georges Cochevelou, Stivell's father, whose research allowed him to construct a Breton harp from a Fender Stratocaster electric guitar. It was the first Breton harp in four centuries. At age 9, young Alain introduced the harp at the Brittany Centre in Paris. He played songs written for other instruments, because there was no Breton harp repertoire. Stivell then learned to play other Breton instruments. He opened for the Moody Blues in 1968, and he won a Grammy Award in 1972. Stivell's albums sold very well; in 1975, he formed a label, Keltia III, to record his work. Over time, Stivell has become a significant spokesperson and educator of Breton Celtic traditions.

70/95 ZOOM   Dreyfus 36–189

This 2-CD set, released in 1997, looks back on 25 years of Stivell's recordings for Mercury/Philips and for his own Keltia III label. CD1 begins with with "Eliz Iza" from 1972's *Renaissance de la Harpe Celtique*; it's a sweeping formal affair with floating choral voices, strings, Breton percussion, and the charming delicacy of Stivell's Breton harp. Remarkably, this arrangement sets the stage for later new age music. "Suite des Montagnes" and "Marig Ag Pollanton" come from 1970's *Reflets*; both are more straightforward solo folk pieces. Stivell's fine Breton tenor voice is heard on the latter song. Several selections from his acclaimed 1991 *Mist of Avalon* album are also included on this CD. "An Advod" is dramatic in the same sense as "Eliz Iza," but with more production sparkle. Various tracks from 1973's *Chemins de Terre* and *Légende* are also CD1 highlights. "Suite Irlandaise" completes CD1 in a traditional arrangement from 1970's *Légende*; the same song opens CD2 in a rocking electric arrangement from 1993's *Again*. The popular live album *Olympia* contributes several tracks to CD2. The crowd sings along on "Tri Martolod"—a more virile approach to Breton music. "Pop Plinn," from the same album, also gets the crowd moving with its electric arrangement, powerful organ, and assorted fireworks. With selections from 1981's *Terre des Vivants*, 1995's *Brian Boru*, and others, CD2 is about audience involvement, lightning, and a clear link to new age music.

LINK▶ *Kornog — Première: Music from Brittany*   Green Linnet 1055

Another key album in the introduction of Breton music to Celtic enthusiasts. Kornog borrows liberally from Scottish, Irish, and Welsh music. Sound mixes guitars, flute, fiddle, bouzouki, and whistle. Released in 1984.

In 1975, Brooklyn-born Quentin Howard was working as a graphic artist in upstate New York. While attending a blues festival, she heard a Montreal-based quartet performing music from the **Andes**. Entranced, she invited the musicians to live at her home for a week.

After they left, she slowly taught herself to play the flute. Howard then visited Montreal, formed a partnership with one of the musicians (who was Swiss), and began researching South American music. The two pooled their funds and spent over a year in the Andes collecting songs and learning Spanish. They also formed an early version of Sukay. By 1985, the band was recording for Flying Fish. Two years later, the group was joined by Bolivian charango player Eddie Navio, well known as the leader of Bolivia's popular Savia Andina folk band. Education is a significant aspect of Sukay's mission; the band offers master classics, lectures, demonstrations, and residencies (3450 Sacramento St., San Francisco, CA 94118; sukay@sirius.com).

Cumbre (The Summit)   Sukay World Music 7

The reason to buy this CD is simple: it contains a traditional version of "El Condor Pasa." The song will be immediately familiar; it was one of Paul Simon's first ventures into world music. "Cumbre" has many of the same sounds: a lighter-than-air melody played on a deep, resonating flute (almost a didgeridoo) and a second, higher flute, as well as pressure-packed rhythms, distinctive harmonies, and a sense of drama. "Tinkuna" adds some vocal shouts and hand claps. Eddie Navia's charango begins "Paloma del Alma Mia," then becomes accompaniment for traditionally passionate vocals. Enchanting music from 1990.

LINK▶ *Flutes & Strings of the Andes*   *Music of the World 106*
The underlying roots music collected in 1983-84. Highlights: the raw, honest emotion of "Wawa Pampay" (an infant burial song), the unabashed whistling and charango on "Entierro de Wawa," and the spirit of "Pares Pares Palomita."

Encuentros (Meetings)   Sukay World Music 20

Superior recording quality captures the medieval voice of the 5-foot toyos, a pan pipe that gets a full-scale workout from Alcides Mejia on "Rebellion de Los Condores." The fast-paced interaction on "Conception" closely resembles small group jazz at its best. The remarkable work is by Eddie Navia and son Gabriel Navia, now the band's charango player. (Eddy Navia plays an unusual combination instrument with guitar and charango in a single unit.) The astonishing duet on "Quebrada Mocha," with its shouts of excitement, is also one of their best. So is "Carnavalito," with Yuri Ortuño's lead vocal and a wonderful chorus. Sukay's best album, released in 1995. No question: start here!

LINK▶ *Savia Andina – Classics*   **Sukay World Music 12**
Before he joined Sukay, Eddy Navia performed with Savia Andina, one of the first groups to popularize traditional rural music. Rafael Arias, who played guitar for Savia Andina, has released a solo album: Andean Guitar *(Sukay 26).*

A modern exponent of the griot musical storytelling tradition, Suso was born in 1953 in **The Gambia** (a small country bordered by Senegal in West Africa). He became a master of the kora (a stringed instrument combining aspects of harp and lute). In 1977, Sosa moved to Germany with hopes of blending his work with contemporary rock and jazz. From there he moved to Chicago, where he found the right combination of African, Cuban, and American musicians; he formed the Mandingo Griot Society, a world music fusion band, and recorded two highly regarded albums. This exposure, plus his work on the soundtrack to the TV mini-series Roots, led to an alliance with Herbie Hancock and his producer Bill Laswell. Together they put together music for the L.A. Olympics in 1984 and collaborated on Hancock's *Sound System* album, as well as other work, including an album of keyboard and kora duets available only in Japan.

Mandingo Griot Society
Flying Fish (Rounder) 70076

This seminal world music was recorded in 1978 with forward-thinking musicians from the U.S.: bassist Joseph Thomas, percussionist Adam Rudolph, and drummer/percussionist Hank Drake. By and large, the U.S. rhythm section plays African music supporting Foday Musa Suso's complex improvisations on kora. The rapid paddling of fishermen in their canoes inspires the fast-paced "Jimbasen." Jazz trumpeter Don Cherry provides a subdued melody in the midst of low-voiced, throaty flutes, tabla, and other percussion on "Sounds from the Bush." It's one of the finest jazz-world music blendings ever recorded. The striking kora sound is heard with an excellent griot vocal on "Janjungo," recalling a great warrior and leader. Essential world music.

LINK➤ *World Saxophone Quartet — Metamorphosis*   Nonesuch 79258
Avant-garde jazz quartet (all saxophones) meets three African drummers. The album's "Lullaby" is similar to some material here, but most songs are tightly played jazz improvisations with African percussion accompaniment.

The Dreamtime   CMP 3001
Multitracking enables Foday Muso Suso to perform as an ensemble. Produced by Bill Laswell in NYC in 1988, this is soothing, hypnotic music. "Morning Light" creates this spell, often making use of repeated patterns highlighted with the sparkles of the kora. A meditative Japanese koto quality is created by the kora on "Bunfa Silence (House Full of Silence)"; it's inspired by the quiet of an audience just before the performer goes onstage. The instrumental "Moving Shadow" is performed with nyanyery (single-stringed violin), dusongoni (six-string hunter's harp), kalimba (thumb piano), and tama (talking drum). The textures, rhythms, and melodies are varied. The execution is masterful.

LINK➤ *Herbie Hancock and Foday Musa Suso — Jazz Africa*
                                                          Verve 847-145
Hancock and several other musicians join the foursome responsible for the Mandingo Griot Society album. Recorded in 1987 for a series of TV specials (it's also available on laserdisc), it includes "Jimbasen" (here: "Jimbasing"), as well as Hancock's "Cigarette Lighter."

Jali Kunda: Griots of West Africa & Beyond

Ellipsis Arts 3510

The Suso family members have been griots since the start of the Malian Empire. For 800 years, father has taught son and mother has taught daughter the Griot ways. Throughout the land of the Mandingo people—which today encompasses Mali, Senegal, The Gambia, and Guinea-Bisseau—Griots are the keepers of living history. (The term "Jali Kunda" means "Home of the Griot.") History is not written down. Instead, men play instruments and recite, or accompany, female griot singers. Griots attend birth ceremonies, accompany heroes into battle, and keep the stories of families and kings. Storytelling, history, praise, and traditions are communicated by the griots. The griot women sing; griot men recite and play the kora (a cross between a harp and a lute made from a large gourd and a tall wooden stick). It's one of several instruments associated with griots (the balafon, a kind of xylophone, is another). This information is contained in the 94-page book that comes as part of this 1-CD package. The book includes a lengthy explanation of griots written by Foday Musa Suso, an essay by noted blues writer Robert Palmer, and a large collection of magnificent color photographs of Suso's family, and others associated with griot music. The CD contains about a dozen griot field recordings, a modern kora composition by Suso and Philip Glass, and two more new tracks. The real joy here is the unadorned griot music, as well as the thorough understanding provided by the text and pictures. This is an essential purchase for every world music library.

LINK➤ *Various Artists - Shaman, Jhankri, and Néle*   *Ellipsis Arts 3550*
Another excellent CD and book project from Ellipsis Arts. This one presents 18 "indigenous sound healers" from all over the world (from Korea to Panama, Tuva to Peru). A full-color book explains how each of these healers works. Producer Pat Moffitt Cook is involved in both music and alternative health care.

June Tabor

As a girl in **England**, Tabor sang the songs she heard on television. She was born in 1947, and grew up in the 1950s, singing along to "Kumbaya" and "Michael, Row the Boat Ashore." She listened attentively to popular British singers, then locked herself in a room for days until she could imitate them perfectly. At Oxford, Tabor involved herself in the local folk music community, recorded a few stellar solo albums in the mid-1970s, and sang with Steeleye Span member Maddy Prior in a duo called Silly Sisters (their first album became a cult favorite, so they eventually recorded a second, years later). Her voice is extraordinary—she truly possesses one of the most remarkable voices in the world of popular music. Over time, Tabor has moved from very traditional music to work by contemporary songwriters. Her recent albums have included tracks by R.E.M., Bonnie Raitt, Los Lobos, and David Byrne.

Ashes and Diamonds
Green Linnet 3063

Mostly traditional songs, performed with a crystalline voice, from 1977. "Reynard the Fox" is typical; a hunter's romp accompanied by accordion and violin. The stark story "The Devil and Bailiff McGlynn" is performed without any accompaniment, but with a cross between rhythmic speech and singing. "The Easter Tree" is similar, a kind of poetry presented by an Old English teller of tales. The eerie calm of the piano adds darkness to the murderer's tale, "Streets of Forbes." The restraint and faithful execution of older music requires a special listening mood; those willing to travel backward through time with Tabor will be rewarded with the likes of "Lord Maxwell's Last Goodnight."

LINK➤ *Cathie Ryan* *Shanachie 78082*
Former singer with Cherish The Ladies, a U.S.-Irish group. Ryan's clarity of presentation, folky material, and artful treatments of work by Dave Swarbrick, Ralph McTell, and Dougie McLean are superb.

Against the Streams
Green Linnet 3096

This 1992 album and 1994's *Angel Tiger* (Green Linnet 3074) attend to a similar muse. In another time, they might have been called folk or folk rock, but today, they're best described as contemporary art songs. Much has been made of Tabor's singing Elvis Costello songs, but the full tone of her instrument and her skill in dramatizing stories are far more remarkable. Eric Taylor's "Joseph Cross" is about an Native American who "killed in the white man's name" but was refused a "white man's funeral." Billy Bragg's "Rumors of War" is spooky with minimalist accompaniment, a town's frightening quiet before the soldiers arrive for battle. Extremely sensitive accompaniment throughout.

LINK➤ *Silly Sisters — No More to the Dance* *Shanachie 79069*
1988 album by two of England's best classic folk singers: Maddy Prior and June Tabor. Harmonies are crisp and magnificent; they're best a capella. Material tends toward traditional. Beautiful work.

In 1981, Pascal Nabet-Meyer left his home in Paris to spend three years in the South Pacific. Inspired by Paul Gauguin's book, Before and After, Nabet-Meyer took his research very seriously. In 1982, he found out about the island of **Rapa**, located 1,000 miles southeast of Tahiti, the last land before the South Pole. Overcoming some remarkable obstacles, he managed to travel to the island. There, he heard a magnificent choir. He vowed to return and to make a recording. Nearly a decade later, Nabet-Meyer came back to Rapa with a tape recorder and other sturdy equipment that could withstand the high humidity. He negotiated with the elders and gained permission to record the choir singing its oldest and most traditional songs. With 126 people singing and crickets chirping outside the village's common room, he recorded enough music to fill two CDs.

Rapa Iti   Triloka 320192

"Oparo E Oparo E" is a song about war. Men tell the story in chorus and with war cries; women's stinging harmonies answer the men. A village has been destroyed; for those who remain, there are only laments. On "Morotiri Nei," men and women again sing different parts, often simultaneously. The women seem to slow down and stop singing (as if the turntable's motor has run down). "Hineme Tatou" sounds less harsh, prettier, and more like a typical Western chorus. Be careful not to dismiss this unfamiliar music; play it a few times over a period of months. Let it get into your soul.

LINK➤ *Rurutu Choir – Polynesian Odyssey*   *Shanachie 64065*
Another in Pascal Nabet-Meyer's series of Polynesian polyphonia.

Rapa Iti, Vol. 2   Shanachie 64055

The more one listens to this primitive music, the more it reveals. Technically speaking, this is about a microtonal scale, polyphonics, and complex harmonies. "Ua Putuputu Tatou E" is a chant for those who are moving from life to death. Several groups sing complementary chants simultaneously; again, the tempo mysteriously slows down to a stop. "Tangi Mahate" includes some giggles; it's about the large size of a local banana. "Te Moko" tells the story of a warrior who saves the island from a giant lizard; a high voice above the harmonizing din creates the necessary tension. Thrusting male grunts and a diminutive singsong female chorus accompany the ritualistic preparation of the Tioo root on "Neki Neki."

LINK➤ *The Bulgarian Voices—Angelite and Huun-Huur-Tu*
Fly, Fly My Sadness   *Shanachie 64071*
Two polyphonic vocal groups singing together, accompanied by traditional instruments. Recorded in 1997. The extremely low male voices on "Legend" and other tracks, contrast sharply with the female harmonies.

Paisley, **Scotland** is a village not far from Glasgow, and there in a pub the Tannahill Weavers got its start in the late 1960s. The band's name merged local writer Robert Tannahill, a Scottish poet laureate, and the area's centuries-old weaving industry. Early members included fiddler Dougie MacLean and Mike Ward, who played violin but recognized the value of adding bagpipes to the folk band. (In fact, Ward had left the band and wanted to return only if Alan McLeod, who played bagpipes, joined as well.) At first, guitar player and lead vocalist Roy Gullane was very much against the idea, but he was outvoted by whistle and bodhrán player Phil Smilie and by Hudson Swan. McLeod joined, and the band became famous for the addition of full-sized Highland bagpipes. The group turned professional in 1975 and has been popular in the U.S., Canada, and Scotland. See also: http://ourworld.compuserve.com/homepages/tannahill_weavers.

Cullen Bay   Green Linnet 1108

Among a handful of albums recorded in the 1990s, Cullen Bay stands out. There's a tenderness to "Joy of My Heart," and there's an innocence in the group *a capella* of "A Night Visitor's Song" that glows. The sheer drama of the bagpipes that open "Cullen Bay," one of many original songs here, is like a sunrise. It begins a splendid medley, which also includes "Alick C. MacGreggor," composed by G.S. MacLennan, one of the century's finest writers of pipe tunes. The work is majestic. The folk simpicity of "Braw Burn the Bridges" sets a mood to recall Scotland's people left on foreign shores. Thoughtful, contemporary work. Recorded in 1990.

LINK▶ *Andy M. Stewart – Songs of Robert Burns*   *Green Linnet 3059*

Scottish poet Robert Burns lived in the 1700s. When he wasn't writing poems or songs, he collected (and often embellished) them. Familiar phrases abound: "green grow the rashes," "my luve is like a red, red rose that's newly sprung in June." From 1989.

Best of the Tannahill Weavers, 1979–1989   Green Linnet 1100

A decade's work is well represented in this 12-song collection. Robert Burns's "Auld Lang Syne" is sung in Scotland for New Year's Eve, but the melody is not the same as the one familiar in the U.S. (it's far prettier). "Tranent Moor" is a Scots battle song, notable for both the fighting spirit in the instrumental and the urgent vocals; the unusual harmonies are most striking, however. "The Highland Laddie" is a love song, again rich with harmonies. In addition, there are "Lucy Cassidy," "Farewell to Fiunary/Heather Island," and other gems. One of the best: "The Cape Breton Fiddlers' Welcome to the Shetland Isles." This album is a good place to start.

LINK▶ *Various Artists – A Celebration of Scottish Music*   *Temple 2003*

Superior collection includes the military precision of Shotts & Dykehead Caledonia Pipe Band (bagpipes, that is), Hamish Moore on Lowland pipes, and Cilla Fisher (who's likely to send chills down the spine). Battlefield Band, too. (And lots more.)

In Malagasy, the native language of **Madagascar**, "tarika" means "group." Tarika Sammy, the group's original name, was "Sammy's Group" (Sammy being a nickname for Sameola Andriamalalaharijaona). Sammy grew up in Madagascar's capital city, Antananarivo. With boyhood friend Solomon Ratianarinaivo (also called Tiana), he formed a folk group, adding two female singers, Claudia Marie Noëlle Ramasirmanana and Hana-triniana Razaonialmiarina (called Hanrita). When Sammy left at the end of 1993, the group reorganized under the leadership of Hanrita and adopted a more contemporary, commercial sound. The members became known simply as Tarika. Hanitra and her sister Noro write the songs and sing. They grew up poor, learned English and several other languages, and in time, Hanitra became a translator, then a tourist guide with a keen interest in her country's unique cultural history. This led to a job in Madagascar's consultate in the U.K., then a job in Tarika Sammy, then, group leadership.

Fanafody
Green Linnet 4003

After recording tracks for various compilations, Tarika Sammy released its first album in 1992. At this point, the group included Sammy (Samoela Andriamalalaharijaona), his cousin Tiana, and two sisters, Hanitra and Noro. Each musician plays multiple instruments unique to Malagasy music. The marovany (double-sided box zither) is featured on "Transport," a song about the isolation of some villages due to the nonexistence of reasonable transportation. The kabosy (small, partially fretted guitar) accompanies the spirited group vocals (which are really good!) on "Fanafody," a song about herbal medicines. "Variana Variana" tells about the stones that poor children use as toys. Acoustic instruments and energetic voices result in a charming, exuberant album. With rhythm support from the 3 Mustaphas 3.

LINK► *Various Artists — Madagaskari I*   *Feur und Eis 704*
Tarika became well-known because of a Madagascar compilation from Henry Kaiser and David Lindley called A World Out of Time *(Shanachie 64041). They worked with a German team who produced this compilation two years earlier. It includes Rossy, Tarika Sammy, etc.*

Balance
Green Linnet 4011

Same musicians (the group is known as Tarika Sammy again), but Hanitra and Noro's enthusiasm is beginning to dominate. Their resplendent joint lead vocal on "Jono (The Catch of Fish)" benefits from a terrific acoustic accompaniment. "Hendry (Wise)," written by Hanitra, adapts a street rhythm to a song about Malagasy unity. Noro's "Vohitsara (Beautiful Town)" is an attractive portrait of Madagascar's capital, Antananarivo; it begins with some lovely strumming, but the magic is in the women's soaring harmonies. "Jijy (Balance, Pay Attention, Recite)" combines a repeating chant-like rhythm with a delightful contemporary lead vocal. It's the best song on this 1994 album, a distant cousin to rap music.

LINK▶ Sibèba — Hijas del Sol   *Nube Negra (Intuition) 3178*
Mostly, the two lead "daughters of the sun" sing flawless a capella, sometimes against their own vocal percussion, sometimes with traditional instruments from Isla de Bioko (part of Equatorial Guinea, near Biafra). Wonderful vocals.

Bibiango
Green Linnet 4028

In 1993, Sammy left, and the group changed its name to Tarika (*the* group). Hanitra and Noro are in charge. Donne and Solo add their experience with traditional instruments, but the youthful power comes from Ny Ony, who previously played salegy dance music. The group vocal sound is smoother than before, with velvety harmonies on "Taraina" backed by an intricate matrix of stringed instruments with distinctive tones and colors. "Bibiango (a wild, hungry, ready-to-kill beast)" is sung as a kind of anthem for this "killer" band. "Kilaloa" adds the melodeon (a kind of accordion) to a children's street romp about games the band members played as kids.

LINK▶ Various Artists — Planet Squeezebox   *Ellipsis Arts 3470*
Superlative 3-CD accordion tour with stops in Scotland, Ireland, France, Italy, Cleveland (for a polka), Mexico, Argentina, Cape Verde, Egypt, even China.

Son Egal
Green Linnet 4042

Hanitra spent 1996 researching the taboo subject of the 1947 fight for freedom against French-African troops trained in Senegal. The album's title has a double meaning: "Sonegaly" means "Senegalese" in Malagasy, and "son egal" means "equal sound" in French. "Avelo (Ghost)" scares up revered ancestors, whose bones are being stolen and sold by desperately poor citizens. "Sonegaly" deals with fear of monstrous Senegalese soldiers, then tries to make peace by explaining that Senegal once fought for its own independence ("Do you want to still keep fighting? Or bear a grudge forever?") "Dive Be (Very Wrong)" attacks an enforced silence about events that happened fewer than 50 years ago.

LINK▶ Sweet Honey in the Rock — Selections 1976-1988
Flying Fish 667/8
With gospel on their side, Sweet Honey in the Rock derives a snappy pop presentation. Extraordinary female voices, a good sense of R&B, and hope for a better world drive this special music. A 2-CD set for every collection.

Beneath Southern Skies
Shanachie 64067

This 1996 album was recorded by a new Tarika Sammy, led by founder Sammy with Tiana. This group's Hanitra is Tiana's wife, not Tarika's current leader—no surprise, then, that this album sounds very much like early Tarika Sammy. There is a greater emphasis on traditional instruments and rhythms, and the female vocals are more choral than lead. There's even the occasional (South African style) male groaner vocal, as on "Arahaba Ririninini (Winter Greeting)." "Arovy Ny Biby (Save the Animals)" is catchy and lovely for its vocal harmonies, guitar, and flutes. Very good vocal songwriting throughout. Nice to have two talented groups develop from a single source.

LINK▶ Machanic Manyeruke & Puritans   *Flying Fish (Rounder) 70553*
Gracious, straightforward songs about the Bible and repentance performed by two harmonizing female vocalists. Accompaniment is provided by a well-played electric guitar and a simple electronic keyboard. From Zimbabwe in the 1980s, but still fresh today.

A four-man polyphonic singing group, Tenores di Bitti follows a tradition on the Mediterranean island of **Sardinia**. The group members have been working together for about 20 years. Daniele Cossellu and Piero Sanna both sing solo, as well as secondary tones (called mesa 'oche, a vocalized song in a high register). Tancredi Tucconi sings contra (a guttural effect produced by pressure on the vocal chords), and Salvatore Bandinu sings bassu (a continuous nasal sound in addition to the guttural effect). The soloist determines how and when to alter the tonality. These musical patterns are associated with sheepherding, and in Bitti (the town in which these tenors work as shepherds), ethnomusicologists have identified more than a dozen different kinds of songs, from fast dances to hymns, all performed in this distinctive style. How old is this music? By one theory, it dates back to 3,000 B.C.

Ammentos   Agogo 9502

The connection between singing voices and the environment is particularly clear here, perhaps not in a direct and concrete way, but it is easily heard in the influences. The bassu (bass) creates images of oxen, the contra (baritone) evokes sheep, and the mesa 'oche (middle voice) sounds like the wind. The voices are polyphonic: gentle pressure on the vocal chords produces a secondary tone, for example. The songs are traditional, but the creative imposition of complex vocal tones requires consummate musical skill. There is no instrumental accompaniment; everything heard in this virile, rustic music is produced by the human voice. The quality on this recording is adequate; the one below is easier to enjoy.

LINK➤ *Huun-Huur Tu — If I'd Been Born an Eagle*   Shanachie 64080
Polyphonic vocals (most often with instrumental accompaniment) from Mongolia. Passion for the land and its beauty is central to the music.

S'amore 'e mama   RealWorld (Caroline) 2362

Often produced with reverb for added effect, the polyphonic combination of four male voices suggests kinship with a surprising range of a capella music. There are strong similarities to monastic choral song, and the occasional reminder of where doo-wop and barbershop harmonies really originated. Various song forms are represented, often with inspiration from nature. One singer frequently takes the lead, and the others provide harmony. But it's far from simple music, as the changes on "Sa Ballarina (The Dancer)" suggest. On the title song (translated as "The Mother's Love"), a tenor calls out lead about the shining light that a mother can provide, and warm harmonies answer. Essential vocal music.

LINK➤ *Hilliard Ensemble — Perotin*   ECM New Series 1385
Seven male voices recreate the polyphonic and harmonic textures of a 12th century composer. The Hilliard Ensemble's work is impeccable and recorded with extraordinary attention to vocal detail.

The members of this idiosyncratic foursome from **Russia** met when they were students at the St. Petersburg Observatory. They first played together in 1986 and gained some renown with an appearance on a local TV talent competition called *You Have Five Minutes*. Oyster Band manager Rob Chalice heard them at a concert in Dresden in 1989 and invited them to tour with WOMAD. A RealWorld recording contract followed. Igor Ponomarenko writes the arrangements and plays alto domra (a three-stringed mandolin). Andrei Konstantinov performs on the soprano domra. They lived together at the Conservatory. Mikhail "Mischa" Dziudze plays the bass balalaika (a large and cumbersome instrument that's quite obscure). Bayan accordion player Andrei Smirnov completes the group. The Russian word "terem" has several meanings. Originally, it was the highest place in the house, where a virgin lived before she was married; it now means any beautiful Russian building, a beautiful place, or a beautiful dream.

Terem RealWorld (Caroline) 2321

While the music is undeniably Russian and the style borrows from folklore, the Terem Quartet creates its own music. "Old Carousel" uses stringed instruments to reproduce every detail, down to the vague feeling of show business and fantasyland: the colorful painted horses, the speed, the feeling of going up and down, and a child's wonder. And the group follows this with a slow folk dance, "Two-Step Nadya." Fierce stomping begins "Valenki," but that's nothing compared to the super speed of the finger picking on the strings. These guys make a significant creative decision every 6 seconds, and never, ever miss! "Barnynia," a traditional Russian song, is the best ride of all.

LINK▶ *The Ukranians* Omnium 2002

The trio is from Britain, but they have some Ukranian blood, and they understand the country's musical traditions well enough to twist them inside out. This probably occupies a place between the real thing and what 3 Mustaphas 3 might do.

Classical RealWorld (Caroline) 2347

Generally more restrained and conventional than one would expect, the group launches a full-blooded folkloric attack on Ponomarkenko's "Funeral March," nicely simulating the enormous sound of a symphony orchestra with just a handful of instruments. Ponomarkenko also contributes "Flea Waltz," crossing overblown Russian classical music with some Looney Tunes slapstick and comic timing. Mozart's "Eine Kleine Nacht Musik" gets the kind of showy treatment that a street band might offer to please the crowd, but the quartet plays Schubert's "Ave Maria" pretty straight. The "Chardash" works best because it's music originally written for a folk ensemble with string instruments. The group's affection for these pieces is infectious. Recorded in England in 1994.

LINK▶ *Borodin String Quartet — Tchaikovsky: String Quartets Nos. 1-3* EMI 49775

The grownups play their serious music.

Texas Tornados

A Tex-Mex, or **Tejano**, supergroup that worked together from 1988 until 1992 (and in 1996, for a reunion). Freddy Fender changed his name from Baldemar Huerta to enter the mainstream music business; a 1960 hit, "Wasted Days and Wasted Nights," made him famous, but he lost momentum after a five-year prison sentence (for marijuana possession); by the early 1970s, he was out of the music business. Fender came back in 1975 with "Before the Next Teardrop Falls" and continued to record hits for a decade. Flaco Jimenez came from a family of accordion players, legendary along the border towns, and better known because of an association with Ry Cooder. Doug Sahm had been recording in Texas for decades when Atlantic Records signed him as a country-rock act; "Is Anybody Going to San Antone?" was one resulting hit during the early 1970s. Augie Meyers, a longtime cohort of Sahm, completed the Texas Tornados.

Best of Texas Tornados   Reprise 45511

At first, songs like "Who Were You Thinkin' Of" and "Is Anybody Goin' to San Antone" feel so familiar; they seem like well-constructed AM radio hits (perhaps because they're sung in English). Flaco Jimeniz keeps his accordion solos brief, but he centers these conjunto polkas. This becomes even clearer on "(Hey Baby) Que Paso." And check out Freddie Fender's electric guitar on the same song. (Yes, his "Wasted Days and Wasted Nights" is here, too.) Some of the Spanish-language songs are better still: the old-fashioned style of "La Mucura" and the rocked-out "Adios Mexico." They're from 1991's *Zone of Our Own* (26683), the group's best album.

LINK➤ *Mazz — Nuestras Mejores Canciones - 17 Super Exitos*
                                                         EMI Latin 42867
A greatest hits collection from 1993 by a very popular Tejano group (Tejano updates conjunto with more of an electric sound). Que Esperbas (EMI Latin 27738), also from 1993, is probably the best single album, but be sure not to miss Mazz Mariachi y Tradicion (74332), a 1997 release performed to mariachi accompaniment.

Ay Te Dejo en San Antonio Y Más   Arhoolie 318

Jimeniz performs in a more relaxed setting, as if he were playing for a small audience at a local bar. Most of the album was recorded in 1985 with Jimeniz on accordion and vocals, accompanied by Toby Torres, who plays bajo sexto (12-string bass). This is about the sheer joy of hearing conjunto and Jimeniz's remarkable skill and talent. The material is nicely varied. In addition to the slower polkas (similar to waltzes), there are some very fast boleros and other Mexican dances. In addition, there's a wild version of "El Barrelio" that might be recognized as "Roll Out the Barrel." Some material from 1979 is also included on the CD.

LINK➤ *Valerio Longoria — Texas Conjunto Pioneer*   *Arhoolie 358*
Conjunto recorded in the 1950s and early 1960s by one of its most expressive musicians. Of three additional tracks recorded in 1990 (two with Freddie Fender), one stands out: "Ramón Delgado," a protest corrido (story ballad) about the 1923 murder of a 70-year-old Mexican immigrant by a white Texan rancher. Extensive notes explain the true story.

Mikis Theodorakis

One of the greatest contemporary artists in **Greece**, Theodorakis was born in 1925 on the island of Chios. Coming of age during WWII, he was active in the resistance, and was captured and tortured—a situation repeated during the Greek Civil War. Theodorakis studied in Athens and Paris and composed his first symphony in 1953. In the early 1960s, he composed film scores (*Zorba the Greek*), song cycles based on classical literature ("Epiphania"), and popular songs. When Papadopoulos took control of Greece in 1967, Theodorakis went underground; he was interned in a concentration camp before being safely exiled through the efforts of international composers and playwrights. His activism became symbolic of resistance against dictatorship. Theodorakis eventually returned to Greece. He has served multiple terms in the Greek Parliament and as the head of music for Greek radio and television. Extensive information about Theodorakis's life and work is available from biographer Guy Wagner at http://members.aol.com/gwagner377/mikihome/.

The Ballad of Mauthausen   EMI Greece 702042
Maria Farandouri is one of the more important singers associated with Theodorakis. Here, she sings a song cycle based on short stories written by Kambanelis. The stories were inspired by people imprisoned in Mauthausen, a concentration camp in Germany. These stories were transformed into lyrics by several writers, including Kambanelis and Gatsos. Theodorakis composed the music. There are bold dreams, and a happy melody accompanying "When the War Is Over." And a slow dance of desperation: "I'm Tired of Holding You." Some songs are heroic, but many just cope with the dark shadows. "Anthony" is a simple song about life on a work line, carrying rocks and picking up friends who fall.

LINK➤ *Mikis Theodorakis — To Axion Esti*   Minos-EMI 7020
Classic recording of one of his finest works, based on religious allegory, featuring the voices of Manos Katrakis (an actor appearing on stage and in films), and Gregoris Bithikotsis (a classical singer often associated with Theodorakis).

100 Years of Cinema   Minos-EMI Classics 37042
This 1995 2-CD set attempts to place film composer Theodorakis in context. CD1 honors Nino Rota and Leonard Bernstein, and features Henry Mancini, John Williams, Vangelis Papathanassiou (*Chariots of Fire*), and Ennio Morricone. CD2 is all Theodorakis—*Serpico, Z*, and works not as well known in the U.S., like 1972's Etat de Siege (like *Z*, directed by Costa-Gravas). George Dalaras sings beautifully, and with full orchestral accompaniment from the Metropole Orchestra. "Beautiful City" from 1962's *Les Amants de Teruel* and "Raining in the Poor Neighborhood" from the 1960s' *The Neighborhood of Dream* are particularly affecting. (On the latter, the audience becomes very involved.) Recorded live at the Acropolis.

LINK➤ *Theodorakis, Xarhakos, Hatzidakis —*
The Sound of Greece...:14 Instrumental Syrtaki   GVRT 1003
"Never on Sunday," "Zorba," and other folk-dance works played on bouzouki. The pieces were composed by three leading Greek composers.

This band is a put-on, a riff on the 1980s obsession with world music. As the story goes, the band has its roots in **Szegerely**, a mythical town between the Balkan and Caucasus mountains, where it started by performing in the village's own nightclub, the Crazy Loquat. The group members' Uncle Patrel helped them defect to London in 1981 (he smuggled them across the border in refrigerators). All six members use the Mustapha surname. The story gets a whole lot sillier, but the success of the band is real: an early 1980s tour was a terrific launchpad; the group's second album entered Billboard's World Music chart at Number 3.

Heart of Uncle   Rykodisc 20156

Sure, it's all a joke. But these guys are skilled musicians with keen ears and a devastating sense of the absurd. "Awara Hoon" is a strident bit of Indian film music, probably the album's best song. The city version of "Trois Fois Trois" is dominated by flashy Latino horns; the country version uses a clarinet and a melodeon for a traditional folk effect. Collectors of rural folk music like Muzsikás are the target of "Ovcepolsko Oro," a lumbering farce of a Bulgarian dance. Afro-pop's ringing guitar and fast dance beat get skewered in "Benga Taxi." To make all of this work, the musicians demonstrate astonishing versatility on a vast number of instruments. From 1989.

LINK▶ _Various Artists – Planet Soup_   _Ellipsis Arts 3450_
The ultimate world beat fusion mix. And a pretty good introduction to world music in its many forms. Some tracks focus on music from a single country (Astor Piazzolla from Argentina, Värttinä from Sweden); many others are hybrids (Indian tabla plus bluegrass banjo, etc.).

Soup of the Century   Rykodisc 10195

The relentless nonsense continues in 1990 with the Albanian drone "Bukë E Kripë Në Vatër Tone" and the dance "Kalazhojnë." (Note the gratuitious umlauts above the e's in these titles.) "Soba Song" is a country-western song about Japanese noodles. "Yogurt Koydum Dolaba/Television (Put Yogurt in Fridge, on Television)" suffers from vaguely Eastern European influences. Don't expect literal parodies; "Zohar No. 2" and "This City Is Very Exciting!" capture Arab, Indian, and North African essences, but they're tough to pigeonhole. Where's the "home country?" Maybe near Bulgaria. "Mamo, Snezhets Navalyalo" comes from around there somewhere. 1991's _Friends, Fiends & Fronds_ (Omnium 2003) comprises mostly alternate mixes and secondary material, but it includes the popular "Linda, Linda."

LINK▶ _Dissidenten – The Jungle Book_   _Worldly Music (Triloka) 7202_
A German group (roots in the 1970s progressive band Embryo) that performs with the Karataka College of Percussion. Western pop meets Indian tradition. Key track: John Coltrane's "A Love Supreme" performed with Indian chants, vocals, and instrumentation.

Toots & the Maytals

Toots is Kingston, **Jamaica**, native Frederick Hibbert. In the early 1960s, he formed the Maytals with Nathaniel "Jerry" Mathis-McCarthy and Raleigh Gordon. By combining gospel, soul, and a Jamaican beat, they helped invent reggae. Like the Wailers, they started with Studio One, but moved on to other producers and labels. The Maytals gained popularity through 1966 in Jamaica and in England, with hit records and festival competitions, but a drug arrest took Hibbert out of action for 18 months. The story picks up again with a new producer and a hit whose title referred to Hibbert's prison ID: "54-46 That's My Number," now a rock steady standard track. Another popular song, "Pressure Drop," appeared on *The Harder They Come* soundtrack. The group broke up in 1981, but Hibbert continued as a solo artist, produced by Sly and Robbie through the 1980s, and became an international star. He formed a new Maytals early in the 1990s.

Time Tough: The Anthology
Mango 524-219

Not just a 2-CD collection by one of reggae's best groups, but a good way to track the music's development from ska and rock steady in the 1960s to reggae connections with rock and other genres in the 1980s. "Six and Seven Books of Moses," produced by Coxsone Dodd in 1963 for Federal, begins the story with a nice harmonica solo, and the next few cuts (1963-68) pre-date reggae. The term "reggae" is first used in 1968's "Do the Reggay," with its tasty and familiar rhythm, released the same year as "54-46, That's My Number." By 1970's "Pressure Drop," the Maytals' sound was focused and distinctive. (The song was included on *The Harder They Come* film soundtrack). With its catchy hook ("na-na-na"), well-placed guitar riffs, and R&B vocal, 1973's "Funky Kingston" made them stars in the U.S. There's also the unlikely "Take Me Home Country Roads" that works remarkably well when remapped onto Jamaica. Their long string of hits had slowed by the early 1980s. Toots went out on his own and did some recording with Sly and Robbie. In 1988, *Toots in Memphis* (Mango 9818) brought a kind of dream-come-true with the uplifting "Freedom Train" sung in his best R&B style with Sly and Robbie and some of Memphis's best musicians (buy this album separately—it's terrific!) A definitive collection (though it does not cover Toots's new Maytals from the 1990s).

LINK▶ *The Heptones — Sea of Love*   *Heartbeat 128*
Very popular 1997 repackaging of a joyous harmony trio's Studio One work from the early 1960s through 1971. Simple and delightful.

When Peter Mackintosh was 18, in 1962, he formed the Wailing Wailers with Bob Marley and Bunny Livingstone. A versatile musician, he played organ, guitar, piano, melodica, and other instruments on early Wailers recordings, and also worked as a session man for Johnny Nash. Renamed Peter Tosh, he stayed with the Wailers until 1973 and released his first solo work in 1976. An aggressive, outspoken man, he enraged **Jamaica**'s police, who beat him soundly several times. Tosh's militancy, marijuana advocacy, and pleas for real justice were often glibly stated (House of Representatives becomes "House of Repre-sent-a-Thief," etc.). He stopped an active schedule of touring and recording in the mid-1980s, seeking help from medicine men in Africa and trying to sort out a multitude of business problems. His life was a mess. Tosh was shot dead in his Kingston home in 1987; some questions about his death remain unre-solved.

Honorary Citizen   Columbia 64681

This 3-CD box from 1997 correctly claims to be a career retrospective, but it's important to understand what's here (and what's not). CD1 collects rare Ja-maican singles. Recorded in 1967, "Pound Get a Blow" was the Wailers' first single for the group's Wail 'N Soul 'M label. Bunny was in jail at the time, so Rita Marley sang in his place. "Once Bitten" was based on Tosh's hit "Maga Dog" (not included in this collection). CD2 is filled with unreleased live record-ings like "Johnny B. Goode" and "Get Up Stand Up" (there are two versions—one is an acoustic one for a Chicago FM station). CD3 offers an incomplete sampling of Tosh's hits. Great liner notes complete a nice package.

LINK▶ _Peter Tosh — The Toughest_   _Heartbeat (Rounder) 150_
Thirteen tracks recorded by a youthful Tosh from 1963 to 1966 for Studio One and producer Coxsone Dodd, with Bob Marley, Bunny Wailer, Rita Marley, and other familiar names on harmony. Plus six later tracks for producer Lee Perry.

The Best of Peter Tosh: Dread Don't Die   EMI 54491

This solid 1996 compilation brings together work from 1981's _Wanted Dread and Alive_ (EMI 17055), 1983's _Mama Africa_ (17095), 1984's _Captured Live_ (17126), and other albums. "(You've Got to Walk and) and Don't Look Back," from 1979, is sung as a duet with Mick Jagger, and it features perfect instru-mentation and flawless backup singers. "Glasshouse," with its shattering glass sound effects and dance-hall mix, offers a rare glimpse of Tosh's more vulner-able, defensive side. He's especially impressive on "Fools Die," a slow and moody folk piece, more like jazz than reggae. And just for fun, Tosh provides a terrific reggae version of "Johnny B. Goode." Very satisfying.

LINK▶ _Mighty Diamonds — Go Seek Your Rights_   _Caroline 1678_
Late 1970s compilation by leading reggae vocal trio. Hits include "Have Mercy," "Bodyguard," and "I Need a Roof." Tight. Some good message songs.

Because of the similarity in tonal colors, Touré's music is often compared with acoustic blues. Born in 1939 to a family whose ancestors were Spanish-African warriors and noblemen, Touré was raised in a small Niger River village called Niafonké (in northern **Mali**, near Timbuktu). He received his musical gift in a mystical experience at age 12, and started playing regularly a few years later (despite his mother's protests: music was unworthy of his noble birth). Through the 1960s, Touré worked on an ambulance boat, led a cultural group, and apparently listened to blues and R&B from the U.S. In the 1970s, he did some touring and recording in Europe. But it was not until 1987, when when he was nearly 50 years old, that a British concert promoter introduced Touré's music to a wider audience. Despite the success, Touré continues to live in his native town, where his income supports a large extended family.

Radio Mali   World Circuit 44

The best of Touré's 1970s work for his nation's radio station. The sound quality is fine, and the performances are captivating. Liner notes are also spectacular; they include English translations of the lyrics, color photos of Touré's life, and a lengthy biography. "Bandalabourou" tells the story of a poor boy told to kill a lion in order to win a rich man's daughter in marriage; the folk-blues piece ends with a dead lion and a paralyzed boy. The dominant feature of "Gambari," a praise song, is its rolling rhythm. "Samarya," sung with a small chorus, is dedicated to Niger's youth movement. "Soko," about a lake where annual sacrifices assure a village's prosperity, is one of several songs performed with ngoni player Nassourou Sare.

LINK➤ *John Lee Hooker — The Country Blues of John Lee Hooker*
OBC (Fantasy) 542
Touré is often compared with Hooker. (And, as world music has become more popular, Hooker has been compared with Touré.) This is the best album for a listening test.

Ali Farka Touré   Mango 9826

Pure acoustic music played on guitar and accompanied by bongos and calabash (a gourd used for a thumping percussion sound). The combination of Touré's piquant guitar style, song structure, repeated phrases, and worldwise tenor might suggest American blues, but there's no reliable evidence of a connection between the two musical forms. His own words express affection for his sister in "Amandrai," but the music comes from the Tamashek culture. Touré's guitar work is lovely on "Bakoye," and the Arab influence informs his vocal and the song's wavering style. He sings in various languages heard in Mali; he sings "Nawiye" in Songhai. Touré's best. From 1988.

LINK➤ *Boubacar Traoré — Kar Kar*   *Stern's Africa 1037*
Increasingly popular guitar player from Mali sings solo—just his voice and his guitar. Try also his earlier album Mariama *(Stern's 1032).*

The River
Mango 539-897

Adding electric guitar, saxophone, and harmonica to the rootsy guitar and calabash proves not at all risky. Touré skillfully maintains the essential structure of his music on this 1990 album; the Western instruments add depth and authority (and, to be honest, a bit of funk) to his resolutely Malian sound. (And yes, it does sound even more like blues....) "Kenouna" is sung as an entire village walks with fishing nets along the riverbank; men in canoes spread the nets, and paddle to the beat (with Touré, there's always a foot-tapping beat). The song is played by acoustic instruments and sung in Bozo. Most songs are sung in Songhai.

LINK➤ Vieux Diop — (Via Jo)　　　　　Worldly (Triloka) 7209

Soothing acoustic music performed on kora, with some acoustic guitar and electric bass in the background. Sweet, dry voice. Recorded in Connecticut in 1994.

The Source
Hannibal (Rykodisc) 1375

On this 1992 album, Touré expertly controls the balance of electric and acoustic guitars, and plays the electric guitar beautifully. Vocals are often unison duets with Affel Bocoum. Hamma Sankare plays calabash and often sings. On several tracks, American musician Taj Mahal plays a bluesy acoustic guitar. Touré also works with Groue Asko, a group of harmonizing backup singers (enormously tasteful, very subtle). "Roucky," a song about beauty and nature, is an impressive showcase of guitar playing. "Cinquante Six" is one of Touré's only recorded solo acoustic guitar songs, and it's superb. "Yenna," sung in Songhai with calabash percussion, showcases his electric guitar. Great album.

LINK➤ Jali Musa Jawara — Yasimika　　　Hannibal (Rykodisc) 1355

Jawara's kora and vocals, a female chorus, and a balaphon (xylophone). Recorded with great care in Abidjan, Cote D'Ivoire. Originally released in 1983, and consistently popular ever since.

Talking Timbuktu
Hannibal (Rykodisc) 1381

Ry Cooder is Touré's creative partner on this 1994 album; he produces and plays various guitars, the mbira (African thumb piano), etc. He's perfect alongside Touré's regular backups, Hamma Sankare (calabash) and Oumar Toure (congas). The presence of some L.A. session players and bluesman Clarence "Gatemouth" Brown (electric guitar, viola) doesn't add much—in fact, it probably detracts from the album's rootsy appeal. The finest moments are simple and uncomplicated. The spellbinding ambience of "Soukora" says nighttime is for lovers. On "Sega," Touré conjures a grass snake by playing a njarka (a stringed instrument made from a gourd). Touré sings in 11 different languages, including Peul, Bambara, Songhai, and Tamashek.

LINK➤ Ry Cooder — Into the Purple Valley　　　Reprise 2052

From way back in 1971, but still one of the best demonstrations of Cooder's versatility and virtuosity on guitar. Not one guitar—lots of different types of guitars and other stringed instruments.

Uttal grew up in NYC, where he studied banjo, electric guitar, and piano. He moved to San Francisco to study at the Ali Akbar Khan College of Music. There he learned sarod and Indian singing, which led to studies in India in the early 1970s. Uttal spent considerable time with folk and temple musicians, but he was most impressed by the Bauls a Bengalese people who passed on musical traditions through generations. The experience sharpened his perception, and he began to hear music in the sounds of everyday life. During the 1970s and 1980s, Uttal was a working musician in all sorts of bands, including punk, soul, blues, and reggae. By the early 1990s, music journalists began to notice Uttal's impact as a **fusion artist** more or less inside the circle that proscribes world music. Uttal is based in San Francisco. His current musical group is called the Pagan Love Orchestra.

Footprints
Worldly (Triloka) 7183

Somewhere between free jazz, new age, and world music, there's a space occupied by Jai Uttal. Jazz trumpeter Don Cherry, whose resumé includes work with artists from Africa and elsewhere, contributes spice, but he's only part of a far larger whole. Uttal's tasteful intermingling of traditional, often ancient, instruments with modern digital devices results in a totally coherent mix. Generally, this relaxing music contains introspective ideas woven into an interesting quilt. Sampled instrumentation from Turkey, Africa, and the Middle East adds to the mix. As artful as these arrangements may be, the music's soul can be hard to find. From 1990.

LINK➤ *Krishna Das — One Track Heart*   *Worldly (Triloka) 697-124-136*
A modern take on Indian chants with Jai Uttal, Jubu Smith (from Tony! Toni! Tone!), producer Jim Wilson. Includes an acoustic folk-blues and gospel version of "The Krishna Waltz" (you know: "Hare Krishna, Hare Krishna, Krishna Krishna, Hare Hare..."). For serious fusion fans.

Beggars and Saints
Worldly (Triloka) 7208

Uttal's journey continued with the formation of his Pagan Love Orchestra and a 1993 album called *Monkey* (Triloka 7194). This 1994 album has the same organization. Once again, Uttal's list of instruments played is long and obscure (included: ektar, gopichand, gubgubbi, kartals). "Lake of Exploits" benefits from a Middle Eastern rhythm, a pleasant groove, an enraptured vocal, and a tight band with good commercial instincts. "Hara Shiva Shanka" further focuses the album's theme: "a tribute to the passionate music of the street singers of India." That said, it's also a dance album with new age tendencies. Everything comes together perfectly on "Menoka," a mystical story.

LINK➤ *Various Artists — Tulku: Transcendence*
Worldy (Triloka) 447-215

By combining sampled vocals (Senegalese songs by Vieux Diop, Tahitian Choir, etc.) with fresh percussion and other instruments (some played by Uttal), producer Jim Wilson creates mid-1990s fusion with high technology.

In 1983, in the village of Rääkkyläa in southeastern **Finland,** a youth group of 15 girls (who sang and played a zither-like instrument) and 6 boys (who accompanied the girls on tin whistle, saxophone, bass, flute, and other instruments) began exploring the traditional music of their home, the Karelia region. The large group began to perform, gained some renown in Finland, and recorded one album, then another. The large group was pared down to ten members, including the best of Finland's roots and rock musicians. Group leader Sari Kaasinen focused the group's material on love, sex, and marriage (all from a distinctly Finnish female perspective). She also emphasized both the unique five-female sound and featured instrumentalists. The formula worked; Värttinä became one of Europe's most popular groups. Still, the roots remain: Värttinä is a showcase for traditional Finnish music. The word "värttinä" means "spindle"; the connotation is sharp and vibrant.

Oi Dai
Green Linnet 4014

The first album by the smaller group, released in 1991, became one of Finland's all-time best-sellers. "Vot Vot Ja Niin Niin" is the classic Värttinä "bad girl" song; the grils like to upset the old women by disappearing around a corner with some boy, and they call out for boys to visit their village to spend the night. Lively Mari dances provide the melody for "Marilaulu." The lyrics are again tough on the elders, who gossip and deserve to have their tongues cut out and their mouths filled up with tin. The combination of sheer energy, harmonies that cut like a knife, and masterful folkloric accompaniment is nothing short of fabulous.

LINK▶ *Väsen − Spirit*   *NorthSide 6004*
Instrumental rural folk trio from Sweden featuring the nyckelharpa (long, thin fiddle with keys on the fretboard). This CD compiles work done from 1990-95.

Aitara
Green Linnet 4026

Irrepressible! The group starts with an unbelievably fast vocal on "Katariina," a song about a girl whose belt was missing, causing endless gossip throughout the village. "Tumula" is no less spunky; the singers try every trick to woo a boy, only to brush him away at song's end. "Mie Tahon Tanssia (I Want to Dance)" bounces to a very unusual rhythm, but the lyrics offer little more than the title does. Very high-speed harmonies lead the (fast) traditional rhythm section on "Kannunkaataja (The Tippler)." The title cut is also a demo of quick vocal high jinks, an edgy song about washing clothes. From 1994. And don't miss 1992's *Seleniko* (Green Linnet 4006).

LINK▶ *Värttinä − Kokko*   *Nonesuch 79429*
No longer young ones who sneak around the corner to steal a kiss, Värttinä women of 1996 are concerned about having babies. Musically, matured. Lyrically, on the abstract and poetic side.

For decades, Veloso has been a popular musician capable of strong social commentary. Born in a small coastal town in Bahia, he moved to the state's capital city of Salvador, befriended Gilberto Gil, and changed **Brazilian** music forever. They introduced Tropicálismo (a.k.a. Tropicália) with electric guitars, violent poetry, kitsch, and touches of free jazz and avant-garde music. As punishment for their radical behavior, the musicians were imprisoned by the military, then exiled in England (1969-71). Their songs were kept alive by female singers Gal Costa and Veloso's sister, Maria Bethânia, and, predictably, both musicians returned home more powerful than before. Among the finest contemporary poets in Brazil, Veloso's music continues to make trouble: one of his 1960s songs, "Allegria Allegria" ("Happiness Happiness"), became popular as a TV theme in 1992, and later, as the chant of crowds demonstrating for the impeachment of Brazil's president.

Sam Lenço Sem Documento (Without Handerkerchief, Without Document)
Verve 836-528

This best-of album begins with seven songs from 1968, then focuses on work just before and after 1980. The CD's title refers to lyrics in "Alegria Alegria (Happiness Happiness)"—Veloso's a happy drifter so carefree he doesn't even own a wallet. The smooth blending of his wordplays and Brazilian rhythms is wonderful on the (very dated) "Superbacana," and amid the electric guitars and racetrack effects on "Atrás do Trio Elétrico." Mostly, this is pretty acoustic work with superior lyrics. 1984's "Podres Poderes (Putrid Powers)" is folk-rock, highly critical of political leaders. Veloso is Brazil's finest singer-songwriter, and the variety of material here is an excellent place to begin a collection.

LINK➤ *Vinicius de Moraes – Minha Historia* *Philips 510-457*
Poet and activist Vinicius de Moraes is well known for his poetry and his lyrics; sometimes, he worked with Jobim as lyricist. The work of Alceu Valencia is in a similar style; seek out Valencia's Minha Historia (514-441), too.

Cinema Transcendental
Verve 512-023

A smile. The purity of Veloso's celebration requires no knowledge of Portuguese on "Lua de São Jorge (St. George's Moon)" as he sings about a beautiful moonlit place. "Oração ao Tempo (Prayer to Time)" is vintage Veloso, a homage to time itself, in which the repeated word "tempo" provides the chorus's rhythmic pattern. This 1979 album is light and easy, and enormously appealing for its simple musicality, Veloso's warm voice, and his obvious joy in his world of words. He loves to put together images: "Trilhos Urbanos (Urban Trails)," for example, explores street corner memories. "Beleza Pura (Pure Beauty)" dances with Brazilian percussion to focus attention on a beautiful woman.

LINK➤ *Luis Bonfá – The Bonfá Magic* *Milestone 9202*
Bonfá's background is samba and jazz, not MPB, but his ability to characterize Brazil in song is in a class with Veloso. Bonfá was 69 when he recorded this album in 1991; it includes many of Bonfá's best-known songs, including "Manhã de Carnaval."

Cores Nomes
Verve 838-464

Mainly Brazilian folk-rock with touches of bossa nova, this 1982 album is one of Veloso's best. The title means "Colors Names" and refers to "Trem des Cores (Train of Colors)." As he looks out the morning train's window, he sees colors: a red caboose and children at play, an olive in a cloud, and the silky blue of a paper covering an apple. Gal Costa made "Meu Bem, Meu Mal (My Good, My Bad)" well known; it's a tender love song that says "you're my everything: my good and my bad, you're my drug and my carnival...." In "Queixa (Complaint)," she's tough and he's delicate—the makings of a bad love affair. Wonderful melodies.

LINK➤ *Madredeus — Ainda* *Metro Blue 32636*

Portuguese fado, made modern, with the stunning voice of Teresa Salguerio out front. As picturesque as Veloso's work—and ultimately, from some similar roots. A lovely album (soundtrack to the film Lisbon Story*).*

Caetano Veloso
Nonesuch 79127

These Veloso classics are accompanied by only a single guitar and soft percussion. Unadorned, Veloso is relaxed, intimate, friendly, even playful. "Luz do Sol (Sunlight Rains)" is soothing dream stuff, and "O Homem Vehlo (The Old Man)" is a dignified portrait of a life that "hurts and shines." After two songs by Jobim, there's a surprise: Michael Jackson's "Billie Jean," followed by a brief bit of "Eleanor Rigby." With his quiet voice and distinctive phrasing, Veloso makes the former song his own. "Get Out of Town" is another of the few songs here not written by Veloso. No matter. Cole Porter fits right in. The liner notes contain Portuguese lyrics and English translations.

LINK➤ *Tom Zé — Brazil Classics 4:*
The Best of Tom Zé: Massive Hits *Luaka Bop 25805*

Zé was also part of the Tropicalia movement, but as he moved into more experimental music (some of this gets strange), he seemed to drop out. Try also Brazil 5: The Return of Tom Zé: The Hips of Tradition *(Luaka Bop 45118).*

Estrangiero
Elektra 60898

1991's *Circuladô* (Elektra Nonesuch 79277) is acoustic and edgy. This 1989 album is electric and edgy, capturing Veloso's melodic sense but adding the spoken word, a threatening percussion, and sharp language. "Os Otros Românticos (The Other Romantics)" gets its edge from Peter Scherer's drum programming, Marc Ribot's guitar, Carlinhos Brown's percussion, and producer Arto Lindsay's guitar and voice. The title song ("The Stranger") is a poetic epic with Bill Frisell on guitar and Naná Vasconcelos on percussion. The song is schizophrenic in its jumps between acoustic prettiness and anger as the lyrics move from images of natural beauty to the acts of madmen. With some acoustic gentility.

LINK➤ *Various Artists — Brazil: Forró: Music for Maids and Taxi Drivers*
Rounder 5044

Forró is a stew of Native Indian, African, and Portuguese, and (to some ears), akin to ska, polka, and Tejano. Dance music from Brazil's northeast, it runs deep in Veloso's influences. Even more on Brazil Classics 3: Forró etc.: Music of the Brazilian Northeast *(Luaka Bop 26323).*

Born Neville O'Reilly Livingstone in **Jamaica** in 1947, Bunny Livingstone grew up with Bob Marley. The two were close friends in the small village of Nine Miles, St. Ann, and then, in the tough Trenchtown ghetto in West Kingston. As teenagers, they sang together and decided to form a band with another boyhood friend from the neighborhood, guitar player Peter Mackintosh. By 1964, the Wailers landed its first hit song, and Livingstone worked with the band for a decade before moving up to the hills to an intensely private existence. He then starting a solo career. He changed his name, in celebration and memory of the band, to Bunny Wailer, and re-emerged with a public performance on Christmas Day, 1982. Wailer easily filled NYC's Madison Square Garden in 1986 and went on to experience U.S. touring success, awards, and consistent acclaim for the artistry and messages in his work.

Blackheart Man
Mango 539-415

Wailer is articulate and poetic, hopeful and reverential, a true believer in the possibilities of change. His lyrics summon mythic images. The music is mellow. The "Blackheart Man" is a mysterious man whom children are taught to fear, a man with whom the singer shares more and more as he ages. A "Rastaman" is stronger than any secular force; great men like Moses were rastamen. "Reincarnated Souls" and "Armageddon" cover similar themes, but Wailer is never more eloquent, nor is his music more magical, than on a reggae version of the folk-gospel song "This Train" (as in: "This train is bound to glory, this train..."). From 1976 with top reggae sidemen.

LINK➤ *The Skatalites —*
Hi-Bop Ska: The 30th Anniversary Recording   *Shanachie 45019*
As studio musicians, The Skatalites played for Bunny Wailer and many other reggae stars. This 1994 career retrospective (all new recordings) includes a big band "Guns of Navarone" and a definitive ska track, "Everlasting Sound." Liner notes tell the group's convoluted story.

Crucial: Roots Classics
Shanachie 45014

Wailer was especially prolific in the late 1970s and early 1980s, when he sang out for change in Jamaica, and his music was often central to the island's political situation. The Jamaica Labour Party adopted his "Crucial" for a 1980 campaign (without his permission) as it battled for power against the Socialist Party, which used Bob Marley's "Bad Card" as its anthem. "Boderation" is one of his best songs; it swings on lists of rhymes (boderation, moderation, creation, inflation, starvation, desperation, eradication, etc.). "Trouble on the Road Again" wonders why blacks kill blacks. Wailer is eloquent. It's easy to understand why this music can seem so threatening.

LINK➤ *Sugar Minott — Slice of the Cake*   *Heartbeat (Rounder) 24*
Major reggae dance-hall songwriter whose own songs, such as "No Vacancy" and "Level Vibes," have become standards.

Liberation

Shanachie 43059

Wailer's sting causes insidious damage. He attacks the soul, spreading his message with music that sounds more soothing than angry. All of this makes a song like "Botha the Mosquito" that much more effective. It's easy to sing along with lyrics like "Botha with the deadly bite that spreads the disease of apartheid...who annihilate Africa." Wailer is a dangerous man. Perhaps even more so on the yearning melody of "Ready When You Ready" with its repeated chorus: "We want to come home, sisters, come home." Whether the standard is songwriting, political passion, arrangements, or the music's spirit, this 1988 album is his best.

LINK➤ *Various Artists — Calypsos from Trinidad*   **Arhoolie 7004**

Political commentary in the islands is not exclusive to reggae. These recordings, made in the 1930s, are striking in their similarity to reggae themes: "The Rats," "The Strike," "The Gold in Africa," "Too Botheration."

Time Will Tell: A Tribute to Bob Marley   Shanachie 43072

In a decision between 1980's *Bunny Wailer Sings the Wailers* (Mango 9629) and this 1990 release, this one wins hands down. Here, he captures the Wailers' spirit; Sly and Robbie are on hand to get the rhythm right, he's got the groove down. With every note and nuance of "No Woman No Cry" so well known, Wailer makes the right decisions as he adds bits of percussion and organ, guitar riffs, and an elegiac singing style. He retains the old Wailers' feeling and makes the song his own. Ditto for "I Shot the Sheriff." Best is Wailer's graceful version of "Redemption Song" ("Won't you help me sing these songs of freedom?").

LINK➤ *Bob Marley and the Wailers —*
Legend (The Best of Bob Marley and the Wailers)   *Tuff Gong 846-210*
Essential originals of the best songs by the best reggae group of all time.

Retrospective   Shanachie 45021

A fine retrospective, but the other albums provide the context and drama that are so important to Wailer's music. In any case, it's fun to hear him loosen up for some dance hits, such as "Cool Runnings," "Ballroom Floor," and "Dance Hall Music" (for several years, Wailer excelled in reggae's dance-hall variation). Wailer's jazz-like improvisation on "Rockers" shows another creative side. Most striking is "Roots, Radics, Rockers, Reggae"— the song also titles an album that's worth owning (Shanachie 430103). All told, this 1995 CD samples the best from nine other albums available from Shanachie.

LINK➤ *Yellowman — Mister Yellowman*   *Shanachie 48007*

Very much the next generation of reggae: a deejay in the 1980s dance halls who played hard with vulgarity, acid satire, and a sharp attack.

Born in the Kasai region of **Democratic Republic of Congo** around 1950, Wemba joined Zaiko Langa Langa shortly after its formation as a student band in Kinshasa. In the early 1970s, the band members did away with horns and quasi-Cuban rhythms; they played loud, fast, and hard, and didn't worry much about precise harmonies or formality on stage. The group was a sensation! Around 1974, Wemba left to play traditional music with Kasai log drums. Looking to become a worldwide star, Wemba formed a new band, named Viva La Musica. He wore expensive European designer clothes, then turned the jacket inside out so the label could be seen. He completed the outfit with a missionary-style pith helmet and cheap African sandals. Wemba moved to Paris in 1984 and recorded his slick African music in ultra-modern recording studios. He still leads Viva La Musica, mainly for African fans. Under his own name, however, Wemba records world music for international audiences.

Papa Wemba   Stern's Africa 1026

Here is music from the late 1980s written and performed by the stylish Wemba. There's an R&B sensibility about the songwriting, and Wemba's voice possesses just the right Memphis tonality to appeal to Western listeners. As he modulates from tenor (with a soulful touch of gravel) to low falsetto, Wemba plays off the percussion with easy timing on "Mambayi Ede." He is supported by a small, tight male chorus. The percussion drives "Makaji Wanyi" and most other songs to a persistent (and infrequently varied) dance beat, but Rigo Star's sharp, bell-like electric guitar cuts through and establishes its own compatible rhythms. Star's longer solos are a highlight: he's one of Africa's best.

LINK➤ *Zaiko Langa Langa — Les Éveilleurs de L'Orchestre 1*
Ngoyarto (Stern's) 13

More rocking than horn-based soukous, ZLL has been one of Zaire's most popular bands for more than two decades. Papa Wemba was a member of the band in its early years, and he's part of this 1973-75 compilation. This and much more available from Stern's in NYC.

Emotion   RealWorld (Caroline) 2351

Wemba called the album Emotion because he was worried about the number of artistic chances taken here. It's a blend of folk, R&B, and Afro-pop with female backup singers. And it works. So well, in fact, that an English-language version of Redding and Cropper's "Fa Fa Fa Fa Fa (Sad Song)," a Memphis hit, fits right in. Although "Mandola" is much like his older work (with a more pronounced falsetto, however), the program is extremely varied. "Sala Keba (Be Careful)" is sung to acoustic accompaniment with a female chorus; "Shofele" gets an unusual shuffling rhythm; "Rail On" is presented as a folk song with a singalong chorus. The album is a delight!

LINK➤ *Papa Wemba and Viva La Musica — Foridoles*
Espérance (Stern's) 72424

Very successful in Africa (and, increasingly, the world). Released in 1994.

Fiddler Willie Royal was born in Texas, spent his early childhood in Turkey, Germany and France, and his school years in Florida. He started on classical violin at age 8, but It's a Beautiful Day, Jean-Luc Ponty, and other progressive rock violinists changed his direction. Royal worked in jazz, reggae, salsa, and country-rock, and he spent time in New Zealand, Canada, Brazil, and Europe before finding his way to Mexico's beaches in the early 1980s. Wolfgang Fink (a.k.a. Lobo) grew up in Bavaria, learned guitar in the German navy, and started hanging out with gypsies in the south of France to learn their music. He formed Lailo, a modern flamenco group, in the late 1970s and settled in Mexico in 1980. The two musicians met while working in separate rooms of Mamma Mia's, a Mexican restaurant in San Miguel de Allende. A decade later, they joined forces. Both are very serious surfers—and legendary characters.

The Music of Puerto Vallarta Squeeze   Mesa 92678

The Bridges of Madison County author Robert James Waller wrote Willie and Lobo into his novel, *Puerto Vallarta Squeeze,* and included their music on the audio version of his book. Waller and his wife chose favorite songs from the duo's first three albums (all top sellers) for this 1996 compilation. Waller narrates "Rockin' Gypsies," which begins his book. "Amsterdam," with its cascading violin and sea sounds, comes from 1993's *Gypsy Boogaloo* (Mesa 79056). "Turkish Dessert" and "Sultan's Dream," also from that album, are two of many songs in the duo's repertoire, inspired by the Middle East. "Vallarta Boogie" comes from *Between the Waters* (92561), and *Fandango Nights* (79079) is nicely represented by the quiet elegance of "Andale."

LINK➤ *Los Pregoneros Del Puerto — Music of Veracruz*   **Rounder 5048**
Authentic mariachi played with three guitars and a harp. A modern band, a good recording.

Caliente   Mesa 92764

If you close your eyes while listening, you can feel the slow burn of the "Desert Sun," an unhurried improvisation with a sizzling violin, a fusion texture built by coproducer Rick Braun's synthesizers, John Menzano's bass, and Scott Breadman's percussion. "Napali" is a more traditional Mexican acoustic guitar piece played with a septet. Lobo takes "El Anclote" and "Lunada," his original flamenco pieces, as unaccompanied solos (very impressive musicianship). "Moorish Reunion" is the only pure duet, and it's probably the best song on the record. Scott Breadman's hard percussion sets a rocking Moroccan rhythm for "Noche de Tangier"; Willie's gypsy violin casts a trance-like spell. Extraordinary recording and mixing. Released in 1997.

LINK➤ *Strunz and Farah — Live*   **Selva 1002**
Costa Rica's Jorge Strunz and Iran's Ardeshir Farah start with flamenco and other Spanish music, then add flavors from Africa and the Caribbean. And they do know how to play fast!

Around 1968, Tom Bee and friends in **Albuquerque** formed a rock band called Lincoln Street Exit. They gigged at the usual bars and parties, playing mostly cover versions and, once in a while, a song of their own. Bee, a tireless promoter, talked his way onto a bill in Bakersfield, CA, that also included Steppenwolf and the Beach Boys. On the way back to Albuquerque, the guys spent some time at the beach in LA, while Bee made the rounds of the record companies. (Actually, he dropped tapes off with lots of receptionists.) Remarkably, Motown called, having liked one of the songs, "(We've Got) Blue Skies," and used it on a Jackson 5 album. Motown was also starting Rare Earth, a label for non-black acts. XIT never became a superstar band, but it sold some records and had an impact on the concert circuit. One of too few examples of Native American culture in the mainstream.

Plight of the Redman   SOAR 101

Native American music is not just about pow wow drumming and wooden flutes. XIT became a popular rock group without sacrificing the integrity of its music or lyrics. The sound is delightfully 1971 (the group was signed to a Motown label when these recordings were made). "We Live" very effectively combines jingle bells and Indian percussion while claiming life for Indian ways. "Young Warrior" strikes out against the Native American who fights for his country ("they have turned you into a killing machine"). Some of the lyrics try too hard, as on "Cement Prairie," but they are no more embarrassing than those of other 1970s songs. SOAR label head Tom Bee wrote the lyrics in his younger days.

LINK➤ *Six Nations Women Singers — We Will All Sing*   SOAR 175
Another reason to rethink stereotypes. This vocal sextet comes from New York state—from the Seneca, Onondaga, and Cayuga nations (three of the six Iroquois nations). Extremely pleasant ceremonial vocals with understated percussion.

Silent Warrior   SOAR 102

The first sounds on this record are the drums, bells, and shouts of a pow-wow—a remarkable breakthrough for a 1973 major label release. In time, "Beginning" becomes a spoken commentary about the Indians' belief that the land would be theirs forever. Many of the songs do not begin in English, but in a chant. This sets the rhythm for "I Was Raised," which hits hard with a definite rock beat based on that rhythm pattern. There's less of an attempt to satisfy hit radio programmers; there is more of an emphasis on good musicianship, and there is more passion. "The Coming of the Whiteman," "War Cry," "At Peace," and "End" all address Native American concerns. Solid work.

LINK➤ *Robby Bee and the Boyz from the Rez — Reservation of Education*   *Warrior (SOAR) 604*
Taking its title from an old XIT tune, an album of rap music from a group led by Tom Bee's son. Very 1993, honest, and earnest. Well done.

Formed in 1986, Yothu Yindi combines the traditional music, dance, and culture of the Yolngu (Aboriginal) people of northeast **Australia**'s Arnhem Land with contemporary Western rock music. In 1988, the band recorded its first album, Homeland Movement, and performed at Australia's bicentennial protest concerts in Sydney. That same year, Yothu Yindi headlined at the first Festival of Aboriginal Rock Music in Darwin, Australia. Vocalist Mandawuy Yunupingu is also an educator; he's the principal of a community school where he advocates a crosscultural curriculum that combines Aboriginal and Western ideas. The band emerged on the world stage in 1991 as a result of a successful series of singles and widespread touring. The group represented Australia at the UN's International Year of Indigenous Peoples. Mandawuy was awarded 1992's Australian of the Year award for his work in forging a greater understanding among Australia's peoples. Tours in the U.S. and Europe in 1994, 1996, and 1997 have expanded the band's popularity.

Tribal Voice
Hollywood 61288

The album features searing guitars, shouting vocals, out-of-control drumming, and songs that build to a climax and then stop. Mandawuy Yunupingu's lead vocal and the repeating chorus on the title song ("better listen to your tribal voice!") could be the work of any number of rock bands. But in the background and during some breaks, traditional instruments identify Yolngu (Aboriginal) roots. After a rock song blasts through, the band returns to roots with didgeridoo and blima sticks, native percussion, and chants for "Dhum-Dhum." The optimistic "Mätjala," one of the few songs that is not sung in English, starts with traditional rhythm and instrumentation, then expertly superimposes a rock aesthetic.

LINK➤ *Dr. Didg — Out of the Woods* *Hannibal (Rykodisc) 1384*
A broader-based approach to the use of the didgeridoo in combination with other instruments (mostly rock and jazz instruments, but also the African thumb piano called the mbira, etc.). Music ranges from samba to heavy metal.

Freedom
Hollywood 61451

The thundering percussion on "Timeless Land" immediately separates Yothu Yindi's 1994 rock music from past work. The drumming is thicker and played to an intriguing beat. The overall mix is rich and dense. "Freedom" follows a familiar rock structure (common in country-rock, for example), and "World of Innocence" is a straight rock song. Roots songs like "Milika" are intriguing, but the most interesting aspects of this band have been its seamless integration of musical genres and its development of a hybrid. "Gapu," with its ocean and seabird sounds, traditional percusssion played on top of a rock drummer, a rock beat, and native improvisational song, is one of many examples of the group's vision.

LINK➤ *Alan Maralung — Bunggridj-bunggridj: Wangga Songs*
Smithsonian Collection 40439
From northern Australia, composer and singer Maralung accompanied by digeridoo. Maralung was well known as a "songman," or someone to whom spirits communicated songs. Here, the emphasis is on instrument sounds and improvisation.

Marie Daulne was born in 1964 in the former Belgian Congo (now, **Democratic Republic of Congo**). Three weeks after her birth, Daulne's Belgian father was killed in a rebellion, and her Bantu mother hid the children in a forest, where they were protected by pygmies. The Belgian Army airlifted the family to Brussels, **Belgium**, where Daulne grew up. As a girl, she listened to her mother sing traditional songs of the pygmies. When Daulne returned (with a Belgian volleyball team), she formed Zap Mama with Brussels schoolmates Sabine Kabongo and Sylvie Nawasadio in 1990. By 1993, the group was opening for 10,000 Maniacs and gaining attention as a world beat group notable for its combination of international influences. Through the 1990s, there have been personnel changes and a general movement from an emphasis on vocal music to a broader combination of vocals and instrumentation. The 1997 lineup places Daulne in the role of lead singer and group leader.

Adventures in Afropea 1
Luaka Bop 45183

An extraordinary a capella debut, released in 1992. This world music classic has several strong points: very imaginative and unusual vocal arrangements, the innocent joy of the women's voices, and demonstration-quality engineering. "Mupepe" begins as a children's chant with principal singer Marie Daulne's musings and even some gorgeous yodeling. "Bottom" is a folk song in English. "Brrrlak!" is even more interesting; it features vocal percussion, the sound of a wooden flute, and a zippy melody. Vocal percussion and a lovely arrangement make "Abadou" special, but the informal break, essentially a musical chat between friends, transforms the song into a small celebration. On "Mizike," the percussion is created by a tapping rhythm on river water. A joyous, essential album.

LINK▶ *Various Artists — Spike & Co.: Do It Acapella*   *Elektra 60953*
Probably the best available a capella sampler. Includes work by Rockapella, True Image, the Persuasions, Ladysmith Black Mambazo. This was the soundtrack to a PBS special that's also available on home video.

Seven
Luaka Bop 45183

Sabsylma (Luaka Bop 45537) from 1994 continues on the path of the group's first album, but this 1997 release takes steps in a different direction. Marie Daulne is accompanied by (mostly) new backup singers. The poetic city stroll, "Nostalgie Amoureuse," is a sophisticated collage of small vocal parts, a cello, and a drum. "Belgo Zairoise" is a modern dance song (for the clubs). A pillow talk version of Phoebe Snow's "Poetry Man" is pleasantly retro. The integration of vocals and instrumentation with a techno tinge is compelling on "Téléphone." The combination of ringing Afro-guitar, waves of female background singing, a didgeridoo, and a cool beat make "Warmth" a highlight.

LINK▶ *Various Artists — Voices*   *Alula 1001*
Pay particular attention to Tam'Echo'Tam, a Belgian a capella group with African members (similar to Zap Mama). Other treasures: Yoon/Bunka Earborn, Trinivox, Hamlet Gonashvili. A unique and varied collection, quite special.

Asia Classics 2: The Best of Shokichi Kina/Peppermint Tea House
Luaka Bop 45159

Min'yo is folk music from Okinawa, performed with sanshin (a three-string banjo). Shoei Kina, the master sanshin player and min'yo singer, was born in 1948; by 1966, he'd recorded a hit record, "Haisai Ojisan." His career took off in 1977 with the formation of Shokichi Kina and Champloose. On "Jing Jing (Firefly)," Takao Nagama's shamisen rides the wild surf as Makoto Kubuto sends off sparks with the electric guitar and three female vocalists warble a dance melody to a martial arts beat. Ry Cooder joins in on slide guitar. It's one of several songs from 1980's *Blood Line* (available from Polydor U.K.). "Celebration" is a relentlessly optimistic toe-tapper from 1982's album of the same name; once again, chirpy female vocalists dodge electric and traditional string instruments.

Yungchen Lhamo: Tibet, Tibet
RealWorld (Caroline) 2363

When Yungchen Lhamo was a child in Tibet, she was sent away to work in a carpet weaving factory. She saw her mother and grandmother only every few months, on brief holiday visits. To keep Lhamo's spirit and dignity, her grandmother encouraged her to sing. In 1989, Lhamo and some friends trekked from Tibet to India, withstanding enormous obstacles, to receive the blessings of the Dalai Lama. After spending time in India's Tibetan communities, Lhamo moved to Australia in 1993, where her pure singing voice astonished audiences and critics. This 1995 recording of Tibetan music is beautiful: Lhamo's fine vocals are often unaccompanied; they're sometimes presented with minimal instrumentation or the voices of Gyoto monks. The purity of Lhamo's voice is matched by the beauty of her message: compassion, dedication to the Dalai Lama, living in harmony with the land, the profound value of a teacher, and taking refuge in religious belief, virtue, and honesty.

Eternal Voices: Traditional Vietnamese Music in the United States
New Alliance 53

This 2-CD survey of Vietnamese music comes with liner notes that clearly explain the music, the instruments, and something about the culture. Prepared by ethnomusicologists Phong Nguyen and Terry Miller, this is a well-recorded sampling. The lovely "Xe Chi Luon Kim (Threading the Needle)" features flautist Nguyen Dinh Nghia on sao and Phong Nguyen on dán tranh (zither). "Ly Qua Deo (Going Through the Pass)" features Doan Trang on tam thamp luc (dulcimer); Nguyen Dinh Nghia's sao simulates the voice of a bird, while the dulcimer provides the natural surroundings. "Name Ai: Trong Tin Nhan (Waiting for News of a Husband Brought by a Wild Goose)" is a well-known Vietnamese song. The vocalist is Thu Van, a South Vietnamese actress who has lived in Seattle since 1975. Throughout the set, there are more songs, improvisations, structured classical pieces, and wonderful variety. Some of this music might be challenging, but most is satisfying and easily enjoyed.

Khac Chi Ensemble: Moonlight in Vietnam
Henry Street (Rounder) 5

This is fascinating music from Vietnam, recorded in Vancouver, Canada. The dinh pa is a percussion instrument made from bamboo pipes; it is played by striking the top end of each pipe with a padded stick. The ko ni is a stick fiddle (essentially a tall, one-stringed violin). Played by Ngoc Bich and Khac Chi, with Hoai Chau on bass dinh pa, these two instruments play a catchy, up-tempo Vietnamese highland song called "On the Mountain Top." Khac Chi performs solo on the dan bau (Vietnamese zither) on "Quan Ho Folk Song," which is based on romantic musical verses traded by young people trying to build relationships with the opposite sex. The suspended xylophone known as the t'rung is played by Ngoc Bich with accompaniment from Khac Chi on sao tre (flute); the sound of the t'rung very effectively recalls a highland stream on "T'rung Stream." All of these instruments are described in detail, and pictured, in the liner notes. For Vietnamese music, start here.

White Elephants & Golden Ducks: Enchanting Musical Treasures from Burma
Shanachie 64087

First, the title: Buddha took the form of a white elephant as the last step toward his enlightenment, and golden ducks are compassionate, happy symbols. This new recording (made in 1996) is full of surprises. On "Phu Pwae Lat Tin (The Hug)," the saung guak (Burmese harp) represents the formality of the royal court; master Zaw Win Maung accompanies one of Rangoon's popular singers, Ko Kyaw Swe. The tiny cymbal-like chime heard as a timekeeper is called the siwa. "Shwe Soan Nyo (Golden Brown Hawk)" is a very simple melody performed with the lightest possible touch on pattala (bamboo xylophone) and palwei (flute). The nasality of the hne (double-reed oboe) contrasts with the maung zaing (thin metal gongs with a sound similar to a steel drum) on "Shwe Kyet Kel Han Chi (Jaunty Air of the Cock)." In addition, the CD contains some piano, mandolin, violin, and a lovely song by Daw Yi Yi Thant.

Gamelan of Surakarta
JVC World Sounds 5263

This is formal music from the Javanase court, recorded in 1992. The choral sound is cultured and very carefully arranged (with some interesting flights of fancy, including whoops). The metal instruments are far more subtle, glimmering in the distance behind the occasional handclaps. Tempos are generally steady and quite slow. "Srinpi Jayaningsih" is a dance that can be performed only at a royal court in Surakarta or Yogykarta. With a sorrowful male chorus and a pair of female singers, "Ronggolawe" tells the 13th-century story of a queen and the downfall of a kingdom. It includes an interlude with metal instruments that's more restrained than the work of Gamelan Gong Kebyar, but it does radiate some excitement. Each of the three selections is meant to accompany a dance.

Gamelan Gong Kebyar
JVC World Sounds 5215

Colorful, dramatic, and carefully recorded, this performance by the Tirta Sari Gamelan Ensemble is an excellent introduction to the Balinese form. The predominant sounds are the metallophone (a xylophone with metal keys), an array of gongs, and drums to thicken the sound. The Gong Kebyar is an enormous gong at the center of it all. "Sekar Jepun (Japanese Flower)" often opens live concerts. The uneven rhythms, bursts of metallic energy, and the small improvisations on one or two instruments make this piece a kind of free jazz within traditional boundaries. "Ujan Mas (Rain of Gold)" emphasizes the melody played on metallaphone. While the music is very easy music to enjoy, it's also sufficiently complex to remain fascinating. A second volume, *Gamelan Gon Kebyar II* (JVC World Sounds 5265), is also available.

Music of Indonesia (Series)
Smithsonian Folkways (as below)

A 9-CD survey put together by ethnomusicologist Philip Yampolsky (whose liner notes are both interesting and extensive). Start with *Music of Indonesia 2: Indonesian Popular Music* (40056). Kroncong is classy string-based music from the 1950s that is popular with a middle-aged, upscale audience. Dangdut is the local dance blend of tradition and rock music; it got started in the 1960s, and its star singers include Rhoma Irama and Elvy Sukaesih, both of whom appear on several tracks. Laggam Jawa is a form of Kroncong popular in central Indonesia. *The Music of Indonesia 4: Music of Nias & North Sumatra* (40420) comes from the west, near Thailand. "Gondang Sabangunan" features the toba (tuned drums) carrying the melody. "Gula Tualah" is ceremonial music featuring a sarune (similar to an oboe, but much smaller and with a higher range), a pair of gongs (gung, the large one, and penganak, which is much smaller), and a pair of very small drums.

The Folkloric Instrumental Traditions 1
JVC World Sounds 5022

Korea supports a thriving and interesting popular and rock music scene, but these recordings are difficult to find outside the country. Traditional ensembles are more easily found, the result of work by ethnomusicologists. This collection features two instrumental forms, the sinawi and the sanjo. Sinawi is a sinuous web of rather challenging tones used to summon gods and spirits. Sanjo is typically performed in a suite of four pieces (two included here) on wind and string insurments. This music is most often heard in the southern Namdo region of Korea. For those interested in Korean popular music, singer Lee Mi-ja and the heavy metal band Sinawe are good places to start.

Cuba: I Am Time

Blue Jackel 5010

The packaging is cute: a CD-sized cigar box containing a 4-CD history of Cuban music with a wonderfully informative 112-page book (with color photos, lots of explanations, interviews, and context). CD1 is the most interesting: it's the early history. There's a song by Merceditas Valdéz, a great singer of both popular and folk music (she often worked with Ernesto Lecuona). And another by Celina Gonzaléz, who kept the rural (campesino) spirit in her salsa; her "¡Que viva Chango!," culled from 1980s recordings made for Cuba's national Egrem label, is recommended. Several heritage groups are in this set, including Los Muñequitos de Mantazas, and Clave y Guaguancó (whose work also keeps the percussion tradition alive). Also included is Conjunto Folklórico Nacional de Cuba, a government-backed education project to collect music, perform, and keep traditions alive. CD2 features some trova (folk singers): Ñico Saquito is here, and so is musical poet Pablo Milanes, representing nueva trova. The popular contemporary Cuban singer Isaac Delgado completes CD2. Beny Moré is the appropriate choice for CD3, which is about dancing. Orquesta Aragon is featured, along with Cachao, whose importance as a composer is clearly explained in the liner notes. The disc also includes a song from Los Van Van and one from N.G. La Banda. Jazz is the topic for CD4; top names include Mario Bauza, Irakere, Paquito D'Rivera, Cachao (once again), and Gonzalo Rubalcaba. A beautiful package (and a fantastic gift).

Ritmo Oriental: Historia de la Ritmo
Qbadisc 9007

The popular dance music of Cuba, and by extension, the origin of salsa, comes from son. It's music that developed by combining native island rhythms and instrumentation with influences from Spain and Africa. Son begins with percussion, guitar, and bass; a charanga band, like Ritmo Oriental, also includes horns, violins (traditionally, three violins), and flute.

Los Van Van, Conjunto Cepedes, and N.G. La Banda are all modern son bands. Ritmo Oriental, however, stays with son's 1950s sound. The interaction of flute and claves (percussion) with guitars makes "La Chica Mamey" a classic son. This essential roots music belongs in every Cuban collection; it's also compelling entertainment. For an earlier look at son, try *Son Cubano* (Tumbao [F.T.C. 3101]), recorded by the classic Sextero Habañero in the mid-1920s.

Los Muñequitos de Matanzas: Vacunao

Qbadisc 9017

Los Muñequitos de Matanzas is a popular rumba group whose music strongly recalls Yoruba rhythms. It's performed with claves (sticks clicked against one another), congas, and a tube called a cata (or guagua, hit with a stick), with a solo or duet vocal and a chorus. No horns, guitars, violins or flutes. (This is not rhumba; that name has been inaccurately applied to son for decades.) This is strangely infectious music with a more popular sound than its rootsy basis might suggest. On this 1995 CD, "Ese Señor" begins with the claves setting the key, or pace, of the song. Then, quickly, the percussion comes in, first as two drums, followed by a single vocalist who establishes the melody. A small chorus builds on the melody. Percussion chugs along, improvising around the vocals. For a clearer look at Cuban music's connection to Africa, try the group's 1996 album, *Ito Iban Echu: Sacred Yoruba Music of Cuba* (Qbadisc 9022).

Ñico Saquito: Goodbye Mr. Cat
World Circuit 35

Ñico Saquito was 81 years old when he recorded this album for Cuba's national label. For most of this century, Saquito was a revered guitar player, composer, and singer of guaracha songs. Saquito performs on lead acoustic guitar; his vocals are a little dusty with age, but still witty and wise. El Duo Cubano offers soft vocals to fill out his sound, along with a second guitar and some percussion. "Maria Cristina" is a son, one of Saquito's best-known songs; here, it's performed as a vocal duet with Virulo. "Estoy Hecho Tierra (I Am Turned to Dust)"—or, in the vernacular, "I Am Totally Exhausted"—is a guaracha with a bigger sound from both El Duo Cubao and El Quarteto Patria. A spirited display with very good guitar playing and a textbook lesson in Cuban acoustic music from a master.

N.G. La Banda: En La Calle
Qbadisc 9002

N.G. La Banda is one of Cuba's hottest bands. It was formed in 1988 by José Luis Cortés, the former flautist for Los Van Van and Irakere. N.G., pronounced "inna-hey," is an abbreviation for "new generation." The band has been wildly popular in recent U.S. appearances, but there aren't many N.G. La Banda albums currently available outside Cuba. This one was put together by licensing two albums recorded and released by Cuba's national Egrem label in 1989 and 1990 (horns are not clearly articulated, particularly in their upper registers). The group's repertoire ranges from traditional son ("Lo Que Siento es Le Lo Ley") to ballads. The best track, however, is "La Expresiva, No Se Puede Tapar El Sol." This bomba-son, which is a jazzy rumba with African drumming and swirling horn arrangements, features the dual lead vocals of two extraordinary singers, Isaac Delgado and Tony Calá.

A World Out of Time
Volumes 1, 2, 3
Shanachie 64041, 64048, 64069

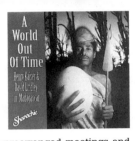

An extraordinary recording project resulting in some of world music's finest albums. In 1991, American musicians David Lindley and Henry Kaiser traveled to Madagascar, the world's fourth largest island, located 250 miles from Africa in the Indian Ocean. They brought a digital recording studio and a German production team with previous recording experience in Madagascar. They'd prearranged meetings and recording sessions with most of Madagascar's leading musicians, and many who were revered but not widely known. Sometimes, they played alongside the Malagasy musicians—not always an easy task because the island's musical development didn't always parallel European and American ideas. Volume 1 introduced two groups that became international successes as a result of these recordings, Rossy and Tarika Sammy. Two other peformers also became well known: the astonishing guitar player D'Gary and Dama Mahaleo (as leader of the group Mahaleo). Tarika Rakoto Frah plays the sodina (a Malagasy flute). He's a 70-year-old virtuoso and brilliant improvser who makes his own sodinas from aluminum ski poles or tent poles. Mama Sana, also 70, plays the valiha (a Malagasy guitar) while swinging her head to click coins in her hair against the valiha's body. This is a sampling, a tribute to the joy of discovery. Volume 2 begins with the kind of happy accident that seemed to enchant all of the Kaiser-Lindley sessions. German engineer Bernard Ramroth had previously recorded animal sounds—the small-group singing of the indri lemurs—and then filled other tracks with Rossy's drum machine. When the tracks were played back together, they lined up perfectly. So "Lemur Rap" begins the album. It's followed by more tracks from Rossy, Mahaleo, Tarika Rakoto Frah, Tarika Sammy, and Dama & D'Gary. Malagasy old-time music from the 1920s and 1930s is performed by Voninavoko. One of the island's best-known dances, "Afindrafindrao," is peformed on valiha by legendary master Sylvestre Randafison with guitar accompaniment. Volume 3 contains some tracks from the original Kaiser-Lindley sessions, plus some songs recorded by Malagasy artists on tour in the U.S. Also included are some new tracks produced by the Ramroth and producer Hostetter in Antananarivo (Madagascar's big city). Rossy and Rakoto Frah perform on several songs together; "Izahay Sy I Malala (Me and My Beloved)" was recorded by Randafison on Volume 1. (Several songs on this album were performed by others on Volumes 1 and 2.) Tovo plays the highlands bamboo harp (Madagascar's unofficial national instrument) on "Echoes of the Savannah." The colorful young Lemaditsy plays the marovany (a harp similar to the valiha). All told, one of the most successful and creatively satisfying world music projects. Start with Volume 1; soon, you'll own a small library of music from Madagascar.

The Sweet Sunny North
Shanachie 64057

Another satisfying excursion with Kaiser, Lindley, and German producer Birger Gesthuisen. This time, it's off to Norway. History plays a big part here; some of these traditions can be traced back over 1000 years. Initially, the attraction to Norway was based on the Hardanger fiddle (similar to a violin, but with extra strings under the fingerboard, and often painted with floral decorations). The big find this time was Hardanger fiddler Annbjørg Lien, who has since released two albums of her own: 1995's *Felefeber* (Shanachie 64060) and 1997's *Prisme* (64082). Both albums feature mainly traditional music; the latter fills out her sound with a small band. Knut Reiersrud is a blues guitarist (try 1994's *Footwork* [Shanachie 64562] with several African musicians and the Five Blind Boys of Alabama). The seljefløte, made of willow bark, is a very unusual flute (no holes); Hans Fredrik employs an unusual technique to produce some surprising tones. There are 28 songs on this CD, and 28 more on the follow-up, *Volume 2* (64061). The second CD contains some astonishing work. A female vocal trio called Tiriltunga not only creates their own harmonies, they reproduce fiddle tunes with original vocal arrangements (they were fiddler players before they became singers). The band called Farmer's Market has become a popular folk group on the Norwegian festival circuit, and here, they break from a repertoire that's heavy on Balkan music to perform a Finnish song, "Polsanitzan." Gabriel Flifet also works Balkan music into his accordion repertoire. The second CD also has more from Lein, and from Reiersrud.

Somewhere along the way, world music became very popular, and ethnomusicologists were left on the sidelines, wondering what happened. Ethnomusicology is a multidisciplinary cluster of related areas of study. Scholars, students, performers, museum researchers, and amateurs visit countries and cultures they find interesting, then report on what they've learned. These reports are often on paper (or now, on the Web), but are sometimes recorded. Studies may concentrate on the music itself or on related issues (dance, music history, sociology, folklore). Many field recordings are now available through record stores and mail order catalogs, notably: Smithsonian Folkways (www.si.edu.folkways), Multicultural Music (800-550-9675), and the World Music Institute (212-545-7536). Several societies and professional organizations are also good sources of information. Contact: The Society for Ethnomusicology (http://www.indiana.edu/~ethmusic/), The American Musicological Society (http://musdra.ucdavis.edu/Documents/AMS/musicology_www.html), and the International Council for Traditional Music (http://roar.music.columbia.edu/~ictm/).

Voices of Forgotten Worlds   Ellipsis Arts 3250

This 2-CD set, packaged with a full-color 96-page book, focuses on one particular aspect of ethnomusicology: recording and reporting on the music and lives of indigenous peoples. In general, there are one or two sample tracks per culture—and a great many cultures and peoples are covered in this set. The Ainu live in Northern Japan; "Ayoro Kotan" describes a garden village that's a nighttime gathering place for dieties. It's a pretty melody performed by Nakamoto Matsuko. "Máhte Lemet Elle" is Ole Larse Gaino's joik. It is his personal song, his acoustic symbol. The joik is one of Europe's oldest musical concepts. It is a Saami tradition; the Saami people (who are sometimes insultingly called Lapps) live in the Scandinavian mountains. The Inuit (formerly called Eskimos) are represented by a hunting song: a single male voice chanting with a percussion instrument. At first, some of this music might seem rough or exotic, but a look at the article describing and illustrating each people's lifestyle and music makes their music feel more familiar. This is certainly true of the odd noises that appear periodically during "Son Sventa N'Ahual San Lórenzo." Those noises are fireworks, intended by the Maya to attract a rain god. The Uighurs, who live in central Asia, tend toward simple instrumentation: a nasal-sounding flute called a sunai and a kettle drum called a naghra. And there's almost nothing exotic about an old man in Turkmenistan playing a guitar (actually, a dutar, with two strings) and singing a melodic song; there, as here, it's folk music.

The Alan Lomax Collection
Rounder 1700

It's 1959. After considerable haggling, Alan Lomax, the white man from the city, has convinced the bosses at Parchman Farm, a miserable Mississippi prison work farm, to record music made by black prisoners. When Ervin Webb harmonizes with a group of fellow prisoners on "I'm Going Home," they sound like a cross between The Five Blind Boys of Mississippi and the Fairfield Four. Hard to say whether the music is gospel or blues...but it's gorgeous. Spencer Moore sings "The Girl I Left Behind" with Everett Blevins on mandolin. Neither became famous, but their expressive folksinging, in the truest sense of the term, is delightful. These tracks are in the *Southern Journey* section of this collection; *Southern Journey* has been released over six CDs. The balance of this remarkable collection is an assortment of diverse music: a Japanese fisherman playing a wooden flute, accompaniment for puppet shows in Bali, work songs from the Mississippi with strong African influence; and some of the first Cajun music heard outside Louisiana. All of these recordings were made in the field long before world music was fashionable by Alan Lomax, one of music's larger-than-life figures. Lomax wasn't a musician—he was a man who recorded roots music, mostly in the U.S., but also in other countries. Rounder is in the process of releasing his complete field recordings on CD, but this single CD is the best place to start. It includes 37 tracks and extensive liner notes that explain the entire series in considerable detail. Highest possible recommendation.

Solomon Islands: The Sounds of Bamboo
Multicultural Media 3007

This disc is one in a series of reissues from JVC's extensive library of ethnomusicological recordings. The musicians are the Are'are people of Malaita (one island east of Guadalcanal in the southern Pacific Ocean). Their music is played on panpipes and consists of lighter-than-air melodies played informally in small groups. The music is made to represent sounds found in nature: rustling trees, crying children, the rippled percussion of a flowing river. The best work, or at least the most interesting, is performed by ensembles of four to eight pipes. "Mani Kinakina (Kinkina bird cries)" is a celebration accompanied by laughing voices, shaking leaves, and striking wooden blocks. The disc's backstage feeling is delightful.

Afganistan: On Marco Polo's Road   Multicultural Media 3003

Another selection from the 80-volume Music of the Earth: Fieldworkers' Sound Collections, released in Japan in 1992 by JVC. In fact, this CD focuses on the northeast region of Afganistan, and so, there's a sampling of nearby Tajik musical influences as well. One common instrument is the ghichak, a guitar-like instrument whose sound box is a large, flat tin can. It's heard in "Badakhshani Charbaiti (farkar)", performed by Saleh Mohammed, a local barber who exceled on the instrument in 1973, when these recordings were made. At first, instruments like the robab (short-necked lute), zirbaghali (vase-shaped drum), and panjtar (long-necked lute) sound very exotic, but the groove quickly becomes comfortable, familiar, and intriguing.

Unblocked: Music of Eastern Europe

Ellipsis Arts 3571 to 3573

One of the best world music collections to date. A full-color 72-page booklet explains the complicated, interconnected cultures of Eastern Europe. It examines the folk music and the marked differences between peoples and musical forms that are too often considered as one. Producer Michal Shapiro did a spectacular job in piecing this story together and in selecting truly outstanding music. CD1 is called *Eastern Voices, Northern Shores*; it's music from Belarus, Poland, the Ukraine, and the Baltic states. Belarus's folk-singing sextet, The Litwins, sing "A Guelder Rose Above a Ravine Stood" and "St. Yuria Had Three Daughters." The group possesses cut-like-a-knife harmonies and plays early instruments recreated by local craftsmen. "Haida-haida (Horseback Rider's Call)" is a zippy fiddle number with manly shouts; it's almost a jig and almost Western swing. The "Estonian Suite," recorded at a 1986 folk festival, is sung by 20,000 people in four-part harmony! CD2, *From the Danube through the Carpathians*, presents music from the Czech Republic, Slovakia, Hungary, Romania, Moldova, and from Gypsy culture. The heat of Martin Hrbác's violin on several Moravian wedding songs, the articulate sadness of Slovakia's Pavel Bielcik's 6-foot shepherd's flute, and the hopeful taragot of Dumitru Farcas from Romania reach out for the heart. Play these for any mainstream listener doubtful about world music! Katice, a polyphonic women's choir from Slovenia opens CD3, which covers the Balkans; it's followed by the thick-throated berda (bass) and the prin, stringed instruments from Croatia, and by Serbian brass bands. The tour winds up in Albania, Macedonia, and Bulgaria.

Global Celebration

Ellipsis Arts 63230

Probably the single best introduction to world music, this 4-CD set collects music from festivals and celebrations from 54 countries and cultures. Each CD is available separately, and each has a name (the names attempt to label very diverse musical traditions that sometimes resist categorizing). *Global Celebration: Earth Spirit* (Ellipsis Arts 3232) begins with an excerpt from a Hopi "Water Maiden Dance," an American Indian chant with drums and other percussion. Then, it's "Over the Moor to Maggie" and other Irish instrumental music performed by a group led by Matt Molloy (who played with the Chieftains, Planxty, and the Bothy Band), followed by Madagascar's Randrianarivo & Lahikoto, a father-and-son duet on the valiha (bamboo zither). This is followed by a chant from Papua New Guinea, a festival song from Cuba's countryside, a Hungarian folk song played on a local bagpipe and a hurdy-gurdy, and a Moroccan harvest festival song. Some songs are pure joy; others require some patience and understanding. *Global Celebration: Dancing with Gods* (3231) ties together a wide range of religious rites. "Ogum Beira-Mar" is a street festival song celebrating the deity in Northern Brazil; it's followed by a surprisingly accessible "Allah, Alik, Allah!" by a popular Egyptian singer. This is one of the few discs that features both a tarantella exorcism from Italy and a selection from an Inca sun god festival. *Global Celebration: Passages* (3233) begins with one of the few well-known artists on this package, Ali Hassan Kuban, who sings a fast-paced Nubian wedding song. Next comes "Hahkamine" by Leiko, a rustic vocal group from Estonia. The Indonesian "Haro-Haro" is performed by the Toba Batak Ensemble. Värttinä, Tarika Sammy, and the Klezmatics also appear. *Global Celebration: Gatherings* (3234) is more of a catchall for joyous festivals: rara from Haiti, "Shoo-Fly" from a New Orleans Mardi Gras, soca from Trinidad's Carnival, a Groit praise song from West Africa, and more. Given the time to read the liner notes and to listen to the similarities and differences, and the sheer pleasure of world music, this is a glorious way to spend one's time.

Photo & Graphic Credits

Thanks to these record companies for the use of CD cover art. Page numbers follow each credit.

Adelphi Records: 110.
AAMP: 82.
Blue Note Records: 15, 61, 114.
BMG Classics: 32, 126.
Caroline Records/RealWorld: 29, 30, 68, 83, 116, 125, 127, 141, 143, 158, 171, 185.
Green Linnet Records, Inc.: 5, 20, 21, 27, 28, 45, 73, 86, 155, 160.
Hannibal Records, a Rykodisc label: 48 (top & bottom), 79 132, 157.
Island Records: 1 (bottom), 7, 16, 22, 36, 75, 111, 175, 177.
JVC Music: 51.
Karen Publishing Co.: 66 (top & bottom).
Luaka Bop, Inc.: 140, 189, 190 top.
Music of the World: 56, 69, 152.
Omnium Recordings, DeSelby Productions, Inc.: 57.
Qbadisc: 193.
RMM Records and Video Corp.: 138.
Rounder Records: 25, 52, 58, 113, 146, 163, 191 (top).
Shanachie Entertainment: 19, 33, 42, 49, 50, 65, 90, 91, 93, 94, 101, 104, 109, 115, 122, 123, 137, 142, 145, 156, 184, 191 (bottom), 195, 196.
Smithsonian Folkways Recordings: 192.
Sonido, Inc.: 10, 37, 40, 129.
Sony Music: 8, 118, 144.
Stern's Africa: 80.
The SOAR Corp.: 13, 24, 64, 187.
Triloka Records: 96.
WEA Latina: 26, 103, 112.

Thank you to the photographers and record companies for photographs used in this book.

Artex/Luaka Bop, Inc.: 74, 194.
BEHZAD: 4.
Adrian Boot/Island Records: 1 (top), 85, 98.
Ray Burmiston/Courtesy of Hannibal Records, a Rykodisc label: 147, 148.
Livio Campos/Luaka Bop, Inc.: 59.
Norman Chalmers/Green Linnet Records, Inc.: 167.
Andrew Cleal/Green Linnet Records, Inc.: 168.
David Cornwell/Dancing Cat Records: 130.
Matthew Donaldson/Island Records: 78.
Ferreira/Luaka Bop, Inc.: 120.
Green Linnet Records, Inc.: 43.
Colm Henry/Green Linnet Records, Inc.: 6.
©ID Photography; Mesa/Blue Moon Recordings, Inc.: 1 (top).
Patricia Leeds/Triloka Records: 81.
Jouko Lehtola/Green Linnet Records, Inc.: 180.
Stephen Lovell-Davis; Caroline Records/RealWorld: 170.
Luaka Bop, Inc.: 14, 38.
Gene Martin/Angel: 153.
Will Mosgrove/Sukay World Music: 162.
Clark Quin/Shanachie Entertainment: 72.
RMM Records and Video Corp.: 39
J.R. Rost/Rykodisc: 77.
Rykodisc: 9.
Roberto Salas/Luaka Bop, Inc.: 97.
Shanachie Entertainment: 71, 159, 183.
Juergen Teller/Island Records: 99.
Matthew Thayer: 12.
Triloka: 166, 179.
Michele Turriani; Caroline/RealWorld: 190 (bottom).
John Werner/Rykodisc: 124.
Dairo Zalis/Luaka Bop, Inc.: 181.

Index: Linked Artists